CRIMINAL TYPOLOGY

CRIMINAL TYPOLOGY

The Legalistic, Physical-Constitutional-Hereditary,

Psychological-Psychiatric and Sociological Approaches

Second Printing

By

JULIAN B. ROEBUCK, Ph.D.

Professor of Sociology
The University of Texas
at El Paso
Formerly, Parole and Classification Officer
United States Bureau of Prisons
Research Assistant
District of Columbia Department of Corrections
Washington, D.C.

CHARLES C THOMAS • PUBLISHER
Springfield • Illinois • U.S.A.

Published and Distributed Throughout the World by

CHARLES C THOMAS • PUBLISHER

BANNERSTONE HOUSE

301-327 East Lawrence Avenue, Springfield, Illinois, U.S.A.

NATCHEZ PLANTATION HOUSE

735 North Atlantic Boulevard, Fort Lauderdale, Florida, U.S.A.

First Printing, 1967
Second Printing, 1971

With THOMAS BOOKS *careful attention is given to all details of
manufacturing and design. It is the Publisher's desire to present books
that are satisfactory as to their physical qualities and artistic possibilities
and appropriate for their particular use.* THOMAS BOOKS *will be true
to those laws of quality that assure a good name and good will.*

Printed in the United States of America

00-2

To my mother,

MAMIE McDONALD ROEBUCK

PREFACE

THIS BOOK deals with the problem of constructing criminal typologies, i.e., the classification and explanation of specific *patterns of criminal behavior* in terms of the particular kinds of offenders who engage in these specific patterns of crime. The author's frame of reference negates any *general* theory of criminal behavior. Given the current definition of crime, which includes such diverse activities as drug trafficking, murder, embezzlement, rape, treason, etc., any inclusive theory of criminal behavior can hardly escape becoming a general theory of human behavior. Attempts at the classification and the explanation of criminal behavior must be directed toward the discovery and analysis of *particular criminal patterns,* manifest as criminal career patterns. Individuals with certain social-psychological attributes tend to embark on certain patterns of criminal behavior. The process that leads to one kind of criminal pattern or type includes several etiological variables and differs from that process which leads to other criminal patterns. Though criminal behavior results from many separate factors, the different causal processes involved in the various criminal patterns may be identified.

First, four typological approaches are presented: legalistic; physical-constitutional-hereditary; psychological-psychiatric; and sociological. Several theoretical problems involved in the construction and use of typological instruments are discussed and evaluated. A discussion follows concerning the functions of a classification system, its form, the basic assumptions upon which it rests and the dimensions of analysis to be considered. The merits of an interdisciplinary approach in the development of criminal typologies is argued, utilizing the services of several different behavioral scientists representing several different disciplines.

Chapters II, III and IV deal with a critical overview of extant criminal typologies selected from the research literature, representative of three typological approaches: physical-constitutional-hereditary; psychological-psychiatric; and sociological. Attention is primarily focused on recent or current typologies within these three camps. The treatment functions, as well as the etiological functions, of these classification systems are considered.

The balance of the book is concerned with the author's inductive criminal typology. A legal, psychological-sociological approach employing statistical and qualitative analyses is utilized. The dimensions of analysis are as follows: (a) offense pattern; (b) *modi operandi*; (c) social attributes; (d) personality type; (e) self-concept; (f) attitudes; (g) situations, stresses and pressures antedating and following criminal behavior.

An intensive research involving a sample of four hundred adult offenders serving felony sentences led to the isolation of thirteen distinct criminal types. Social-psychological profiles of six of these criminal patterns are presented in detail: single pattern of armed robbery; single pattern of violation of narcotic drug laws; single pattern of gambling; single pattern of fraud; double pattern of drunkenness and assault; mixed pattern. The remaining seven patterns are less intensively described: double pattern of larceny and burglary; triple pattern of drunkenness, assault and larceny; no pattern; single pattern of burglary; single pattern of sex offenses; single pattern of auto theft; single pattern of forgery and counterfeiting.

Guidelines for the control and/or treatment of each offender type described are outlined. Additionally, "indicators" within each type which might be of interest to future typological researchers are discussed in terms of their value and focus to representatives of the four typological approaches: legal; constitutional; psychological-psychiatric; and sociological.

Hopefully, this volume will make a contribution to the criminological, typological literature. The criminal patterns delineated herein should be of heuristic use to the theoretical criminologist. For the correctional worker and correctional practitioner, the material can, in part, form a theoretical framework for planning methods of control and treatment, particularly for the specific pattern of crime analyzed. Law enforcement personnel may be able to relate some of the data contained in these typologies to processes of detection and apprehension.

JULIAN B. ROEBUCK

ACKNOWLEDGMENTS

A NUMBER of people have contributed to the development of this monograph. Peter Lejins initially encouraged the author to do research in the typological area. Donald Clemmer not only made a position available in a prison setting possible for the empirical research, but also gave encouragement, interest and assistance. He was scheduled to write an introduction to the volume, but his untimely death made this impossible. The late Paul Tappan encouraged me to write the book, and I am particularly grateful to him for many suggestions and criticisms which have influenced my frame of reference. However I, alone, remain responsible for any errors of omission or commission found herein.

J.B.R.

CONTENTS

CRIMINAL TYPOLOGY

Chapter I

APPROACHES TO CRIMINAL TYPOLOGY

T HE QUEST for an all-inclusive typology by which criminal behavior can be predicted or explained has long intrigued laymen, literary men, lawyers, judges, penologists and scholars in the physical and social sciences. Usually, the orientation of the searcher foretells the typology and makes for etiological approaches to crime and delinquency that are varied, if not often contradictory, inconsistent and inadequate. Historically, classification based on the study and observation of the criminal has differentiated offenders in accordance with the prevailing *zeitgeist*.

Currently, criminologists, in their typological attempts, may be roughly divided into four camps, albeit there is certainly some overlapping among them: (a) legalistic approach; (b) physical-constitutional-hereditary approach; (c) psychological-psychiatric approach; and (d) sociological approach. A residual group of scholars frown upon typologies of offenders.[1]

The *legalistic approach* holds that criminology is obligated to function from the base of statutory and judicial definitions of criminal acts. The criminal is defined in terms of his intent and act; e.g., a robber is one who has been convicted of robbery, a murderer one convicted of murder, etc. Legal classifications represent the earliest and most commonly used categories in dealing with the criminal. The legalist's position is that adjudicated offenders represent the closest approximation to those who have in fact violated the law. Furthermore, legal classifications do not preclude the study of offenders falling into legal categories and legal sub-categories by behavioral scientists. The late Professor Paul Tappan, a lawyer and a sociologist, claimed that criminals are a sociologically distinct group of violators of specific

3

legal norms, subjected to official state treatment. To him, legal
norms, their violation and the mechanics of dealing with breach
constitute major provinces of criminology.[2]

The constitutionalists center on inferiorities of the constitution
which are derived in large part from heredity and disease. They
utilize varying combinations of morphological, physiological and
mental characteristics in their typological attempts, e.g., physical
trait deviation, physical trait inferiority, endocrine malfunction,
somatotype and temperament, malstructure of nervous system,
disharmonies of physical growth, unregulated bodily functions,
epilepsy, encephalitis, mental disease, brain damage, mental
deficiency, senility, paresis, infant diseases, abnormal brain waves,
constitutional psychopathy (psychopathic personality), etc.
Homosexuality, alcoholism, suicide and criminality are generally
included as manifestations of indirect hereditary predisposition.
Criminality is viewed as a resultant of the impact of environment
upon defective or abnormal organisms.

The psychological-psychiatric approach holds that criminal
typologies should be delineated in terms of different motivational
patterns arising out of personality structure and various psychological states or disabilities. Explanation of delinquent and
criminal behavior is viewed in terms of personality disorders
and neurotic mechanisms by psychoanalysts (dynamic rather
than constitutional orientation), psychiatrists and clinical psychologists. Offenders with specific personality structures are
studied in reference to their stressful situations. In such a
representation, the various forms of crime are considered, by
and large, as symptomatic of underlying mental conditions. Trait
disorders are traced to faulty personality development. Neurotic
mechanisms stem from mental conflicts and guilt reactions.
Character disorders are psychogenically determined in early
childhood as a result of faulty interpersonal relationships. The
cardinal thesis is that criminals are emotionally deficient in
some way.

The sociolgical approach centers on a classification schema
which regards criminal behavior as a product of social interaction
and culture. Crime is viewed as a social phenomenon; therefore,

criminals must be classified in accordance with their social orientation and in accordance with the values and cultural definitions in the social world in which they live. Criminal behavior exhibits recurrent patterns which reflect the sociocultural organizations of society. Criminal behavior systems (e.g., Edwin Sutherland, *The Professional Thief*, Edwin M. Lemert, "The Behavior of the Systematic Check Forger")[3] comprise a sociological typology which ideally discriminates among various offenders in terms of degree of commitment to criminal culture in organization of their lives, self-concept, identification of self with other criminals, criminal subculture membership and status, and progression in acquisition of criminal techniques. The sociologists' offender categories refer to role behavior in specific types of situations of more or less enduring response and not to types of personality organization. Sociologists are concerned with the "social criminal" and crime rates; psychiatrists and psychologists are concerned with the "individualized criminal." Sociologists, historically, have been more interested in the relationships of the social characteristics of age, sex, race, nativity, social class, ethnic and subculture membership to crime than in the construction of typologies.

While the preceding frames of reference are obviously at variance, it is clear that all four share a common assumption which makes for some similarity in their classification attempts. The legalistic approach implies that a certain type of crime is committed by a certain type of person. The constitutionalists, who stress that physical and hereditary influences are causally related to personality and behavior, point to peculiarities disposing the offender to specific criminal roles. The psychological-psychiatric approach suggests that certain character types in certain stressful situations commit similar kinds of crime. Sociologists maintain that certain types in given social situations commit similar offenses.

Regardless of approach, the criminal act *per se* is initially the cardinal focus of attention. Therefore, the criminal categories of the latter three approaches often approximate the legal nomenclature, despite the fact that their purpose is to distend or extend the legal categorization. The "criminal constitution" (often alluded to by the constitutional school) serves not only to distinguish habitual criminals from occasional criminals in the research and diagnostic work of European criminologists, but it has been incorporated into the penal codes by way of prescribing measures for the protective detention of prisoners who exhibit gross signs of "degeneracy," "abnormality" and "defectiveness." Terms such as "recidivist" and "habitual criminal" existed in the legal nomenclature before their use by the behavioral scientist.

Abrahamsen, a psychiatrist, in his book, *The Psychology of Crime,* alludes to situational offenders who commit theft, associational offenders who commit robbery, accidental offenders who are involved in tragic traffic accidents, kleptomaniacs who shoplift, pyromaniacs who commit arson, obsessive-compulsive persons who gamble, psychopaths who assault or murder, etc.[4] Murderers, drug addicts, child molesters, rapists, swindlers, gamblers, etc., have been analyzed in terms of their personality motivation by psychiatrists and psychologists. Sociologists have analyzed several offender types in terms of social types or behavior systems and role adaptations, e.g., professional thieves, robbers, pickpockets, confidence men, embezzlers, check writers, drug peddlers, auto thieves, numbers game operators, prostitutes, murderers, hobos, vandals, O.P.A. violators, conscientious objectors, etc.

Despite some similarity in the four approaches (a similarity often unrecognized), serious divisive elements in point of view and methodology obtain among them.

DIVISIVE ELEMENTS IN TYPOLOGICAL ATTEMPTS

Many behavioral scientists reject the legalistic approach on the following bases: (a) It is not concerned with criminal motivation and etiology; (b) it relies on the "legal fictions" underlying the criminal codes of "hedonism," the "reasonable man" and "free will"; (c) it ignores individual differences and defines the criminal only in terms of his act, i.e., the crime is classified but not the criminal, since an offender may easily fit into two or more legal categories; in short, an offender may commit several different kinds of crimes; (d) it comprises a set of legal, non-behavioral categories irrelevant to the understanding of individual or group behavior because of the variability and relativity of criminal law from time to time and place to place; (e) it questions the types of behavior defined as criminal and the graduated provisions of the criminal codes, e.g., some sociologists would define violators of Federal administrative agency regulations (Securities Exchange Commission, Federal Communications Commission, Federal Trade Commission, National Labor Relations Board, etc.) as "white-collar" criminals; (f) adjudicated criminals constitute an artificial and nonrepresentative category which restricts researchers to a study of only those persons convicted of violating the law, thus blocking the inclusion of nonconformists, social deviants and unconvicted offenders who resemble criminals in their personality structure and behavior; (g) it supports a false impression of homogeneity, since a legal category, e.g., embezzlement, may include varying types of embezzlers and embezzlement.

Legalists answer that the law, in addition to actions and consequences, concerns itself with variable intent, responsibility and accountability. Certain characteristics of the offender and certain extenuating circumstances of his situation constitute grounds for withholding or attenuating legal sanctions, e.g., insanity, mental defect, mental disease, extreme youth, self-defense, coercion, etc. The legalist considers motivation insofar as it operates to prove intent. Legal procedure has incorporated some behavioral science techniques, e.g., psychiatric examinations, pre-sentence investigations, sentencing boards, parole boards, probation and parole selection techniques. Though the concepts of hedonism, the reasonable man and free will may be limited in value, what better does the behavioral scientist have to offer except a hodgepodge of conflicting personality and sociological theories?

Granted that all social norms, including legal norms, are relative, variable and impermanent, this does not preclude an analysis of norms and those who deviate from them. Criminal norms, especially the major felonies, are less relative and less variable than general conduct norms. Criminal norms and their violators must be separated from other conduct norms and their violators. The concepts of "nonconformists" and "social deviants" are loose and ambiguous. Moreover, where are the formal agreed-on measures to select, study and classify them? Legal norms, contrariwise, are precise and technical, requiring procedures of formal proof. The law has defined with greater clarity and precision the conduct which is criminal than have anti-legalist criminologists. The branding of businessmen who violate the regulations of Federal administrative agencies as criminals is to equate antisocial behavior with crime. Unless the so-called white-collar criminal has in fact violated a criminal norm, he is not a criminal. He may be defined as greedy, crafty or unfair by some, and a good businessman by others. The white-collar criminologist is actually concerned with acts of a financial nature that he thinks should be defined as crime and with people whom he thinks should be defined as criminals.

Paul Tappan concludes that the criminal law establishes substantive norms of behavior and includes standards more clear-cut, specific and detailed than the norms in any other category of social control.[5] At no other junction in the field of social control is there directed a comparable rational effort to elaborate standards conforming to the predominant needs, desires and interests of the community. Adjudicated criminals may not be representative of all criminals, but they represent the closest possible approximation to those who have verifiably violated the law. Unconvicted offenders are important but remain an unselected group with no specific, ascertainable membership. Certainly, the researcher would not give up an ascertainable for a non-ascertainable group of subjects. Clinical psychologists and psychiatrists continue to study and treat various types of personality aberrations, although these aberrations do not necessarily constitute a representative sample of all aberrations.

The legalist has no quarrel with the criminologist or other behavioral scientists who study social deviancy and deviance on the basis of an operational definition which is not covered by the criminal law. Such studies might prove fruitful in many ways to all students of human behavior. He would reject such deviancy and deviance from criminological research, *per se*.

Certainly in heterogeneous, modern society there is some overlap in behaviors defined as illegal and deviant; and there is no complete agreement on what should be defined as legal or deviant behavior. There is consensus in the definition of some behaviors as criminal and deviant. Such types are probably most susceptible to explanation. Certain illegal acts are not in violation of the social norms of some groups and therefore do not constitute deviant behavior for them. Obviously, certain kinds of deviant acts are not illegal. To some degree, criminal law has developed as a formal system of maintaining social order in differentiated societies. Where conduct cannot be agreed on, the criminal law operates, in part, to control the behavior of all persons. Although criminal behavior and deviant behavior must be treated as separate entities, studies are needed to determine the correspondence between them instead of proceeding on the basis that the two are the same. Any study of the relationship between legal norms and extralegal norms would necessarily include the study of the process of law-making, the groups influencing legislation and the social norms supporting the criminal law. Such study could contribute to the explanation of illegal behaviors.[6] In the meantime, the research criminologist must confine his studies to adjudicated offenders.

The criminologist who confines his research and typological attempts to known offenders suffers from no paucity or variety of data. He may study traditional felons, e.g., robbers, burglars, confidence men, assaulters, etc., or he may center on atypical offenders, e.g., draft-dodgers, traitors, saboteurs, conspirators to overthrow the government by violence, tax evaders, violators of health or safety regulations by members of religious sects, hit-and-run drivers, civil rights violators, etc. Convicted persons are nearly all criminals, and they offer sizeable and varied samples of many criminal types.[7]

Sociologists have spilled much ink in claiming that crime is not inherited, that biology does not determine behavior, and that constitutional researchers in criminology have not supported the conclusions of their investigations. They contend that biologists erroneously begin with constitutional assumptions and eventually find what they are looking for. Sociologists and psychologists have noted the faulty sampling techniques and dearth of control groups in constitutional studies. Sociologists hold that the influence of sociocultural factors is not given adequate consideration by the criminal biologists. The clinical psychologist and psychiatrist on the American scene since the third decade of the twentieth century have been psycho-dynamically oriented, and therefore they would disagree with the constitutionalists in reference to hereditary predisposition.

The constitutionalists answer that structure influences function and that structure has a genetic base. Man is an animal and is not strictly a product of social determinism. Additionally, (with some justification) they aver that social and psychological factors are included in their investigations. The criminal is seen as a product of nefarious social conditions and psychological pressures affecting inferior biological organisms.

Sociologists maintain that the psychological-psychiatric approach tends to ignore situational and cultural factors as causal elements. They also refute the psychoanalytical interpretation of personality, and they substitute in its place role theory and the socialization and maladaptive behavior process. Most criminal behavior, according to the sociologist, is not related to some form of personality disturbance. Furthermore, they point to the frequent unrepresentative samples utilized by the clinicians. Psychologists and psychiatrists note the sociologist's neglect of personality structure and dynamics and man's differential response to similar social situations. They are keenly aware of the fact that the sociologist does not possess adequate learning theory to support his conception of crime as normal learned behavior.

Consequent polemics dealing with the issues among the four typological approaches have resulted in many extremist positions, whereby some classifiers pledge their allegiance to typologies based exclusively on legal norms, constitutional types, psychiatric nosology or sociological constructs. Others maintain eclectic positions. Still others throw out all attempts at classification. For them, typological attempts suggest a false impression of homogeneity which merely transfers from the behavioral to the diagnostic level.[8] Moreover, most sociologists and some clinicians would deny the applicability and feasibility of con structing a typology.

Martin and Fitzpatrick, in their comments on criminal typologies constructed on a broad interdisciplinary basis, point to their usefulness as heuristic and practical devices of intervention required to meet the challenge of prevention and control. They go on to say that, due to the undeveloped state of typologies, there are two defects in attempting construction on an inter-disciplinary base: (a) Current typologies separate cases along a psychogenic-sociogenic continuum, offering no solution for the case in which there is the blend of these factors in a single causal process; (b) current typologies limit their explanation to personality growth and development and how the individual case became delinquent—thus not meeting the additional requirement of epidemiological studies aimed, not at explaining individual cases, ". . . But at accounting for differences in the concentrations of different types of delinquency in different sectors of society."[9] Certainly no current typology meets the needs mentioned in the first defect; however, this does not preclude future efforts from meeting it. Moreover, as Paul Tappan points out, there are many pitfalls in the holistic approach. The cases representing a psychogenic-sociogenic blend may not result from a single causal process but from a related interplay of causes.[10] In reference to the reported second defect, the author suggests the construction of several typologies appertaining to offenders taken from different population groups throughout society rather than universal typological attempts. This is made explicit in subsequent discussion. Admittedly, the criminal typologist must examine individual cases, but this does not preclude his concern with situational elements involved in criminality.

REACTION AGAINST CLASSIFICATION

The position of the non-classifiers is similar to that of Thomas Szasz, who postulates there is no such thing as mental illness, and that what we categorize as such can more appropriately be described as problems in living.[11] Similarly, Karl Menninger and his associates in their recent book, *The Vital Balance,* suggest that the urge to classify is beset by many pitfalls and sources of error implicit in the classification process. Tracing the changing conceptualizations of mental illness from ancient times to the influences of logical positivism, these authors argue that trends in the categorization of mental illness have moved from pluralism and ontogeny to monism and leave us with one unitary concept, i.e., that all classifications are arbitrary, and there is only one kind of mental illness.[12] In this writer's opinion, this position casts doubt on the nature of the scientific method.

Boring contends that science began when organisms began to generalize, to see similarities between themselves and members of their own species or to see differences and other similarities between other species and themselves.[13] Thus, the nature of science requires that one first observe and then attempt to categorize, compare and classify observations. While some data based on observation is systematic and stands in a defined relation to other data, some other data is unsystematic and unrelated. The scientist, monist or otherwise, is required to organize as well as to acquire knowledge. In the process of organizing data, given bits of knowledge have differential consequences, depending upon the structure into which they are fitted. A single observation may require reorganization of existing theory. The discovery of the spirochete reorganized all former conceptions of the causation of syphilis and its consequent physical and mental degeneration. Such observations stand out as landmarks in the history of scientific knowledge. Another observation may do nothing more than settle the immediate question to which the investigative work was directed. The discovery of delusions and hallucinatory phenomena common to most advanced states of psychoses is an example. While it failed to revolutionize the understanding of etiology, prognoses and treatment of psychotic disorders, it meshed with existing theory.

If Menninger is saying that we do not have enough idiographic or nomothetic data to allow for adequate classification in categorizing types and kinds of psychiatric groups, most scientists would agree. On the other hand, explanation is precluded by classification. Menninger's point that the simple illnesses have allowed easy categorization and diagnosis, while the present complicated and unexplained afflictions, e.g., mental illness and cancer, have defied such diagnosis and classification schemes does not negate the fundamental contributions preceding the delineation, diagnosis, explanation and treatment of the so-called simple illnesses What is forgotten, however, is that the explanations of the so-called simple illnesses were also seemingly unconquerable at earlier periods in history. Their explanation was preceded by technological advance, research findings and professional skill. Diagnostic attempts have had to rely on useful terminology, descriptive explanation and syndrome appellations because of a lack of knowledge which would permit us to consider one classification scheme as synonymous with the behavior it represents. The scientific method resorts to inductive description and nomothetic designations prior to the establishment of systematized classifications and explanations.

Several scholars, in addition to Menninger, have noted the inadequacies of psychiatric and psychological classifications.[14] Psychiatrists who disparage clinical classifications on the basis of the inadequacies of prior antiquated classical systems make a similar error to that of some criminologists who refute the establishment of criminal typologies on the basis of errors found in Lombroso and his followers. If we consider the increasing complexity of man's culture, the complex interaction of sociological, economic and psychological conditions, one cannot help but realize that a concept so uncrystallized as mental illness must undergo change as man's culture also changes. We have already seen that the nature of science serves a self-corrective purpose. Thus, finer and closer approximations to the truth are continually made until at last the one single fact or variable explains the crucial link in the mystery. One can suggest that the fault of those reacting against classification lies not in the inadequacies of classification *per se,* but in the misuse and failure to understand the purposes for which classification schemes are intended.

In his attempt to replace the void created by the removal of classification schemes, Menninger substitutes five levels of personality disorganization and reorganization. The nature of these five levels (five orders of dysfunction) is such that they characterize differing individuals as they depart in kind and degree—ranging from the normal individual who is successfully able to cope with recurrent stress and anxiety to those who are plagued by malignant depression so severe that it inevitably eventuates in death.[15] To make such a substitution, is, in the writer's view, simply removing our inductive state of knowledge one step farther from the hoped-for label which gives the disease its name and provides the clue or shorthand to its etiology, its meaning, nature and treatment. If we examine these disorders, labels and illnesses which fit into the broad levels, or "syndrome appellations," we recognize the fortuitous nature in this process. The nature of these disorders or illnesses now becomes circular, substantiating the levels of dysfunctions and behavioral syndromes from which they were originally derived. Further, inherent in this conceptualization is the assumption that all behavior exists on a continuum. Although the positing of a continuous model has allowed meaningful methods of categorizing and anlyzing behavior, there is some suggestion that its premise is ill founded. Commenting on the war neuroses, which Menninger uses as a prototype to substantiate the continuity hypotheses, Kardiner points out that there is no disintegration of the ego in the war neurosis, and it thus cannot be considered similar in any way to mental illnesses as found in everyday life.[16]

Baughman and Welsh have pointed out that three broad characteristics of human behavior have led people to postulate personality: (a) Behavior patterns differ from one person to another; (b) behavior patterns are consistent; and (c) there is also inconsistency in that behavior patterns can be and frequently are changed.[17] It is the quality of inconsistency which hinders our efforts in developing highly refined and systematized categorizations of personality variables and behavior types and allows critics to discredit classification schemes. To focus entirely on the inconsistencies of behavior, however, while disregarding or negating the consistent quality, is to leave us with a biased point of view. It is the consistency, similarity between events and the reliability found in behaviors which enables the behavioral scientist to classify, predict, control and understand the nature of behavior. The scientific method takes into account the inconsistencies of behavior through statistical control. The consistent elements would be unacceptable unless they revealed a significance beyond that of the inconsistent qualities.

The preceding exposition and criticism of Menninger's conception of classification is admittedly a digression; but hopefully it sheds light on the over-all problem of typological attempts. Recapitulating, up to this point we have discussed various typological approaches to criminal behavior. We have concluded that typological constructs are a must for behavioral scientists. What concrete problems, then, face the criminologist in his typological attempts and what solutions to these problems are in the offing?

ASSUMPTIONS, CRITERIA, FORMS AND FUNCTIONS OF CRIMINAL TYPOLOGY

As Gibbons has cogently pointed out, the major criteria required for a specific classification of offenders are as follows: (a) functions the classificatory system is to serve and the form it should take; (b) assumptions upon which the classificatory device is based; (c) dimensions of analysis along with their specific attributes. Typologies may function in two ways: (a) they are needed in the construction of etiological types; and (b) they may provide diagnostic, treatment types.[18] The writer holds that the research criminologist could more profitably concern himself with the first function because the second function involves a normative dimension. Moreover, the nature of cause ideally if not generally precedes treatment. Regarding form, a classificatory system should focus on offense patterns existing within longitudinal criminal careers defined in terms of legal nomenclature.

The author's orientation is based upon the following assumptions: (a) There is no adequate, general theory of criminal behavior; (b) behavioral scientists are concerned with and can only explain patterned behavior; (c) many adjudicated offenders demonstrate a patterning of offense behavior in their criminal careers; offenders with similar offense behavior patterns are likely to share certain social and psychological attributes which differentiate them from offenders with other offense behavior patterns; (d) though behavioral and social-psychological changes occur in the development of criminal careers, such changes are limited and identifiable; it is possible to define definite and stable criminal career patterns; offenders tend to close on specific offense behaviors; (e) adjudicated offenders may be classified on the basis of legal categories of offense behavior; (f) the etiological process that leads to one kind of criminal career differs from that which leads to another criminal career; (g) criminal behavior results from multiple causation; and (h) an interdisciplinary approach is necessary to any typological approach.

The selection of dimensions of analysis depends upon the researcher's theoretical approach. The writer views criminal behavior as resulting from an interaction of sociological and psychological factors. Pertinent sociological factors include role successions, interactive factors and social backgrounds. Pertinent psychological factors include personality traits and structure plus motivational factors.

An amplification and justification of the preceding criteria follows along with suggestive guidelines for the construction of a criminal typology.

Students of human behavior who have interested themselves in criminology have suggested a number of general theories for use in criminological research. These include, among others, differential association, culture conflict, social class conflict, ecological, psychodynamic, constitutional, containment, differential opportunity structure, conflict of values, sex role conflicts, lower-class value system, anomie and delinquent subculture theories, all of which have been utilized by some scholars in the classification of criminals and which have led to either a clearly postulated or an implied criminal typology by others. These theories have been repudiated by articulate critics who have pointed to certain negative cases that cannot be explained by a particular theoretical frame of reference. Criminologists appear to delight in the destruction of each others' theories.[19] Attempts at a grand, universal, unitary theory may be a chief source of difficulty. Given the present state of knowledge, general theories endeavor to explain too much and therefore actually explain too little.

Some scholars contend that, eventually, several specific orders of delinquency and crime will have to be recognized and that a different explanation for each order of criminal behavior may be found.[20] This middle-range theory approach, they reason, will ease the struggle and frustration of the criminologist who, for the purposes of study and explanation, has been seeking to bring together into a single capsule the diversity of criminal behavior. Certainly, any *general theory of criminal behavior,* given the current definitions of such disparate kinds of crimes as murder, embezzlement, rape and shoplifting, can hardly escape being a general theory of *all* human behavior.

Crime is relative in time and space. Different geographical areas are represented by different kinds of crime, e.g., smuggling is prevalent in border regions, as is the illegal manufacture of corn whiskey in Southern hill regions, while teenage "jack rolling" is a city phenomenon. Criminal forms and styles change as the characteristics of the sociocultural organization in which crime is committed change. The professional safecracker and the flamboyant gangster of the twenties and thirties are no longer as prevalent as in yesteryear. Moreover, criminals vary in motivation, developmental history of criminality and types of behavior. For these reasons, researchers might accomplish more if they confined their quest to one particular group at a time and if they sought for criminal typologies which vary according to political jurisdiction, geographical area and specific population instead of seeking for a universal criminal type.

General theorists have usually assumed that criminals could

be differentiated from noncriminals without the necessity of first finding out how criminals differ from one another.[21] This has led to a false dichotomy of criminals *versus* noncriminals as comprising two homogeneous groupings. Comparing indiscriminate samples of criminals with samples of noncriminals, no matter how careful the sampling and matching technique, leaves much to be desired. No wonder some criminologists claim their findings reveal no significant differences in personality type between criminals and noncriminals.[22] It is granted that some criminologists have demonstrated that offenders as a class share some psychological and social characteristics (as do noncriminals). This finding does not preclude significant differences among offenders. What are these differences, and on what behavior and personality dimensions may they be measured? Significant differences between sub-categories of offenders may indicate similarities within certain subgroups. Similarities within and differences between subgroups would permit the development of a criminal typology consisting of general summary statements about carefully observed facts about particular classes of criminals. A reliable set of general summary statements on each sub-category of criminals would help solve the following crucial questions: What factors lead to a particular pattern of criminal behavior? Why do some individuals end up in one category of crime and others in another? How and why do offenders differ from one another to the extent that they qualify for different categories?

If this latter approach were used, the research criminologist could set up certain criteria within dimensions of behavior by which he would include or exclude cases in his sample, thereby establishing homogeneity of cases or a specific order of crime, e.g., armed robbery, special kinds of assault, special kinds of forgery, etc. Other criminologists with the basis for the specific order of crime at hand would be in a position to replicate the study. Findings could be confirmed or rejected. Currently, the samples of delinquent and criminal behavior of any one criminologist are quite different from those of others.[23]

CRIMINAL TYPOLOGY AND LEGAL OFFENSE CATEGORIES

At the start of any effort in the construction of a criminal typology, a decision must be made in regard to the use of legal offense categories. It has been noted that many of the categories of crime in the various criminal codes cover a range of different behaviors.[24] For this reason, some sociologists suggest that the researcher must set up his own behavioral categories which cut across the legal categories.[25] This method would make for a loss of preciseness in the definition of criminal types and would lead to several kinds of amorphous groupings. The dimensions of the so-called behavioral categories would then depend upon the particular criminologists who were constructing them. A criminal typology must be precise and parsimonious. The criminologist must remember that he is dealing with criminals as defined by legal nomenclature. He is not studying antisocial or deviant behavior. Moreover, the accessible official data concerned with criminal histories exist in terms of the legal nomenclature, i.e., arrests and convictions by criminal charges.

Perhaps the answer lies in the construction of behavior categories within the confines of the legal categories, e.g., *narcotic drug laws offenders* could be differentiated into those who use and sell drugs (the common variety of small-time street peddlers, the professional wholesaler (a nonuser), the young addict, the marijuana user, the heroin addict). *Gamblers* could be broken down into professional promoters, "numbers men," racetrack bookies, sports pool operators, gambling house operators, nonprofessionals who engage in gambling, e.g., the compulsive gambler. *Burglars* could be subdivided into housebreakers, safecrackers, professional burglars, amateur burglars (depending upon modus operandi). Those charged with *prostitution and commercialized vice* could be differentiated as call girls, street walkers and bar hustlers, madams, pimps, etc.

Several criminologists have used this method; e.g., Lottier divides embezzlement into two kinds—"group embezzlement" and "individual embezzlement;"[26] Lemert studied both "naive" and "systematic" check forgers;[27] Riemer delineated several types of embezzlers;[28] Roebuck researched armed robbers, addicted drug peddlers, numbers men, assaulters and drinkers and short con men;[29] Clinard and Wade have suggested the delineation of vandalism as a subtype in juvenile delinquency.[30]

The thorniest problem facing the criminologist espousing legal labels hinges on the question: Do legal labels merely classify crimes and not criminals? Legal labels act to classify both crimes and criminals. An offender demonstrating a pattern of robbery in his criminal history is a robber even though at some stage of his career he may have violated other criminal norms. It has been established that many offenders violate several different criminal norms in their career spans; however, this does not preclude the fact that some of them do close on specific types of criminal behavior. Sociologists, psychiatrists, policemen and prison classification officers have reported criminal patterning in the criminal careers of many offenders. Some psychiatrists note that each person selects his own type of crime, depending upon his personality structure, albeit the selection may also depend upon circumstances frequently created by the offender.[31] The criminal act a man chooses to carry out, in short, is typical of his own special characteristics though it may be colored by the situation. Criminals then often concentrate on one type of crime, and in fact, may specialize on a certain technique, or *modus operandi*, within this type. The technique may be significant in determining the direction of police investigation.

Moreover, a study of the *modus operandi* may enable the behavioral scientist to differentiate professional from nonprofessional criminals, habitual criminals by virtue of a personal vice (e.g., alcoholics, drug addicts, compulsive gamblers, etc.) from other habitual offenders, "loners" from gang, mob and syndicate-affiliated offenders, violent from nonviolent offenders, etc.[32] Additionally, the *modus operandi* may indicate motivation, e.g., economic gain, alienation from the reference group, loyalty and conformity to in-group membership, revenge, direct aggression, symbolic aggression, obsession-compulsion, reaction formation, displacement, victim proneness, etc.

THE NECESSITY OF A MULTI-DISCIPLINARY APPROACH

In the construction of criminal typologies, we must utilize the services of several behavioral scientists: anthropologists; neurologists; psychiatrists; psychologists; sociologists; social workers; and legalists. All of these could work together as a research team formulating research designs and collecting data. Behavioral scientists have pooled their brains and research efforts in the study of other problems. Heretofore, in the area of criminology, behavioral scientists have generally been loners ignoring each other's efforts and failing to read each other's literature. Moreover, the proponents of the various disciplinary approaches to crime have been hesitant to accept each other's contributions when they were cognizant of them.[33] Specialized perspectives, whether appertaining to psychiatric, psychological, constitutional, sociological or legal studies are likely to be resolved in their own delimited frames of reference. Such efforts make it extremely difficult to relate the findings of one specialized area to the results in adjacent fields. Cooperative research would work not only to lead to the pooling of findings but also to the development of new frames of reference. There is evidence available that the constitutional, psychogenic, legal and sociocultural approaches to crime have made some contributions to the etiology of crime.[34]

Certainly, the multi-disciplinary approach involves problems. Proponents of the four preceding typological approaches concern themselves with different data and address themselves to different levels of analysis and explanation. Selected sections of these levels may be integrated. Psychologists and psychiatrists have generally concerned themselves with the push toward crime and delinquency rather than the form that it takes. Push is interpreted in terms of the acting out of hostilities and frustrations resulting from an assortment of personality aberrations. Sociologists, on the other hand, have concerned themselves to a greater extent than the psychologists and psychiatrists with the form or kind of crime persons commit and, more specifically, with the kind of crime a person is likely to have the opportunity, need or occasion to commit. These levels of push and form could be linked in a team approach.[35]

Some sociologists (e.g., Herbert Bloch, Arthur Niederhoffer, Albert Cohen, Lloyd Ohlin, Richard Cloward), influenced by the theories of Talcott Parsons and Robert Merton, pose stress-strain situations in society as a consequence of differential ethnic, social class and age-grade subculture memberships which, in some instances, lead to crime and delinquency. These sociologists see crime as a result of status frustration, group reinforcement, cultural innovation, anomie, reaction formation, contra-culture, differential opportunity, role confusion, etc. Though these theories focus upon socially induced stress, they interpret such strain as a chief source of personality tension.[38]

Sociologists, however, are not equipped, if indeed interested, in testing the validity and reliability of the preceding hypothetical causal elements in the individual case. Some psychologists are equipped to test for these hypothetical claims. Psychoanalysts as theoreticians and as practitioners in examining interpersonal relations within the family have concerned themselves primarily with the family as a unique internal structure. On the other hand, sociologists have been more concerned with the family as a social institution existing within a larger social system. The sociologist's knowledge of family patterns and problems stemming from the social processes of industrialization, urbanization, mobility, etc., is appreciable. They also have accumulated a wealth of material on the family relating to the ethnic background and social class position. Both the sociologist and the psychoanalyst are interested in the process of socialization; therefore, the knowledge of the sociologist could be utilized by the psychoanalyst in the area of interpersonal relations within the family. Conversely, the sociologist could learn much about differential family behavior patterns within the same ethnic and social class positions.

The multi-disciplinary approach will also face conceptual problems because of the complexity of language habits in the field of criminology. The diversity of backgrounds among criminologists makes for language confusion at the theoretical levels. There is evidence, however, that the constructs and concepts of the various disciplinary approaches to crime may be clarified and in part agreed upon, thus permitting cooperative research.[37] The varying degrees of precision or the measuring and judgmental approaches of the different disciplines would offer some impediment. Every effort would need to be made to make decisions involving psychiatric and social data as precise as possible. Researchers could be assigned specific roles in gathering and analyzing data on the basis of their specialties.

Currently, there is no systematic approach which attempts to link the legal, constitutional, sociological, psychiatric-psychological variables to specific patterns of criminal behavior. As Bloch and Flynn point out, however, a fruitful and encouraging beginning is already taking place in what is known as the multidisciplinary approach to the problems of human relations and motivations, which includes the beginning of a coordinated and cooperative attack upon the problem of crime and delinquency.[38] Marshall Clinard's *Report of the Representative to the Fourth International Criminological Congress* reveals that European as well as American criminologists are advocating an interdisciplinary approach to the study of crime.[39] Moreover, within the past twenty years there has been a movement, among some scholars, away from general theories to account for all criminal behavior toward separate theories for specific patterns of crime.[40]

DIMENSIONS OF ANALYSIS AND METHODOLOGY

The author's findings reveal (elsewhere) that individual offenders may be classified on the basis of their criminal careers, criminal pattern categories, including *modi operandi,* and that thus classified they exhibit psychological and social characteristics common to the category. Recent research indicates that certain kinds of people select (and are selected) for certain occupational roles in the upper world. A parallel may exist in the criminal world.[41]

The author concludes that what is needed in the construction of criminal types is the linkage of certain types of criminal behavior patterns (along with levels of *modi operandi*) to certain social and personal background factors, including family and cultural background, social pressures, personality traits and structure, self-concept, psychogenic pressures and constitutional predispositions, should they exist. The dynamics involved in the resulting criminal behavior pattern must be studied in the individual case; however, it must be demonstrated that a sizeable group of offenders who engage in the same type of crime share personality and social background factors. In short, to establish a criminal typology it must be shown that certain kinds of people in certain situations commit similar kinds of crime. We must find dimensions of measurement on which offenders (probationers, inmates, parolees) may be differentiated into homogeneous groups. The following dimensions are suggested: (a) offense pattern; (b) *modi operandi;* (c) social attributes; (d) personality type; (e) self-concept; (f) attitudes; and (g) situations, stresses and pressures antedating and following criminal behavior. *Any definition of criminal types must specify variation along the first dimension (offense pattern). In regard to the other dimensions, criminal types might include similar attributes in some but not in all dimensions.*

The following outline includes study areas essential to the above dimensional analysis.

1. *Delinquent and Criminal Career:* (a) time of onset; nature, number and types of official and unofficial delinquent and criminal acts; (b) time periods between acts; (c) police contacts, arrests, adjudications, dispositions and commitments; (d) adjustment during commitment; (e) level of *modus operandi* in delinquent and criminal acts; (f) solitary acts, group acts (juvenile gang, criminal gang or mob, syndicate); (g) role in delinquent and criminal groups— leaders, followers; (h) type of delinquent and criminal patterning; (i) definition of self as delinquent or criminal; (j) level of aspiration in pursuit of a criminal career.

2. *Family Background:* (a) age, occupation, work habits, education and marital status of parents and siblings; (b) mental, emotional and physical health status of parents and siblings; (c) delinquent and criminal history, deviant

habits (drugs, alcohol, prostitution, philandering, incest, violent behavior, gambling, etc.) of parents and siblings; (d) number and nature of parent and sibling contacts with public and private social agencies (welfare, mental health clinics, psychiatric clinics, child behavior clinics, marriage counseling clinics, etc.); (e) marital adjustment of parents and siblings; (f) degree of family cohesion; (g) parents' attitude toward each other; (h) parents' attitude toward the children; (i) parents' attitude toward religion; (j) family activities, amusements and cultural interests; (k) relations existing among children.

3. *Developmental History, Family:* (a) kind and quality of parental supervision offender received, e.g., lax, regimented, erratic, adequate; (b) nature and kinds of stressful situations offender faced in family; (c) nature of conflicts offender had with parents and siblings; (d) offender's type of disciplinary problem in family, e.g., active and passive disobedience, lying, stealing, fighting, running away from home, temper tantrums, etc.; (e) offender's reactions toward parents' disciplinary measures, overt and covert; (f) offender's emotional relationships and identifications with parents and siblings; (g) offender's present emotional ties with parents and siblings; (h) offender's academic and behavioral school adjustment.

4. *Developmental History, Community:* (a) type of area reared in—urban, rural, slum, non-slum, neighborhood mobility; (b) presence of delinquents, delinquent gangs, criminals and criminal gangs in neighborhoods reared in; (c) nature and persistency of associations with juvenile delinquents, juvenile delinquent gangs, criminals, criminal gangs; (d) nature of delinquent and criminal acts offender participated in as a "loner" and as a member of a delinquent or criminal group; (e) recreational pursuits in childhood, adolescence and adulthood; (f) adjustments within supervised and unsupervised play groups; (g) time of onset and developmental circumstances surrounding the following

habits—smoking, drinking, gambling and the use of drugs, heterosexual and homosexual experiences; (h) participation in and adjustment to church and other community organizations; (i) employed at street and other trades as a juvenile; (j) occupational history as an adult (occupational type: unskilled, semiskilled, skilled, clerical, other; work history: work habits and present attitude toward work); (k) military adjustment—disciplinary history and type of discharge; (1) marital status and marital adjustment including number of spouses and children.

5. *Reference Group Orientation and Identification:* (a) social class; (b) occupational group; (c) ethnic group; (d) delinquent or criminal subculture; (e) self-concept.

6. *Attitudes:* Attitudes toward the basic social institutions and especially toward law enforcement machinery, the judicial processes and correctional institutions.

7. *Developmental History, Physical:* (a) chronological age; (b) serious illnesses during infancy, childhood, adolescence, adulthood; (c) amputations, deformities, crippling diseases, head injuries; (d) epilepsy, brain damage, abnormal brain waves, encephalitis; (e) communicable disease history; (f) somatotype.

8. *Developmental History, Personal:* (a) IQ reports; (b) personality profile based on psychiatric and psychological inventory evinced from reports of clinical interviews and examinations and objective and projective psychological tests.

The next three chapters embody critical overviews of several typological attempts. No endeavor is made at complete coverage, but rather the presentation of representative constructs emanating from several frames of reference—the constitutional, psychological-psychiatric and sociological. It is recognized, as Garrity, and Gibbons point out, that criminal and delinquent typologies are generally of two kinds: (a) those which purport to classify the universe of offenders and (b) those which identify specific patterns of criminal behavior for analysis.[12] Since this dichotomy is not always explicit in the typological literature, no precise attempt is made to follow it in this review.

REFERENCES

1. MARTIN, JOHN M., and FITZPATRICK, JOSEPH P.. *Delinquent Behavior*. New York, Random House, 1964, pp. 155-163.
2. TAPPAN, PAUL W.: Who is the criminal? *American Sociological Review*, 12:96-102, February, 1947.
3. SUTHERLAND, EDWIN H.: *The Professional Thief*. Chicago, University of Chicago Press, 1937; LEMERT, EDWIN M.: The behavior of the systematic check forger. *Social Problems*, 6:141-149, Fall, 1958.
4. ABRAHAMSEN, DAVID: *The Psychology of Crime*. New York, Columbia University Press, 1960, pp. 124-144.
5. TAPPAN, PAUL W.: *Crime, Justice, and Correction*. New York, McGraw-Hill, 1960, pp. 7-10.
6. QUINNEY, RICHARD: Is criminal behaviour deviant behaviour? *British Journal of Criminology*, 132-140, April, 1965.
7. The pros and cons of the legalist approach are discussed in NEWMAN, DONALD J.: Legal norms and criminological definitions. In ROUCEK, JOSEPH S. (ed.): *Sociology of Crime*. New York, Philosophic Library, 1961, pp. 55-85. See also JOHNSON, ELMER H.: *Crime, Correction and Society*. Homewood, Ill., The Dorsey Press, 1964, pp. 3-15, 226-227; SACHAR, EDWARD J.: Behavioral science and criminal law. *Scientific American*, 209:39-45, November, 1963.
8. ZIGLER, EDWARD, and PHILLIPS, LESLIE: Psychiatric diagnosis: A critique. *Journal of Abnormal and Social Psychology*, 63: 607-618, November, 1961.
9. MARTIN, JOHN M., and FITZPATRICK, JOSEPH P.: *Delinquent Behavior*, pp. 160-162.
10. TAPPAN, PAUL: *Crime, Justice and Correction*, pp. 70-71.
11. SZASZ, THOMAS: *The Myth of Mental Illness*. New York, Harper and Brothers, 1961.
12. MENNINGER, KARL, MAYMAN, MARTIN, and PRUYSER, PAUL: *The Vital Balance*. New York, The Viking Press, 1963, pp. 9-34.

13. BORING, EDWIN G.: *A History of Experimental Psychology* (2nd ed.). New York, Appleton-Century Crofts, 1957, pp. 5-7.
14. ZIGLER, EDWARD, and PHILLIPS, LESLIE: Psychiatric diagnosis: A critique, p. 607.
15. MENNINGER, KARL: *The Vital Balance,* pp. 162-163.
16. KARDINER, ABRAM: The traumatic neuroses of war (Vol. I). *American Handbook of Psychiatry, 1,* New York, Basic Books, 1959, p. 251.
17. BAUGHMAN, E. EARL, and WELSH, GEORGE S.: *Personality: A Behavioral Science.* Englewood Cliffs, N. J., Prentice-Hall, 1962, pp. 22-23.
18. GIBBONS, DON C.: *Changing the Lawbreaker.* Englewood Cliffs, N. J., Prentice-Hall, 1965, pp. 39-44.
19. HARTUNG, FRANK E.: A critique of the sociological approach to crime and corrections, pp. 703-734; and HAKEEM, MICHAEL: A critique of the psychiatric approach to crime and correction, pp. 650-682. *Law and Contemporary Problems,* Autumn, 1958. CLINARD, MARSHALL B.: Criminological research. *Sociology Today, Problems and Prospects.* New York, Basic Books, 1959, pp. 509-536. GLUECK, SHELDON: Theory and fact in criminology. *The Problem of Delinquency.* Boston, Houghton Mifflin, 1959, pp. 241-252.
20. CLINARD, MARSHALL B.: Research frontiers in criminology. *The British Journal of Delinquency.* October, 1956, pp. 110-122; CLINARD, MARSHALL B.: *The Sociology of Deviant Behavior.* New York, Rinehart and Company, 1957, pp. 200-229; RECKLESS, WALTER C.: *The Crime Problem* (3rd ed.). New York, Appleton-Century-Crofts, 1961, pp. 324-325; SUTHERLAND, EDWIN H., and CRESSEY, DONALD R.: *Principles of Criminology* (5th ed.). New York, J. B. Lippincott, 1955, pp. 237-250.
21. KORN, RICHARD R., and McCORKLE, LLOYD W.: *Criminology and Penology.* New York, Henry Holt, 1959, pp. 317-319.
22. SCHUESSLER, KARL F., and CRESSEY, DONALD R.: Personality characteristics of criminals. *American Journal of Sociology,* 55:476-484, March, 1950.
23. RECKLESS, WALTER C.: *The Crime Problem* (3rd ed.). New York, Appleton-Century-Crofts, 1961, pp. 324-325.
24. RECKLESS WALTER C.: *The Crime Problem,* p. 75.
25. GIBBONS, DON C., and GARRITY, DONALD L.: Definitions and

analysis of certain criminal types. *Journal of Criminal Law, Criminology, and Police Science,* 53:27-35, March, 1962.

26. LOTTIER, STUART: A tension theory of criminal behavior, *American Sociological Review,* 7:840-848, December, 1942.

27. LEMERT, EDWIN M.: An isolation and closure theory of naive check forgery. *Journal of Criminal Law, Criminology, and Police Science,* 44:296-308, September-October, 1953; LEMERT, EDWIN M.: The behavior of the systematic check forger. *Social Problems,* 6:141-149, Fall, 1958.

28. RIEMER, SVEND: Embezzlement: Pathological basis. *Journal of Criminal Law and Criminology,* 32:411-423, November-December, 1941.

29. ROEBUCK, JULIAN B., and CADWALLADER, MERVIN L.: The Negro armed robber as a criminal type: The construction and application of a typology. *Pacific Sociological Review,* 4:21-26, Spring, 1961; ROEBUCK, JULIAN B.: The Negro drug addict as an offender type. *Journal of Criminal Law, Criminology, and Police Science,* 53:36-43, March, 1962; ROEBUCK, JULIAN B.: The Negro numbers man as an offender type. *Journal of Criminal Law, Criminology, and Police Science,* 54:48-60, March, 1963; ROEBUCK, JULIAN B.: and JOHNSON, RONALD: The Negro drinker and assaulter as a criminal type. *Crime and Delinquency,* 8:21-23, January, 1962; ROEBUCK, JULIAN B., and JOHNSON, RONALD: The short con man. *Crime and Delinquency,* 10:234-248, July, 1964; see also ROEBUCK, JULIAN B., and JOHNSON, RONALD: The Jack-of-all-trades offender. *Crime and Delinquency,* 8:172-181, April 1962.

30. CLINARD, MARSHALL B., and WADE, ANDREW L.: Toward the delineation of vandalism as a sub-type in juvenile delinquency. *Journal of Criminal Law, Criminology, and Police Science,* 48:493-499, January-February, 1958.

31. ABRAHAMSEN, DAVID: *The Psychology of Crime,* pp. 123-126.

32. CAVAN, RUTH SHONLE: *Criminology* (3rd ed.). New York, Thomas Y. Crowell, 1962, pp. 96-185.

33. FERRICUTI, F., and WOLFGANG, MARVIN E.: Clinical vs. sociological criminology: Separation or integration? *Excerpta Criminologica,* 4:407-410, July/August, 1964.

34. BOVET, LUCIEN: *Psychiatric Aspects of Juvenile Delinquency.* Geneva, World Health Organization, 1951; AARON J. ROSANOFF, et al.: Criminality and delinquency in twins. *Journal*

of Criminal Law and Criminology, 24:923-934, January-February, 1934. For an overview of the constitutional, psychogenic and social-cultural factors in the causation of crime, see BLOCH, HERBERT A., and FLYNN, FRANK T.: *Delinquency: The Juvenile Offender in America Today.* New York, Random House, 1956, pp. 96-237; TAPPAN, PAUL W.: *Crime, Justice and Correction.* New York, McGraw-Hill, 1960, pp. 83-188.

35. MARTIN, JOHN M., and FITZPATRICK, JOSEPH P.: *Delinquent Behavior,* pp. 144-148.

36. MARTIN, JOHN M., and FITZPATRICK, JOSEPH P.: *Delinquent Behavior,* pp. 63-69.

37. NAESS, SIRI: Comparing theories of criminogenesis. *The Journal of Research in Crime and Delinquency,* 1:171-180, July, 1964.

38. BLOCH, HERBERT A., and FLYNN, FRANK T.: *Delinquency,* pp. 96-98.

39. CLINARD, MARSHALL: *American Sociological Review,* 26:999-1000, December, 1961.

40. GIBBONS, DON C., and GARRITY, DONALD L.: Some suggestions for the development of etiological and treatment theory in criminology. *Social Forces,* 38:51-52, October, 1959.

41. JOHNSON, ELMER HUBERT: *Crime, Correction and Society.* Homewood, Ill., The Dorsey Press, 1964, pp. 227-238. See also HENRY, WILLIAM E.: The business executive: The psychodynamics of a social role. *American Journal of Sociology,* January, 1949, pp. 286-291.

42. GIBBONS, DON C., and GARRITY, DONALD L.: Some suggestions for the development of etiological and treatment theory in criminology. *Social Forces,* p. 51.

Chapter II

THE PHYSICAL-CONSTITUTIONAL-
HEREDITARY APPROACH

T HE CONSTITUTIONAL approach to crime has had few adherents in the United States since the early decades of the twentieth century. Neither the reported findings of the criminal anthropologists (Lombroso and his followers) nor the constitutional studies of recent European criminal biologists (on criminal twins, physical constitution, psychopathic personality and prognosis of unimprovable recidivists which stress the indirect rather than the direct influence of heredity) have had much impact on American behavioral scientists in their study and classification of criminals. Ernest A. Hooton, William Sheldon and, in part, Sheldon and Eleanor Glueck are exceptions; and the studies of all of these have been sharply criticized by American psychiatrists, psychologists and sociologists. The following representations begin with Lombroso and end with recent constitutional studies.

Cesare Lombroso (1836-1909), a physician, the founder of the Italian or Positive School of Criminology, attempted to apply Darwin's biological theory to the criminal. The criminal behaved as he did because he was born with a certain biological constitution characterized by a direct tendency to commit criminal offenses. Certain physical stigmata and physical deviations found through anthropometric measurements indicated the born criminal an anatomical, atavistic type. His investigations included the measurement of skull and various other organs in postmortem observation and the examination of living criminals with reference to blood pressure, emotional reactions, hearing, taste, smell and handwriting. He divided criminals into: (a) the born criminal; (b) the epileptic criminal; (c) the criminal of irresistible passion; (d) the insane and the feebleminded criminal, including those of borderline mentality; and (e) the occasional criminal, subdivided into the pseudocriminal, the criminiloid and the persistent offender of non-abnormal type. Lombroso in his later career modified his earlier theories and recognized many sociological and psychological factors in crime causation. Epilepsy and degeneracy received more attention than atavism.[1] Though he failed to demonstrate an anatomical criminal type, it is not for naught that he is often referred to as the "father of modern criminology." Criminology is indebted to Lombroso for the following contributions: (a) He recognized the prevailing inadequacy of methods being utilized to discover the causes of criminal conduct and was among the first to focus attention on the individual criminal; (b) he made the first attempt to establish a scientific criminal psychopathology; contemporary endocrinological and biological typological studies reflect the direct influence of Lombroso; (c) he stressed determinism, rather than free will; (d) he made comparisons between offender types as well as comparisons between criminals and noncriminals; (e) he utilized measurements and statistical methods (though crude) with anthropological, social and economic data; (f) he made an attempt to classify criminals; (g) he insisted that the personality of the offender be examined—paving the way for the idea that the criminal was the cause and that the crime was the result; (h) he described the psychological traits which the criminal manifested (instability, impulsiveness, meagerly developed affections, vanity, lying, gambling, lack of restraint, etc.); (i) he called attention to a relationship between epilepsy and violent crime.[2]

Enrico Ferri (1856-1929), a student of Lombroso, classified criminals as: (a) the born or instinctive criminal (criminals, alcoholics, syphilitics, subnormals, insane, neuropathics, etc.) who suffers a reduced resistance to criminal stimuli and a precocious propensity to crime; (b) the diseased or those burdened with neuropsychopathic condition; (c) the passional criminal of two subtypes—passion (a prolonged and chronic mental state) and emotion (explosive and unexpected mental

state); (d) the occasional criminal who constitutes the majority
of lawbreakers, a product of family and social milieu more than
of abnormal, personal physico-mental conditions; (e) the habitual
criminal, the criminal by acquired habit, who is mostly a product
of his social environment, e.g., abandonment by family, lack of
education, poverty, bad companions, contacts with criminals in
prison; (f) the involuntary criminal, the pseudocriminal who
causes damage and peril through lack of foresight, imprudence,
negligence or disobedience of regulations rather than through
malice. Some of these have a weak sense of moral sensitivity,
some lack technical knowledge, some are inattentive, and others
are exhausted.[3] He stressed the importance of age, sex, organic
and psychological conditions, industrial, economic, political,
climatic, geographical and family conditions in their relationship
to crime.[4]

Raffaele Garofalo (1852-1934), another member of the Positive
School, focused on the criminal as a psychological, rather than a
body, type. He analyzed the criminal's personality in relationship
to the circumstances and *modus operandi* of the criminal act.
Garofalo classed criminals into four groups, though distinct, yet
related in that each was characterized by deficiency in the basic
altruistic sentiments of pity and probity. The classifications
were: murderers; violent criminals; criminals lacking in probity;
and lascivious criminals.[5]

More recently, Ernst Kretschmer posed a constitutional classification based upon the study of people as psychobiological or
mental physiological entities: the athletic; the asthenic-schizothymic-leptosomic; and the pyknic. He claimed that there exists
a clear biological connection between mental disposition toward
schizophrenia and the asthenic-schizothymic-leptosomic and the
athletic body builds and also between mental disposition toward
a manic-depressive condition and the pyknic body type. Applied
to the classification of criminals, this theory holds that offenders
who commit serious crimes are of the asthenic-schizothymic-
leptosomic body build, while those offenders who commit less
serious crime are of a pyknic body build.[6] Dr. Adolph Lenz and
Dr. Louis Vervaeck, criminal biologists, have also posed a

criminal type based on inherited constitutional determinants and "predispositions to maladjustments."[7]

Lombroso and early anthropological criminologists assumed that there was a direct tendency to commit offenses on the part of those characterized by a certain physique. The nature of the relationship between physique and criminality was neither spelled out nor established. Critics were quick to point out the lack of evidence for the inheritance of innate tendencies directed toward the violation of laws, which vary in definition in space and time. To overcome this difficulty, the constitutionalists postulated the existence of certain biological tendencies, e.g., cruelty, dishonesty, the lack of the sentiments of pity and probity, degeneracy, moral insanity, etc., which, in themselves, were not necessarily directed against specific legal codes, but which, as personality traits, under certain conditions, lead to a crime. Still later, the constitutionalists postulated certain predispositions or general "moral weaknesses" which, when allied with adverse environmental conditions, might manifest themselves in criminal behavior. The fundamental question remains unanswered—the nature of the relationship existing between whatever it is that is constitutional and criminal behavior. Additionally, the claim of those who pose a criminal typology on the basis of physical type or on the basis of inherited constitutional factors have not been validated by research findings on a representative sample of offenders. Their studies do not contain standard measurable norms by which they can compare the physical and mental traits of observed criminals with the noncriminal population of the same age, class, sex and race.

Though the constitutionalists have been primarily concerned with demonstrating that criminals in general (at least recidivists) possess a physical and mental makeup that decreases their ability to live a law-abiding existence, a number of them have concentrated on the psychopathic personality type as a criminal type. Despite complete agreement as to the psychopathic syndrome, the following characteristics are generally included: asociality; uncontrolled desires; impulsiveness; aggressiveness; lack of guilt feelings; inability to relate to or love others. Many criminal biologists will insist that most of the "real" criminals are psychopaths.

There exist three schools of thought in reference to psychopathic causation: (a) the genetic; (b) the neurological; and (c) the psychogenic. Since we are interested at this point in the constitutional approach, the first two schools are discussed. Patridge,[8] Mohr[9] and Newkirk[10] in three separate studies of psychopaths report a high incidence of psychopaths in their cases' ancestral lines. The studies of Lenz, Vervaeck, Exner and Frey, although concerned with several biological factors, report a high incidence of psychopathic personalities among their criminal case studies and also high incidences of psychopathy in the ancestral lines of these cases.

Twin studies to date designed to examine connections between genetic factors and psychopathy are inconclusive. Kallman demonstrated that the children of psychopaths have a higher percentage of psychopathy than the siblings of psychopaths.[11] Slater studied the life histories of nine pairs of twins, some of whom were psychopathic, some neurotic. Only two pairs had similar personality traits, though he concluded that psychopathy results from a genetic base precipitated by environmental conditions.[12] Newman and Holzinger reported on twins reared in separate environments and claimed a close resemblance in the incidence of psychopathy and the date of its incipience.[13] Cleckly, in a study of the psychopath's ancestral line, found no evidence of genetic succession.[14]

The problem of a concise definition of the psychopath, differentials in study samples and the dearth of adequate control groups have plagued the twin studies. The genetic factor in psychopathy remains an important, open question.

The neurological approach to the causation of psychopathy (psychopathic personality) has yielded more conclusive results than the genetic approach to date. McCord and McCord have reported the findings of a long series of studies on the relationship of brain damage, damaged neural structures, encephalitis, chorea, epilepsy, and abnormal EEG patterns to psycopathy. Some of these studies included criminals; some did not. Some made use of control groups; others did not. The McCords' provisional summation of these studies follow. (a) Psychopaths, more frequently than normal people, show EEG abnormalities; (b) a greater proportion of psychopaths, when compared with normal people, exhibit signs of neurological disorder (tremors, exaggerated reflexes, tics); (c) psychopaths are probably more physiologically responsive to physical changes in their environment than non-psychopaths; (d) a greater proportion of psychopaths, when compared with normal people, have a history of early diseases which damage the brain.[15]

Recent European "criminal biologists" have attempted to differentiate between two types of offenders: (a) the *real criminal*, the recidivistic serious offender, whom they claim is a product of inherited predispositions linked with adverse surroundings and (b) the *occasional petty offender*, the situational type. Inherited predispositions are not ruled out for this second type. They reason that, as a group, all criminals are inferior or defective when compared with noncriminals. Differences are of degree rather than kind. These predispositions, or "loadings" against the individual, are considered to be paramount in the making of the real criminal. Data is presented by Franz Exner in his work, *Kriminologie,* from his own research and the research of other German researchers, such as Riedl, Schnell, Schmid, Stumpfl, Bemmelen, Buttkus, Schwaab, and Krassnuschkin. These data exhibit a reported high incidence of one or more of the following factors in the family strain of the real criminal: mental abnormalities; epilepsy; feeblemindedness; alcoholism; psychopathic personality; suicide; sex perversion; and criminality. The reported incidence of these factors is high in offenders, higher for the repeaters than the first offenders and higher for the early-starting than for the late-starting offenders.[16]

Erwin Frey, a Swiss criminologist and a student of Exner, analyzed several series of juvenile delinquent cases from the courts in Basel and from the institutions for delinquent youth in Switzerland. He suggests the same dichotomy as Exner: (a) the *habitual serious offender* who is "loaded" and whose family strain is "loaded" with one or more of the following— mental disease, defective intelligence, psychopathic personality, alcoholism, criminality; (b) the *occasional offender* or situational type who evidences in his own makeup or his family line less frequent loading of these characteristics. Frey, as many other European criminologists, considers the appearance of such blemishes in the personality of the individual offender and in the personalities of his ancestors as evidence of the biological inheritance of weaknesses predisposing to antisocial and criminal behavior.[17]

Although both Frey and Exner failed to demonstrate a linkage between a particular criminal-behavior pattern and a particular personality structure, they did exhibit (at least with the cases under study), as have others, that the onset of delinquency and crime in early youth foretells criminality in adulthood. Their research also indicates that the habitual serious offender may vary from the occasional offender in hereditary predisposition to antisocial and criminal behavior.

On the American scene, Sheldon and Eleanor Glueck claim to have established a correlation between physical type and delinquency. The dedication of their book, *Physique and Delinquency,* a monograph growing out of a comprehensive research into persistent juvenile delinquency, encompassed in their *Unraveling Juvenile Delinquency,* to the late Ernest A. Hooton is meaningful. Their reported findings not only support but extend Sheldon's thesis. For the first time, a mechanism is suggested which connects a specific kind of physique and personality (mesomorphic dionysian) with a specific kind of criminal behavior (aggressive and predatory). Moreover, their reported results go much further than indicating the high incidence of mesomorphs among delinquents; what is more important from a typological frame of reference, they report different characteristic patterns of response for each of four body types. Certain sociocultural stresses operate to modify or enhance the characteristic behavior patterns of each type.[18] Professor Peter Lejins maintains that the Gluecks have found for the first time a plausible suggestion for a way out of the long-standing controversy between the role of the hereditary endowment expressed in the physique of the individual and the roll of the environmental influences.[19]

The constitutionalists may, through research findings, contribute data which, when coupled with psychological and sociological findings, might lead to the construction of a criminal typology. The efforts of the following constitutionalists are of note in this direction: Lange; Legras; Kranz; Stumpfl; and Rosanoff.[20] Yoshimasu in twin studies has concluded that the greater frequency of concordance (both being criminal) in identical twins than in fraternal twins implied an inheritance of criminality.[21] The greater similarity in the behavioral history of the identical twins may be accounted for in part by the fact of their closer companionship and identification. Though such studies do not specifically prove hereditary influence, they do indicate the need for further twin-study research.

Schlapp and Smith,[22] Berman,[23] Podolsky[24] and Grimberg[25] have emphasized the role of the endocrine glands in causing criminal behavior. Podolsky claims that certain offense types are associated with specific glandular dysfunctions. Berman claims that there are various endocrine types of personality in which one or another of the hormones may connote the pattern of the individual's behavior, e.g., the uninhibited, irresponsible and criminalistic thymocentric type.

Further glandular research is necessary before an evaluation of the relationship between glandular dysfunction and criminality can be made. There is evidence to indicate that glandular dysfunction is a precipitating factor in the development of behavioral disorders among some people.[26]

Recent EEG studies indicate the persistent delinquent with serious, aggressive behavior problems may vary neurologically from normals. Daniel Silverman did electroencephalographic studies on criminal psychopaths, finding that 80 per cent of his subjects had abnormal or borderline tracings.[27] George N. Thompson found 280 severe delinquents to have a significantly higher rate of neurological abnormalities than 100 controls (non-delinquents).[28] In Yoshi, *et al*, in a comparison of delinquents with controls, EEG's of the two groups were significantly distinguishable. In delinquents, the theta waves were observed more frequently on the frontal, central and temporal cortices. Spikes appeared more frequently on the temporal and central cortices of delinquents. Results of the Rorschach and Yatabe-Guilford tests demonstrated asocial and impulsive traits or anxiety in the spikegroup and asociality and emotional immaturity in the theta group. A significant relationship between EEG patterns and the criminal classification of the delinquents was found.[29] Dr. Sara G. Geiger, in an examination of 623 acting-out juvenile delinquents with severe behavior disorders received at the Milwaukee County Guidance Clinic, found 453 with abnormal EEG's.[30] Jenkins and Pacella studied delinquent boys and found no high correlation between criminal behavior and abnormal encephalographic tracings but did find correlations between abnormal tracings and epilepsy and organic brain disease.[31] Abrahamsen maintains that EEG's may be more related to epileptic manifestations than to antisocial or criminal behavior.[32]

The relationship of types of criminal behavior to EEG's and epilepsy remains unclear. It is known that some epileptics are prone to crimes of violence and that still others commit acts varying from petty assaults to rape and murder during states of altered consciousness as well as during states of clear consciousness.

In concluding this section it may be fitting to remark that, contrary to the beliefs of many American criminologists, the constitutional school is not dead. Research continues in this area, and it behooves the skeptic whether he be sociologist, psychiatrist or psychologist to at least keep an open mind toward it. Enrico Altabilla, professor at the University of Naples, in a recent article, "Criminal Anthropology, Old and New," recapitulates the contributions of the Positive School and comments on various current constitutional approaches to the study of crime in Europe.[33]

REFERENCES

1. LOMBROSO, CESARE: *L'Uomo Delinquents* (1876). Translated, with modification by Henry P. Horton as *Crime, Its Causes and Remedies*. Boston, Little, Brown and Company, 1918.
2. WOLFGANG, MARVIN E.: Cesare Lombroso. In Mannheim, Her-

mann (ed.): *Pioneers in Criminology*. Chicago, Quadrangle Books, 1960, pp. 168-225.

3. FERRI, ENRICO: *L'Omicida Nella Paicologia e Nella Psicopatologia Criminale* (2nd ed.)—*L'Omicidio-Suicidio. Responsabilita Givridica* (5th ed.). Torino, UTET, 1925, pp. 45-55.

4. SELLIN, THORSTEN: Enrico Ferri. In *Pioneers in Criminology,* pp. 277-300.

5. ALLEN, FRANCIS A.: Raffaele Garofalo. In *Pioneers in Criminology,* pp. 254-276.

6. KRETSCHMER, ERNST: *Physique and Character*. New York, Harcourt, Brace, 1925.

7. LENZ, ADOLPH: Die Bedeutung Der Kriminal-Biologie. *Archiv fur Kriminalbiologie, LXXXVIII*:222-234, 1931; VERVAECK, LOUIS: *Syllabus De Cours D'Anthropologie Criminelle, Donne a la Prison de Forest*. Brussels, 1926, p. 57.

8. PATRIDGE, G. E.: A study of 50 cases of psychopathic personality. *American Journal of Psychiatry*, 84:953-973, May, 1928.

9. MOHR, PETER: Die Forensische Bedeutung der Psychopathen. *Schweizer Archiv fur Neurologie, Neurochirurgie und Psychietrie*, 60:244-268, 1947.

10. NEWKIRK, P. R.: Psychopathic traits are inheritable. *Diseases of the Nervous System, 80*:52-54, 1957.

11. KALLMAN, FRANZ J.: *The Genetics of Schizophrenia*. New York, J. J. Augustin, 1939.

12. SLATER, E. T. O.: Psychiatric genetics, Part II. In Fleming, G. and Walk A. (eds.): *Recent Progress in Psychiatry* (Vol. 3). New York, Grove Press, 1959.

13. NEWMAN, H. H., FREEMAN, F. N., and HOLZINGER, K. J.: *Twins: A Study of Heredity and Environment*. Chicago, Chicago University Press, 1937.

14. CLECKLEY, HERVEY: Psychopathic states. *American Handbook of Psychiatry* (Arieti Silvano, ed.). New York, Basic Books, 1959.

15. McCORD, WILLIAM, and McCORD, JOAN: *The Psychopath: An Essay on the Criminal Mind*. Princeton, New Jersey, D. Van Nostrand, 1956, pp. 61-70.

16. EXNER, FRANZ: *Kriminologie*. Berlin, Springer Verlag, 1949, pp. 115-120.

17. FREY, ERWIN: *Der Frukriminelle Ruckfallaverbrecher*. Basel, Verlag Fur Recht Und Gessellschaft [A.G., 1959], pp. 59-348.

18. GLUECK, SHELDON and ELEANOR: *Physique and Delinquency.* New York, Harper and Bros., 1956, pp. 161-273.
19. LEJINS, PETER P.: Hereditary endowment, environmental influences and criminality, as found in Bloch, Herbert A. (ed): *Crime in America.* New York, Philosophical Library, 1961, pp. 315-328.
20. MONTAGU, M. F. ASHLEY: The Biologist Looks at Crime. *Annals,* 217:46-53, September, 1941.
21. YOSHIMASU, S.: The criminological significance of the family in the light of the studies of criminal twins. *Excerpta Criminologica,* 2:723, November/December, 1962.
22. SCHLAPP, MAX G., and SMITH, E. H.: *The New Criminology.* New York, Boniand Liveright, 1929.
23. BERMAN, LOUIS: Crime and the endocrine glands. *American Journal of Psychiatry,* 12:215-238, September, 1932.
24. PODOLSKY, EDWARD: The chemical brew of criminal behavior. *Journal of Criminal Law and Criminology and Police Science,* 45:175-679, March/April, 1955.
25. GRIMBERG, LEIZER E.: *Emotion and Delinquency.* New York, Bretano's, 1928.
26. YOUNG, WILLIAM C.: *Glandular Physiology and Therapy* (5th ed.). Philadelphia, J. B. Lippincott, 1954, pp. 513-518.
27. SILVERMAN, DANIEL: Clinical and electroencephalographical studies on criminal psychopaths. *Archives of Neurology and Psychiatry,* 1:18-20, 30, 31, July, 1943.
28. THOMPSON, GEORGE N.: *The Psychopathic Delinquent and Criminal.* Springfield, Illinois, Charles C Thomas, 1953.
29. YOSHI N., SHIMOKOCHI, M., and TANI, K.: In *Excerpta Criminologica,* 2:545, September/October, 1962, Excerpta Criminologica Foundation, Amsterdam, The Netherlands.
30. GEIGER, SARA G.: Organic factors in delinquency. *Journal of Social Therapy,* 6:224-237, 4th Quarter, 1960.
31. JENKINS, R. L., and PACELLA, B. L.: Electroencephalographic studies of delinquent boys. *American Journal of Orthopsychiatry,* 13:107-120, 1943.
32. ABRAHAMSEN, DAVID: *The Psychology of Crime,* p. 139.
33. ALTAVILLA, ENRICO: Criminal anthropology, old and new. *Excerpta Criminologica,* 2:505-511, September/October, 1962.

Chapter III

THE PSYCHOLOGICAL-PSYCHIATRIC APPROACH

PSYCHIATRISTS rather than psychologists have pioneered in criminology in the United States as practitioners in clinics, guidance centers, courts and institutions. They have also been more interested and prominent in the study and classification of offenders, *per se,* than have psychologists. The names of the following "criminal psychiatrists" quickly come to mind: Benjamin Rush; Hamilton D. Wey; William Alanson White; Bernard Glueck; William Healy; Herman Adler; Benjamin Karpman; Winfred Overholser; David Abrahamsen; Ralph Brancale; and Manfred S. Guttmacher. Psychiatrists and clinical psychologists who have constructed criminal typologies have, for the most part, relied heavily on psychoanalytical theory. Their constructs were envisioned and structured in treatment terms. Among others, Alexander and Staub, Alexander and Healy, Walter Bromberg, Robert Lindner, Walter F. Argon, J. F. Brown and Douglas Orr, and Corsini illustrate this point in their typologies.[1]

Recently, some psychiatrists, though remaining psychoanalytically oriented, have combined a social-psychological approach in their criminal typologies. The classification systems of Abrahamsen and Guttmacher mark this trend. Abrahamsen contends that personality structure and environmental (situational) elements determine the types of crime a person may commit. The person's emotional state and kind of immediate pressures determine the outlet he chooses, whether it be in the form of antisocial or criminal behavior or a neurosis or psychosis. Emotionally disturbed non-offenders are similar in some respects and different in others. Both are reared in tense family situations; however, the offender, unlike the non-offender, is more likely reared in a family where ethical standards resulted in the formation of a strong superego. The criminal acts out his criminalistic aggressions. The individual suffering from an emotional or mental illness generally turns his hostile feelings toward himself. He may, however, depending on the strength of his superego, his abnormal personality type and the situation, commit a crime by acting out. Neurotic, psychotic or character disorders are all predisposing factors toward criminal behavior. Why the presence of these factors in some cases leads to crime and in other cases does not lead to crime is to be understood in a study of the individual case.[2]

Abrahamsen holds that classification of offenders will enable the court, district attorney, prison official, probation officer and psychiatrist to deal with criminals in a natural way. Classification has to be based upon personal, psychiatric-psychological factors and a combination of psychological and situational elements. Three dimensions of study are suggested: (a) history of criminal and antisocial behavior, including type, seriousness and frequency (also time spans between acts) of criminal, delinquent and anti-social acts; (b) ego involvement in each criminal act; and (c) the relationship, if any, between the criminal's aggressive drive which manifests itself in criminal behavior and his emotional and mental condition. Abrahamsen advocates a case-study approach, including a careful psychiatric examination to get at these dimensions. From his clinical examinations of criminals in New York State he postulates the following typology: (a) acute criminals subdivided into situational, associational and accidental offenders; (b) chronic offenders subdivided into neurotic offenders, offenders with neurotic character disorders, genuine psychopathic offenders, and psychotics and mentally defectives.

Acute Offenders

Acute offenders commit minor crimes once or twice with little personality involvement under circumstances that tempt them to succumb to their antisocial impulses. They do not possess marked antisocial traits and therefore make up a group of "normal criminals" who feel guilty after their criminal acts. Acute offenders are usually not essentially dangerous. Some are, and from these, chronic offenders may develop, depending on the quantity and quality of antisocial character traits present in the individual personality. Depending upon ego involvement in the crime and the ability to learn from previous situations, an offender may either commit other crimes as situations arise, or he may learn to check his criminal inclinations. *The situational offender* acts out on the basis of opportunity and need; e.g., he is the man without means who fails to return a found wallet to its rightful owner, the hungry man who steals from a bakery shop when the owner is not present. *The associational offender* is influenced by antisocial patterns in his environment, e.g., by bad companions and criminal family members. External circumstances mobilize his criminalistic tendencies, e.g., a gang man who accompanies a group of companions "just for the ride" in an unplanned robbery. *Accidental offenders* are involved in criminal acts by chance or mistake, e.g., careless driving resulting in traffic accidents, throwing away a burning match which causes property damage, the hit-and-run driver, etc.

Chronic Offenders

Chronic offenders include the following. *Neurotic offenders* are obsessive compulsive persons who are driven into action by unconscious drives, e.g., repressed sexual drives. Behind their aggressive motive is oral dependency, a passivity which they try to deny by antisocial aggression. They are unable to endure anxiety. Another group of neurotics commits crimes because of unconscious guilt feelings as a result of their deeply embedded hostility and hatred and consequent guilt feelings. The unconscious desire for punishment is a wish fulfilled by the commission of a crime. The criminal acts of neurotic offenders are kleptomania, pyromania, dipsomania, dromomania, homicidal mania, gambling, and vagrancy. *Offenders with character disorders and genuine psychopathic offenders*, include offenders with character disorders who do not exhibit neurotic symptoms *per se*. Their actions are substitutes for neurotic symptoms. They are markedly aggressive, antisocial, impulsive, narcissistic, unstable, hedonistic, orally fixated and emotionally flat individuals who have weak superegos. Frequently reared in unstable homes characterized by poor emotional relationships, emotional depriva- tion, alternating rejection and overindulgence, they have failed to identify with proper role models. Persons with character disorders are likely to commit all types of criminal acts. Distinc- tions between the offender with neurotic character disorder and the genuine psychopath are a matter of degree rather than kind. The genuine psychopath is reared under conditions of extreme deprivation, etc. He demonstrates pronounced absence of guilt feelings, anxiety and gross lack of identification. Among both we find a greater proportion of neurologically abnormal findings than among non-offenders. *Psychotic and mentally defective offenders* include those offenders who, because of defective reasoning, are unable to understand (either emotionally or intel- lectually) that their criminal acts are wrong. Factors causing impediment of mind of these criminals may be functional, psychogenic, toxic, infectious or degenerative. They comprise schizophrenics, mentally defectives, persons with severe head injuries, manic-depressives, paretics, epileptics, etc. Crimes of psychotics are often bizarre and seemingly nonsensical. Mental defectives commit a variety of simple crimes, e.g., simple theft, assault, arson, exhibitism, rape, incest, homosexuality, cruelty toward animals, murder, sex offenses.[3]

Dr. Manfred S. Guttmacher, Chief Medical Officer, Supreme Bench of Baltimore, Maryland, claims that there has been no psychiatric study which gives us a true measure of the incidence of psychiatric mobility in the criminal population. He holds that various statistical surveys by competent psychiatrists with ex- perience in the field of criminal psychiatry show that about 80 per cent of criminals are psychiatrically normal. In his opinion, no classification of criminals to date is adequate; however, he supports typological efforts as necessary. He sees disposition as the chief purpose of criminal classification. Guttmacher postu- lates the following classification. (a) The normal or dysocial offenders who have identified with the asocial members of society (generally with morally and socially defective parental figures) comprise 75 to 80 per cent of criminals. He recommends work therapy and group therapy as treatment measures for this group. (b) The accidental or occasional criminals belong to a very small group with healthy superegos, who have become pressured into criminal acts by a special set of circumstances. These make ideal probation material. (c) The organically or constitutionally predisposed criminals constitute a small and disparate group: the intellectually defective; the post-encephalic; the epileptic; the senile deteriorative; the post-traumatic, etc. Treatment must be based on the causative factors involved, e.g., the urban, recidivistic, mentally deficient should be placed in a farm-type prison colony, the senile-deteriorative group generally involved in sex offenses with children belong in a mental hospital. (d) The psychopathic or sociopathic criminals present the most difficult treatment challenge. Many of them are serious recidivists. Others are persistent nuisances. These non-psychotic persons become involved in irrational, antisocial and criminal behavior as a probable result of unconscious neurotic conflicts. They comprise 10 to 15 per cent of the criminal population. Psychopaths should be subdivided on the basis of behavioral manifestations. Causation is unknown, but early emotional deprivation and the lack of early love objects with whom identification could be made probably resulted in childhood defense mechanisms of hostility and aggression which persisted into adulthood. They would include many check forgers, swindlers, confidence men, violently aggressive and sadistic criminals, neurotic sexual offenders, immature and recidivistic neurotic offenders, who because of antisocial impulses and compulsions, turn to law enforcement officers and penal administrators for help. Treatment for these psychopaths (including some neurotics) entails individual and group psychotherapy. (e) The psychotic criminals whose antisocial behavior is a symptom of insanity comprise one and one half per cent of criminals. They suffer from one of the major mental disorders, marked by regressive behavior in which the ego is overwhelmed by primitive aggressive drives. Their acts are bizarre and seemingly nonsensical. They should be sent to the criminal division of state psychiatric hospitals for psychiatric treatment.[4]

The typologies of Abrahamsen and Guttmacher are noteworthy and plausible in relationship to their clinical findings; however, they are not based on representative samples of offenders confined and defined within a tight research design. The inclusiveness of their scope might preclude research attempts at validation.

These scholars fail to make a clear distinction between antisocial behavior and criminal behavior. In the writer's view, such a distinction is a must in the construction of a typology. Many writers would also criticize Abrahamsen and Guttmacher's failure to draw lines between persons suffering from character disorders, sociopathic personality and neurotic syndromes.

A number of psychiatrists have examined specific orders of crime. To mention a few, Ellis and Brancale have classified variations of the abnormal sex offender; Karpman has focused on the criminal psychopath and the sexual offender; Bernard Glueck, Jr. identified five types of major abnormal sex offenders in a sample of sex offenders sentenced to Sing Sing Prison; Seliger has classified alcoholics and the personality motivations he found among them; Reichard and Tillman studied murder and suicide as defenses against schizophrenic psychosis; Guttmacher has classified various types of murderers; Podolsky has analyzed what he calls "the mind of the swindler;" Bromberg and Keiser have made a psychological study of the swindler; Barbash analyzed a group of short con men; and Ausubel has classified drug addicts according to personality types.[5]

Recent psychiatric and psychological research in the typology of offenders has been concerned primarily with a typological classification of delinquents. The current psychiatric-oriented approaches are represented by the works of Jenkins and Hewitt, Redl, Erikson, Aichorn, Bloch and Flynn, Argyle, the Illinois State Training School Treatment Committee and the California Youth Authority Standard Nomenclature Committee.[6] The psychological approaches are represented by the social perception and interaction classifications of: Gough and Peterson; Sarbin; Peterson, Quay and Cameron; Studt; Sullivan, Grant and Grant.[7]

The works of Reiss, Beck, Topping and Mueller, which recommend different treatment assignments for different delinquent types, may also be included in the psychological-psychiatric approach.[8]

Composite sketches of four delinquent types may be extrapolated from the behavioral and personality descriptions given by the preceding authors. Type I, the emotionally disturbed delinquent is neurotic, anxious, dependent, a social isolate, with few well-developed environmental controls. Actual behavioral manifestations, however, take two forms: the over-inhibited boy, with delinquency expressed in a compulsive manner, and the acting-out boy, whose reactions to frustrations or threats to self-esteem are manifested in emotional disturbances, temper tantrums and attention-demanding behavior. Type II, the socialized delinquent, primarily an environmental product, has identified himself strongly with delinquent rather than middle-class models, ideals and goals. Within a gang, he is highly socialized, controls his aggression, subordinates his needs to those of the group and is a loyal participant. Against others, particularly the school and authority figures, he is aggressive and antisocial. Sociologists such as Peter Lejins would refer to this type as the conformist delinquent who learns delinquent behavior from a "criminalistic subculture."[9] Many psychologists, however, would question the "conformist delinquent" concept as too limited. They would additionally point to the general functional failure of the parental family group and also to the impaired interpersonal relations existing between the delinquent and his parents and between the delinquent's parents as motivating factors in the making of the so-called socialized delinquent. Type III, the unsocialized aggressive delinquent, is a boy without strong group loyalties. He perceives other people as unfriendly and threatening. He vents his hostility in aggressive acts and in maladaptive domineering behavior. Negative reactions to his aggressive behavior by others further serve to isolate this type. Type IV, the accidental delinquent, is a boy pressed by unusual or extreme circumstances into single or rare law violations. With relatively integrated personal controls he will, in all probability, become a mature, independent, conforming adult. He is like the socialized delinquent in his relations to others and in his feelings of security, but he is quite different in his positive identification with conformist models and goals. This type, in the parlance of the sociologist is the situational offender, and in the opinion of the writer is infrequently found among adjudicated delinquents.

Probably the typology of Lester E. Hewitt and Richard L. Jenkins in their stimulating work, *Fundamental Patterns of Maladjustment,* marks the most significant attempt at the typology of juvenile delinquents, utilizing the psychiatric approach, to date.[10] Sociocultural factors are also included. They examined five hundred unusually good case records at the Michigan Child Guidance Institute, upon which extensive and detailed statistical analysis was performed in an attempt to classify types of behavior patterns among them and their linkages to specific personality structures and situational determinants. They found three major types of "maladjusted youth" in their study: (a) the unsocialized aggressive delinquent, (b) the socialized delinquent, and (c) the over-inhibited neurotic.

The neurotic has an over-inhibited personality structure fraught with internal conflict between impulses and repressive forces. The typical behavior pattern is marked by shyness, seclusiveness, fears, tics, sleep disturbances, nailbiting and jealousy of parental love and attention that is directed to sibs. The parents are repressive, cold and unsocial. The mother compensates for some rejection by overprotection and overrestriction, whereas the father tends to be an intolerant perfectionist. Both parents are inconsistent, restrained, socially disciplined. The social class position of the family group is above that of the other types in the clinic. The subject has continual fear of loss of his parents' love, and his insecurity stems from the lack of a close emotional contact with his parents. The boy must be very good in order to hold his parents' love, and he feels rejected when he violates his parents' conformist taboos. He feels secure only by being excessively good. He screws down the safety valve on primitive impulses and pressure produces acute situations of internal conflict.

The personality structure of the unsocialized aggressive type is akin to that of the sociopath. The boy is cruel, defiant, remorseless, quarrelsome, mischievous, boastful, bossy, selfish, jealous, rude, suspicious, negative, evasive, sullen, hostile and bitter. He destroys property, attacks others physically and fights. He demonstrates his defiance toward people in authority and is antagonistic toward teachers. He refuses to accept blame for his acts and views himself as a victim, though in reality he is often the aggressor. He has little superego and therefore experiences few guilt feelings. Since he cannot relate well to others, he has few if any friends. He comes from the lower end of the social scale and was raised in a deteriorated neighborhood. He is likely to be illegitimate or a product of a discordant family broken by desertion or divorce. Most likely, he has grown up in several different family groups, none of which have really wanted him. His family is in disfavor by neighbors, and delinquent and unconventional sex behavior is frequently found among parents and sibs.

The mother is an unhappy, unstable individual of low mental ability who got married to get away from her parents. Both parents, but particularly the mother, have denied the boy affection from birth. The mother is most likely to be hostile or rejecting. The parents are both violent and abusive toward each other or the children. The mother, usually an alcoholic, does not accept the responsibility of motherhood and is likely to be unfaithful to her husband. One parent is extremely domineering. Family loyalty is split into opposing factions. Sex relations between the parents are unsatisfactory. Discipline is lax and inconsistent.

Exposed to generalized and continual parental rejection, lack of an effective affectional tie to any adult by which he could incorporate standards of behavior, and subject to selfish, inconsiderate and delinquent patterns in the family group, the unsocialized aggressive delinquent, motivated by revenge, openly expresses hostility toward his parents and other authority figures. His behavior pattern may be marked by arson, murder and petty theft at home and at school. His language is profane and obscene, and he demonstrates a marked interest in sex. This blundering, acting-out type of individual is likely to be engaged in a variety of delinquent and unconventional acts.

The pseudo-social boy is usually a member of a gang in which he is socialized, accepted, and adjusted. The product of a delinquent subculture, his antisocial acts are vented against people in the larger society. His behavior pattern is in some respects similar to the unsocialized aggressive boy. He, too, is defiant toward authority, avoids accepting the responsibility for his own acts and expresses little guilt. Should he violate the code of his peer group, he feels deeply guilty. Unlike the unsocialized aggressive boy, he is capable of relating to others.

He is the product of a deteriorated, delinquency-area type neighborhood. The home is overcrowded and physically inadequate. The family is large, frequently on relief, and considered to be unwholesome by neighbors. The boy notes the unfavorable contrast of his home conditions as compared with the more favorable home conditions of others he knows. The failure of paternal function rather than overt maternal rejection is the problem in this type of home. The lack of parental supervision and training is present. Both parents are violent tempered and possess different cultural values. One or more of the sibs has been an adjudicated delinquent. There is a lack of family solidarity and loyalty.

The father, more than the mother, is unwilling or unable to fulfill the parental role. He may be an alcoholic or suffer from poor health or physical impairment. He is likely to be overtly indifferent to the boy and more rejecting than the mother who frequently is overprotecting. Feeling resentment for his father, the delinquent identifies with the mother against the neglectful father. This boy was initially socialized in his relationship with the mother. The parents' failure to supervise, train, and control their children, led to a breakdown in family socialization. As a result the boy is socialized within a delinquent group rather than his family.

Though the family is wrought with conflict, the consistent sibling rivalry and jealousy found with the over-inhibited boy and the unsocialized aggressive child is not in evidence. This socialized delinquent engages more frequently in petty stealing at home or school than the unsocialized aggressive type, but his behavior is motivated by *acquisitiveness* rather than by a desire for *revenge*. He, too, is antagonistic toward school attendance, but he expresses this in truancy rather than by direct attack, such as fighting. He is popular among a wide circle of friends, including delinquent companions. He steals as a "loner" as well as in the company of others. He loiters on the street late at night, smokes and has sex relations with girls.

The chief weakness with this scheme lies with the so-called neurotic personality type. The characteristic pattern of his delinquencies is not reported. When and under what circumstances does he become delinquent? The attempt of Hewitt and Jenkins to link similar emotional patternings and environmental pressures to characteristic delinquent acts seems feasible. The sociologist would probably quarrel with the psychiatric definition of personality explicit in the typology; however, other constructs of personality type could be used in parallel research efforts.

Recently (1964), Jenkins has reported the findings of several other researchers which support the original Hewitt-Jenkins typology with minor variation. Moreover, Jenkins outlines the form of treatment for his typology as follows.[11]

1. Treatment of the over-inhibited neurotic should be directed to canalize the shell of inhibition so that the primitive impulses may find some expression in a socially acceptable way. Therapy follows the method of Freudian psychoanalysis—rapport, transfer, free association, dream analysis, behavioral and ideational interpretation, etc.

2. Therapy with the unsocialized aggressive type aims not at superego analysis, but rather an attempt to synthesize a superego. The therapist does not seek to relieve guilt-anxiety, but rather to create it. This is done in the way that taboos are planted at any time of life. It requires the use of authority, firmness, planned limitation and, at times, punishment. First, by a warm accepting attitude, the therapist endeavors to convince the child that he has a fundamental interest in his welfare. The next step is to establish and effectively maintain pressure toward required kinds of behavior and against objectionable kinds of behavior.

This is accomplished in small steps at a time. Motivation to conformity is enlisted by an appeal to the child's personal loyalty to and identification with the therapist and if possible other socialized adults. Such an appeal is also oriented in terms of the child's self-interest. Abused privileges must be withdrawn and returned step by step. Constant reassurance of the therapist's personal interest and warmth is required while particular types of behavior are disapproved. The reason that requirements are set must be explained repeatedly and enforced. Sanctions, along with authoritative management, should be interpreted as punishment and as necessary parts of treatment. The therapist should be in contact with the child much of the day. Contacts with other adults should be held to a minimum and experienced only with stable, mature, even-tempered and strong personalities. Freedom and responsibility are increased step-by-step as the child demonstrates his ability to manage them. Attempts are made to help the child accept and recognize the therapist as a substitute parent, interested in his welfare, who at times must enforce reasonable restrictions on his behavior.

The ultimate goal is the development of inhibition, the stimulation of foresight, in enlightened self-interest, and the implanting of patterns of conformity. Jenkins recognizes the difficulty of treatment with this type and admits that with some only an improvement in the capacity for institutional adjustment may be realized. He advocates an institutional setting for the treatment of older children and adolescents of the unsocialized, aggressive type because adequate control is difficult in an open society.

3. With the socialized or pseudo-social boy one is dealing with a child who had initial, fundamental socialization, but later, because of impairment of family function and the presence of a delinquent milieu, became a member of a delinquent gang. The circumstances under which rapport is established should be such that the boy interprets the "break" as a result of personal interest and confidence, not as a result of weakness, fear or an effort to "buy him off." This type usually despises weakness. The treatment process aims at enlarging the delinquent's concept of his

in-group through the development and utilization of his loyalty. In order to neutralize the delinquent group's influence he should be either removed from it or group-treated along with the other members. Therapists working with this type should have strong masculine personalities with capacity for warmth and fairness and an uncompromising fixity of purpose.

Recently, the California Youth and Corrections Agency, including the Youth Authority and Department of Corrections, has become very much interested in developing juvenile delinquency treatment typologies utilizable in various types of correctional institutions as well as in the community. Several research projects in this vein are currently in progress. Many typologies have been already suggested, but since they are quite akin to the typology of Hewitt and Jenkins previously discussed, they are not included here.[12]

Hurwitz has developed a threefold, delinquent typology also similar to that of Hewitt and Jenkins based on a study sample of 196 male, white alleged delinquents appearing on official complaint in a New England juvenile court over a two-year period.[13] This typology utilized several conceptual levels or dimensions—socio-environmental; intra-familial; interpersonal and intrapsychic—by means of rigorous multivariate analytic techniques. Hurwitz's Types I and II correspond closely to Hewitt and Jenkin's socialized delinquent and unsocialized delinquent respectively. Hurwitz's Type III agrees in part with Hewitt and Jenkin's overinhibited neurotic type but differs in certain aspects. Hurwitz's cases come frequently from physically broken or psychologically disrupted homes marked by death of a father, or by extremely poor father-son and parent-parent communication. They experience seductive relationships with mothers who are eager to compensate their sons for this lack of a father figure and/or to find substitute gratifications for their own emotional deprivations due to the death or verbal inaccessibility of their husbands. Though possessing strong superegos, they were emotionally disturbed and conflicted cases whose difficulties developed after their early developmental period. Behaviorally, they acted out much more frequently and aggressively than did

Hewitt and Jenkins's cases. Probably Hewitt and Jenkins would include many of these so-called acting-out neurotics in Hurwitz's Type II category in their unsocialized aggressive delinquent category.

REFERENCES

1. ALEXANDER, FRANZ, and STAUB, HUGO: *The Criminal, The Judge, and the Public: A Psychological Study.* New York, Macmillan, 1931, pp. 145-152; ALEXANDER, FRANZ and HEALY, WILLIAM: *Roots of Crime.* New York, Knopf, 1935; BROMBERG, WALTER: *Crime and the Mind: An Outline of Psychiatric Criminology.* Philadelphia, Lippincott, 1948; LINDNER, ROBERT M.: *Stone Walls and Men.* New York, Odessey Press, 1946, pp. 42-58; ARGON, WALTER F.: A proposed functional classification of criminal behavior. *Journal of Criminal Psychopathology,* 687-701, April, 1943; BROWN, J. F., and ORR, DOUGLAS: The field-theoretical approach to criminology. *Journal of Criminal Psychopathology,* 236-252, October, 1941; CORSINI, RAYMOND: Criminal psychology. In Branham, Vernon C., and Kutash, Samuel B. (eds.): *Encyclopedia of Criminology.* New York, Philosophical Library, 1949, pp. 108-114.
2. ABRAHAMSEN, DAVID: *The Psychology of Crime,* pp. 105-116, 134-150.
3. ABRAHAMSEN, DAVID: *The Psychology of Crime,* pp. 115-204, 208-243.
4. GUTTMACHER, MANFRED S.: The psychiatric approach to crime and correction. In Nice, Richard W. (ed.): *Criminal Psychology.* New York, Philosophical Library, 1962, pp. 112-142.
5. BRANCALE, RALPH, ELLIS, ALBERT, and DOORBAR, RUTH: Psychiatric and psychological investigations of convicted sex offenders: A summary report. *American Journal of Psychiatry,* 109:26-27, November, 1952; KARPMAN, BENJAMIN: *Case Studies in the Psychopathology of Crime.* Washington, Mental Science Publishing Company, 1933; KARPMAN, BENJAMIN: The sexual psychopath. *Journal of Criminal Law, Criminology and Police Science,* 42:185-186, July-August, 1951; KARPMAN, BENJAMIN: *The Sexual Offender and his Offenses.* New York, Julian Press, 1963; GLUECK, BERNARD C., JR.: *Report*

on a Study of 102 Sex Offenders at Sing Sing Prison, as submitted to Governor Thomas E. Dewey, conducted under the
auspices of the Commissioner of Mental Hygiene and the
Commissioner of Correction. Albany, State of New York,
1950, p. 13; SELIGER, ROBERT V.: Psychiatric orientation of the
alcoholic criminal. *Journal of the American Medical Association, 129*:421, October, 1945; REICHARD, SUZANNE, *and* TILL-
MAN, CARL: Murder and suicide as defenses against schizophrenic psychosis, as found in Podolsky, Edward (ed.):
Encyclopedia of Aberrations, A Psychiatric Handbook. New
York, Philosophical Library, 1953, pp. 245-353; GUTTMACHER,
MANFRED S.: *The Mind of the Murderer.* New York, Farrar,
Straus and Cudahy, 1960; PODOLSKY, EDWARD: The mind of
the swindler, as found in Podolsky, *op, cit.,* pp. 516-517;
BROMBERG, WALTER, and KEISER, SYLVAN: The psychology of
the swindler. *American Journal of Psychiatry,* 94:1441-1458,
May, 1938; BARBASH, JAMES T.: Compensation and the crime
of pigeon dropping. *Journal of Clinical Psychology,* 8:92-94,
October, 1951; AUSUBEL, DAVID P.: *Drug Addiction: Physio-
logical, Psychological, and Sociological Aspects.* New York,
Random House, 1958, pp. 39-56.

6. JENKINS, RICHARD L., and HEWITT, LESTER: Types of personality
structure encountered in child guidance clinics. *American
Journal of Orthopsychiatry, 14*:84-94, January, 1944; JENKINS,
ROBERT L., and GLICKMAN, SYLVIA: Patterns of personality
organization among delinquents. *Nervous Child,* 8:329-339,
July, 1947; REDL, F.: In Witmer and Kotinsky (eds.): *New
Perspectives for Research on Juvenile Delinquency,* Children's
Bureau Publication No. 356, 1956; ERIKSON, E. H.: *Childhood
and Society.* New York, Norton, 1950; AICHORN, AUGUST:
Wayward Youth. New York, Viking, 1935; BLOCH and FLYNN:
Delinquency, pp. 151-175; ARGYLE, MICHAEL: A new approach
to the classification of delinquents with implications for treatment, as found in *Inquiries Concerning Kinds of Treatment
for Kinds of Delinquents,* Monograph No. 2, California, Board
of Corrections, 1961, pp. 15-26; Illinois State Training School
for Boys, Treatment Committee: *Report on Diagnostic Categories,* 1953; Youth Authority of California Report on Standard
Nomenclature, 1958.

7. GOUGH, HARRISON G., and PETERSON, DONALD R.: The identifi-

cation and measurement of predispositional factors in crime and delinquency. *Journal of Consulting Psychology, 16*:207-212, June, 1952; SARBIN, THEODORE R.: A preface to a psychological analysis of the self. *Psychological Review, 59*:11-23, January, 1952; PETERSON, DONALD R., QUAY, HERBERT C., and CAMERON, GORDON R.: Personality and background factors in juvenile delinquency as inferred from questionnaire responses. *Journal of Consulting Psychology, 23*:395-399, October, 1959; STUDT, E.: Social work in correction. Unpublished manuscript in preparation for Russell Sage Foundation, 1960; SULLIVAN, CLYDE E., GRANT, MARGUERITE Q., and GRANT, DOUGLAS J.: The development of interpersonal maturity: Applications to delinquency. *Psychiatry, 20*:373-385, November, 1957.

8. REISS, ALBERT J.: Delinquency as a failure of personal and social controls. *American Sociological Review, 15*:196-207, April, 1951; BECK, B. M.: What we can do about juvenile delinquency. *Child Welfare, 33*:37, 1954; TOPPING, RUTH: Case studies of aggressive delinquents. *American Journal of Orthopsychiatry, 11*:485-492, July, 1941; MUELLER, PAUL: Success rates as a function of treatment assignment and juvenile delinquency classification interaction, as found in *The Treatment of Delinquents in the Community: Variations in Treatment Approaches*, Monograph No. 1, California: Board of Corrections, 1960, pp. 7-14.

9. LEJINS, PETER: Pragmatic etiology of delinquent behavior. *Social Forces, 29*:320-321, March, 1951.

10. HEWITT, LESTER E., and JENKINS, RICHARD L.: *Fundamental Patterns of Maladjustment: The Dynamics of Their Origin.* Springfield, Illinois State Printer, 1947, pp. 25-36.

11. JENKINS, RICHARD L.: Diagnosis, dynamics and treatment in child psychiatry. *Psychiatric Research Report, 18*, American Psychiatric Association, October, 1964, pp. 91-120.

12. *The Treatment of Delinquents in the Community: Variations in Treatment Approaches.* Monograph No. 1, California, Board of Corrections, 1960; *Inquiries Concerning Kinds of Treatment for Kinds of Delinquents.* Monograph No. 2, California, Board of Corrections, 1961.

13. HURWITZ, JACOB I.: Three delinquent types: A multivariant analysis. *The Journal of Criminal Law, Criminology, and Police Science, 56*:328-334, September, 1965.

Chapter IV

THE SOCIOLOGICAL APPROACH
JUVENILE DELINQUENT TYPOLOGIES

SOCIOLOGISTS such as Cohen, Short, Ohlin, Cloward, and Miller have attempted to classify and analyze delinquent subcultures. Their theoretical interpretations are directed to lower-class, urban, male subcultural delinquency. Cohen envisions working-class gang delinquency as a delinquent subculture. Many working-class boys are driven to develop the delinquent subculture as a means of recapturing self-esteem destroyed by middle-class institutions. The working-class boy's socialization has not prepared him to function and compete in middle-class institutions, e.g., the school; but at the same time, he has partially internalized middle-class values. In the process of failing to measure up to the middle-class measuring rod, he receives disapproval, rejection and punishment. The punishing experiences of not measuring up plus self-derogation result in status deprivation. A number of working-class boys collectively sharing this problem of status deprivation work out a collective solution by forming a delinquent subculture based on a set of values antithetical to those of the middle class—nonutilitarian, malicious, negativistic and characterized by versatility, short-term hedonism and an emphasis on group autonomy. This subcultural solution to status deprivation and guilt is effected through the mechanism of reaction formation.

The delinquent subculture's delinquent activities are not motivated by utilitarian motives, e.g., stealing for economic gain, but rather by irrational desires to attack, in a variety of ways, the middle-class value system. In response to the criticism that there might be several kinds of lower-class gang delinquency,

58

Cohen and Short have suggested four delinquent subculture types (a) the parent-male subculture (based on Cohen's original thesis); (b) the conflict-oriented subculture; (c) the drug-addict subculture; (d) the semiprofessional-thief subculture.[1]

Cohen has not demonstrated empirically that a delinquent subculture exists. It must be shown that individual members of a delinquent subculture share attributes which identify them as members of a specific subculture group. This would require longitudinal case histories on specific groups of gang boys. To date, no such empirical findings are reported by any of the delinquent subcultural theorists. In this respect the earlier findings of Shaw and McKay and Thrasher are more precise and meaningful. The processes of norm internalization, punishment, self-derogation, status deprivation, reaction formation, irrational behaviors, etc., must be identified and described in the case histories of real delinquents; and furthermore, it must be shown that they are interrelated in a chain of causation.

Cohen probably exaggerated the aspirations of working-class boys to attain middle-class approval and membership. It is unlikely that the so-called working-class members crave success as it was once defined in the "American Dream." On the other hand, it is likely that a sizeable number of lower-class boys who attain to middle-class status achieve it. In any event, Reiss and Rhodes in a recent study of the distribution of juvenile delinquency in the social-class structure demonstrated the existence of a large number of boys in the blue-collar class, both "conforming non-achievers" and "nonconforming achievers" who were not delinquent. In an analysis of 9,238 white boys, twelve years old and over, in Davidson County, Tennessee, they were unable to isolate Cohen's "nonutilitarian, malicious and negativistic subculture." They found that delinquent boys, regardless of their ascribed social status and social-status structure of the area in which they lived, come in larger numbers than expected from the high rate delinquency areas, that there is no simple relationship between ascribed social status and delinquency, that there is not much evidence that the lower-class boy is more likely to be delinquent the more he is subjected to pressure from middle-class norms, that substantial numbers of delinquents come from residential areas where the majority of residents are from other than the lower class, and that lower-class status is not a necessary and sufficient cause of any type of delinquency.[2]

In summing up, Cohen offered a theory of the origin of delinquent subcultures. His frame of reference is provocative, and it has influenced many researchers in the field of juvenile delinquency. Probably Cohen's most lasting contribution is his brilliant description of the differential life experiences and values of those growing up in the lower class and those growing up in the middle class.

Ohlin and Cloward analyzed delinquent subcultures in terms of a theory of "opportunity structure" borrowed from Robert Merton. American culture makes mandatory the seeking of success goals (measured primarily in material terms) but differentially distributes the morally acceptable means to these goals. The gap between goals and structurally limited means creates a structural strain experienced among lower-class youths who aspire to material success. This structural strain leads to the formation of delinquent subcultures. In short, the aspiring lower-class male who finds legitimate avenues to success goals blocked may blame the system and resort to illegitimate means of success. In so doing he legitimates illegitimate means. Means-ends disjunction vary from one neighborhood to another; therefore, there is the presence of more than one type of delinquent subculture.[3]

Ohlin and Cloward differentiated delinquent subcultures into three types. (a) The criminal subculture develops in a neighborhood milieu characterized by: integration; the presence of criminal role models; the existence of class bonds between different age-levels of offenders, between criminal and conventional elements; and social control. The legitimate means to success are blocked; the illegitimate means are open in that regularized, organized criminal patterns are present and in that the criminals who carry these patterns are accessible role models. (b) The conflict subculture develops in disorganized, mobile, new slums where organized crime is not present. The young in such areas are exposed to acute frustration because access to success goals is blocked by the absence of any institutionalized channels, legitimate or illegitimate. They are blocked not only by a dearth of conventional opportunity, but also deprived of criminal routes to material success. Adolescents from this type of neighborhood close upon the manipulation of violence as a route to status. The principal requirements for success are "guts," the capacity to endure pain, "heart," a "rep" for violent behavior. (c) The retreatest, or drug-use subculture, develops among persons who are double failures. Double failures result from three causes: internalized prohibitions against theft and violence; failure to "make it" in the criminal gang or in the violent gang; and the objective unavailability of violence or theft as solutions. Some adolescent double failures turn to drugs as a solution to their status dilemma.[4]

Intervening between structural stress-strain and the development of the conflict subculture of whatever type, there occurs a withdrawal of attributions of legitimacy from established social norms. Ohlin and Cloward, as opposed to Cohen, claim that it is not the boys who aspire to middle-class status who form the material for delinquent subcultures, but those boys who aspire only to improve their economic status without change in social class membership. Ohlin and Cloward's boys, as opposed to those of Cohen, are rational "system blamers" who are qualified to succeed. They are justified in their interpretation of the differential opportunity structure.

Justification of a delinquent subculture does not explain motivation. Ohlin and Cloward did not use case histories; and therefore their claim that the boys who form delinquent subcultures are normal, intelligent, strong and agile people who could easily succeed in our culture if given an opportunity is not supported. In reference to the relationship of neighborhoods to delinquent subculture type, Ohlin and Cloward have no explanation for differentials in response among individuals who live in certain kinds of slum neighborhoods. The dimension of personality type was not included in their analysis. It would seem that certain personality types are more prone to violence or to the use of drugs than others.

Ohlin and Cloward's major contribution was probably their conceptual analysis of different types of slum areas. Variation in slum organization and structure may account for behavioral variation within certain slum neighborhoods; however, people have something to do with making slums. Different kinds of people may develop and may be attracted to different kinds of slum neighborhoods.

Walter B. Miller viewed gang delinquency as evolving directly from the lower-class community. The processes of immigration, migration, ethnic succession and vertical mobility have resulted in the sifting out of a hard-core lower class in the United States. The carriers of and the adaptors to this lower-class culture are primarily unsuccessful immigrants and Negroes. The lower-class way of life which generates delinquency and crime, in common with that of all distinctive cultural groups, is characterized by a set of focal concerns—"areas or issues which command wide spread and persistent attention and a high degree of emotional involvement"—(a) female-based household, (b) trouble, (c) toughness, (d) smartness, (e) fate, (f) autonomy. These focal concerns involve kinds of behaviors frequently defined as illegal.[5]

Participation in the lower-class street group may produce delinquency in several ways. (a) Following cultural practices which comprise essential elements of the total life pattern of lower-class culture automatically violates certain legal norms. (b) In instances where alternate avenues to similar objectives are available, the non-law-abiding avenue frequently provides a relatively greater and more immediate return for a relatively smaller investment of energy. (c) The "demanded" response to certain situations recurrently engendered within lower-class culture involves the commission of illegal acts.

Miller's lower-class delinquent boys are not suffering from status deprivation, and they are not "system blamers." They conceive of themselves as acting like "real men" in their cultural milieu. Middle-class values and institutions have no impact on their value system. They are completely committed to a lower-class culture.

Miller's analysis neither accounts for different types of delinquent gangs nor different types of delinquents. The thesis that lower-class culture directly generates crime and delinquency needs refinement and qualification. It also suffers from cultural determinism. Again, the personality dimension is lacking, and there are no life-history materials to support the thesis. Miller, in his analysis of lower-class "focal concerns," has certainly made a contribution. These "focal concerns" attributed to a total class as generators of delinquency need to be empirically identified. Moreover, once identified, their relationship to the specific motivations of gang members is necessary to demonstrate causation.

In closing this section on the delinquent subculturists, it should be pointed out that most delinquent gangs are "near groups" with a changing and marginal membership. Though they may share some problems, much of their behavior does not constitute a culture pattern. It has not been demonstrated that gang members are homogeneous in their norms or lack of norms. No less a scholar than Paul Tappan states: "This analogic term (criminal subculture) can be misleading if it is taken to suggest a structured and homogeneous social organization having a set of uniform cultural patterns distinct from those prevailing in the community at large. There is no separate and coherent 'culture' here in any ethnologically meaningful sense."[6]

The majority of boys reared in "lower-class" deprived neighborhoods are not adjudicated delinquents. Whether or not antisocial and criminal norms will prevail in particular families depends very largely, as the Gluecks have indicated, upon the "under-the-roof" patterns of the particular home, upon its reference groups and upon the controls that are effected through the family line.[7]

The most definitive study on juvenile gangs since *The Gang* (1927) by Frederick Thrasher is *The Violent Gang* by Yablonsky.[8] While directing a crime-prevention program on the upper West Side of Manhattan, Yablonsky compiled research information on over one-hundred gangs and gang-warfare incidents covering a period from 1953-1957. Methods used in collecting data included:

(a) depth interviews with gang members, some of which were office and other street interviews—both individual and group interviews were conducted; (b) tape recordings of field notes; (c) tailor-made, printed questionnaires; (d) employment of two former gang leaders as paid research interviewers; (e) the diary of a gang leader; (f) conversations with and observations of gang boys in all sorts of social situations. Yablonsky lived and worked in the research area during the four-year study.

Yablonsky identified three types of modern gangs. (a) The first is the social gang—for the most part a law-abiding group of adequately socialized youths who "hang together" because of comradeship and a "we" feeling. Gang activities are "socially dominated" and include organized participation, personal discussions, organizing dances and other socially acceptable activities characteristic of youth. Membership is long-enduring and is not based upon self-protection. Leadership is based on popularity and constructive leadership qualities. (b) The delinquent gang is primarily organized to participate in various illegal acts motivated by profit and not simply kicks. Gang offenses include burglary, petty thievery, mugging, assault for profit. Membership is likely enduring and includes a small, mobile clique of emotionally stable youths "socialized" into accepting delinquent patterns of behavior. The leader is generally the most effective thief and the best organizer and planner of delinquent acts. The delinquent gang member lives in the present and does not anticipate a future criminal career. (c) The violent gang is organized for emotional gratification. Violence is its central theme. All other activities, including delinquent activities, are incidental to its paramount violent pattern. The violent gang's organization and membership constantly shift, depending upon the emotional needs of its members. Leaders of violent gangs exaggerate membership size as a psychological weapon against other gangs and for self-aggrandizement. Weapons, e.g., switchblades, hunting knives, zip guns, standard guns, pipes, blackjacks, machetes, etc., are accumulated as gang arsenal. Intra-group conflict is characteristic of the violent gang in that members are continually "putting each other down" verbally and physically. Violent gangs seem to emerge spontaneously.

The origin of the gang, according to the verbalized rationale by gang boys, is related to their felt needs for defense and protection. Actually, the gang serves as a vehicle for adjusting the gang boys' personal problems and feelings of inadequacy. Gang membership satiates the need for power, especially for gang leaders. The gang also serves to channel aggressive feelings and overt violence. In short, boys with personality problems may act them out through the gang. The violent gang is created by and attracts sociopathic youth who enjoy fighting and violence for its own sake.

Joining the violent gang is an informal matter. One approaches the gang leader and requests membership which is rarely denied because the leader desires a large membership for prestige and power purposes. Violent gangs are near-groups with little formal or permanent character. The core members (3 to 6) include the leader and his close associates who are at the center of the gang's structure. These core members are on intimate terms and usually grow up within the same neighborhood. They play together, fight among themselves, "sound" each other, and plan and execute gang warfare.

Beyond the core members, the violent gang is not well integrated. Most of the violent gangs' membership comprises temporary, marginal members who shift their allegiances from one gang to another. They join any violent gang which provides them with an immediate opportunity for violence. When the gang to which they are loosely attached experiences a lull in violent activities, they move on to another gang or "roll their own" form of violence as individuals or in groups of twos or threes. Under pressure from without, whatever the source, most violent gang members leave the gang, although leaders and core members rarely resign. Gang leaders are self-appointed, and they initially organize their own gangs. They, along with core members, tend to be more sociopathic than the marginal members, though most members of violent gangs are to a degree sociopathic. Violent-gang leaders are socially ineffectual in that they have failed to make adequate adjustments to other groups prior to violent-gang membership. Their "leadership qualities" are not transferable to other groups. The violent-gang leader is an epitome of idealized violence to his followers. He has heart and will shoot, smash or knife an adversary without expression of fear or regret. Coupled with fantasies of power, the leader has delusions of being persecuted. He projects the blame for his violent tendencies onto others, society in general, and other gangs.

Yablonsky maintained that the sociopathic youth "growing up" in the disorganized slum has a personality that interlocks with the paranoid pseudo-community of the violent gang. He suggested the following sequence of events as processes of violent gang development. Step 1: *Defective Socialization*—The socialization vacuum of the disorganized slum, with its many inconsistencies, produces sociopathic youths. Step 2: *Alienation and Disassociation*—The sociopathic youth is further separated from the more constructive part of his community because of his psychopathic tendencies, negative self-feelings of "difference" and social failure. Rejection becomes reinforced and hardened by the disorganized world to which he is exposed. Step 3: *Paranoid Reactions*—The paranoid patterns of delusions of grandeur and persecution are articulated out of self-defense in reaction to the hostile world around him. Responsibility is shifted to others, which relieves the pressures on his weak ego. Gang leaderships, a false claim of the control of large divisions of youth, belonging to a conjured-up vast youth gang army and a violent "rep" gives the unsuccessful depressed youth illusionary ego strength. Preoccupation with enemy gangs (sometimes real but at other times imagined), expulsion from school and other group fears and failures enable the sociopathic youth to shift the responsibility from himself to society. Step 4: *The Pseudo-community of the Violent Gang*—The violent gang of both reality and unreality becomes for this sociopathic youth a pseudo-community. In this community he can at least partially adjust and receive some relief from personal problems and inadequacy feelings.

Yablonsky brilliantly described the disorganized slum as a producer of asocialized youths. His analysis of the origin, membership, structure and function of the violent gang marks a significant contribution to the discipline of criminology. Moreover, in revealing the interlocking nature of the sociopathic personality with the violent gang, he demonstrated the importance of the personality dimension in delinquent gang research. This has irritated some sociological criminologists— particularly those who have an over-socialized view of man. The author thinks that Yablonsky's research findings dictate the need of an alliance between sociologists and psychologists in the study of delinquent gangs. Certainly, the violent acts of the Egyptian Kings may not be explained in terms of "normal learned behavior."

The sociological approach has been utilized exclusively by some and in part by others in the study of specific patterns of delinquent behavior. Schepses, from a study of juvenile car thieves utilizing control groups, concluded that car thieves, when compared with other delinquents (no history of car theft), are more frequently Caucasian, begin their delinquent behavior at a later age, are brighter and more literate, come from homes with better economic circumstances, come less often from broken homes. Delinquent car thieves usually commit their offenses in groups for the purposes of joyrides and not in connection with other offenses.[9]

Clinard and Wade have reported on juvenile vandalism as a subtype of delinquency. Acts of juvenile vandalism are rarely accompanied by theft or other delinquent acts. Property destruction is seen as functioning for the adolescent as a protest against his ill-defined role and ambiguous status in the social structure.[10] Reiss has concentrated on the sex offenses of adolescents.[11] Chein has reported on the social and psychological characteristics of juvenile drug users.[12] Hill has specialized in the study of juvenile delinquency among Negroes. He advocates a structural-functional approach to the analysis of Negro delinquency, i.e., within the contact of reference group, status-role behavior and the self-images of individual and groups possessing minority-group consciousness.[13]

Gibbons has developed a more inclusive and significant typology of juvenile delinquents than has any other sociologist.[14] He described nine types in terms of delinquent roles explicated from descriptions of offender patterns in the criminological literature. Patterns of treatment were suggested for each type. Gibbons attempted to articulate treatment theory based on diagnostic categories. The typology was based on seventeen assumptions which reflect a sociological orientation. Several definitional dimensions (etiological or background dimensions) were utilized in this analysis: offense behavior; interactional setting; self-concept; attitudes; role career; and background dimensions, including social class, family background, peer group associations and contract with defining agencies. Descriptions of each of the nine types, along with their patterns of treatment, follow.

I. *Predatory Gang Delinquent*—defined as a repetitious, serious property offender who engages in deviant acts with different collections of delinquent peers over time. These boys conceive of themselves as "cool," "tough" kids and as delinquents, and they evince antisocial attitudes toward the police, probation officer and law-abiding citizens generally. All work roles are viewed as rackets. "Only slobs work." Delinquent careers are initiated at the age of eight or nine, and, generally, delinquent acts become more numerous and serious from childhood throughout adolescence. Boys of this type develop "delinquent personalities" as a result of differential association. They come from lower-class, high-delinquency areas; and they are products of lower-class families who fail to supervise their children properly. Though their parents and sibs are often criminalistic or delinquent, interpersonal relations within the family are devoid of pathological overtones. They are well socialized into a delinquent peer group or subculture which provides them with support of their hostile and cynical attitudes. This type has frequent contacts with police, probation officers and juvenile courts. Many end up in correctional institutions. They do not suffer from personality aberrations.

Proposed Treatment. The task of treatment is to convert offenders well socialized in a delinquent group into members of an "anti-delinquent society" by using group members as the agents of behavioral change, group therapy, milieu management of the Highfields form, physical and social segregation of gang offenders from other types, the use of juvenile wards as treatment agents, deliberate manipulation of an incentive system, halfway houses, environmental change programs designed to alter the social environment of the community areas in which gang delinquency is common, e.g., Chicago area Project, detached gang worker programs.

II. *Conflict Gang Delinquent*—defined as "tough guy" type who engages in "bopping," violent attacks on others and gang fights. Such boys make up a clearly-defined, well-organized peer group; however, they do not define themselves as delinquent, but rather "tough guys." They are products of more "disorganized" neighborhoods than Type I. Though residing in "sociological jungles," they are not particularly hostile, though they are aware of their dearth of opportunity to obtain a conventional job. Their parents, generally newcomers to the city, are confused and frequently unemployed. Unlike parents of Type I offenders, they are prosocial, but unable to control their children. Delinquency begins later for these "hanging-gang" boys (adolescence) than is the case with Type I. Possessing normal personalities, they usually develop noncriminal, adult adjustments.

Proposed Treatment. Gibbons suggested the same treatment devices for this type as Type I. The difference between the two types tends to be one of offense behavior rather than of social-psychological characteristics. Gibbons was opposed to breaking up this type gang and reasoned it could be redirected into non-violent, legal channels by detached gang workers.

III. *Casual Gang Delinquent*—defined as a lower-class, high-delinquency area product who engages in relatively minor and infrequent acts of delinquency, often as peripheral members of delinquent gangs. Most behavior is non-delinquent. Such boys engage occasionally in conflict activities as well as theft. They are only fringe members of delinquent gangs who do not consider themselves to be "real" gang boys or delinquents. In attitude they are no more hostile toward the police than are working-class persons. They are conventional in their attitudes toward legal-work roles. Casual gang delinquents begin their delinquent activities at a relatively early age, but they eventually make good adult adjustments. Though similar to Types I and II in that they are products of urban working-class neighborhoods and families, they differ from Types I and II in that their families exert adequate supervision and are less criminalistic. Personality-wise, they are normal. The families of the casual gang delinquent, unlike the families of Types I and II boys, have succeeded in indoctrinating their children with prosocial norms.

Proposed Treatment. Varied types of group therapy are recommended, as long as they include the isolation of this type from older, more sophisticated delinquents. Therapy should be designed to reinforce the existing non-delinquent self-image and attitude.

IV. *Casual Delinquent, Non-gang Member*—defined as "hidden delinquent" who engages in infrequent minor delinquent acts as a loner or as a member of a non-gang, peer groups. Typical delinquent acts include petty theft, driving without a license, smoking and drinking, vandalism. These boys define themselves as non-delinquents and express remorse and shame when apprehended for delinquent acts. They are prosocial in attitude and unlikely to commit delinquent acts after graduating from high school. Casual, non-gang delinquents are usually from middle-class families who have, for the most part, been successful in attempts to socialize their children. Boys of this type have minimal contacts with the police, who regard them as "pranksters." Official action is rarely taken with them. Personality-wise, they are normal.

Proposed Treatment. Gibbons suggested "no treatment" for this type beyond severe and dramatic warnings by the police.

V. *Automobile Thief Joyrider*—defined as a "wild" boy who steals cars for joyriding purposes rather than for profit. Such boys are not usually involved in other types of property offenses. Joyriders steal cars in friendship groups; they are not gang boys. Though defining themselves as non-delinquent, they have self-notions as "tough" and "cool," and they frequently have adjustment problems in school and at home. They are essentially prosocial in attitude, but frequently look upon the police as stupid and inefficient people. Joyriding begins in adolescence and may persist until adulthood. Repetitive car thefts often result in arrest and placement on probation. Some of these boys are committed to training schools.

Most car thieves terminate car thefts in the late teenage years. Joyriders are usually from middle-class backgrounds marked by occupational and residential mobility. Usually there is a lack of intense interaction with their fathers, which breeds a problem of masculine identity. Despite this problem, joyriders have no serious personality problems and as a rule grow up and make adequate adult adjustments.

Proposed Treatment. Gibbons suggested group therapy and attempts to involve these boys in legal, "masculine lines of activity" which would substitute for stealing cars, e.g., the use of autos as a therapy tool within "hot rod clubs." Family counseling was indicated in some cases.

VI. *Drug User (Heroin)*—defined as a delinquent who, by virtue of addiction to heroin, engages in delinquent acts in order to purchase drugs. Juvenile drug addicts are members of a drug-user subculture characterized by mutual aid, the hustle, "cool-cat" self-image and a disdain for squares. The addict usually rationalizes away his drug problem as a "kick" no more deviant than many other "kicks," e.g., drinking. He argues that the use of narcotics should be legalized and conceives of himself as a victim harassed by the police. Heroin users have negative attitudes toward work, the police and "square society." Drug users may begin their delinquent careers as gang boys, but they drop out after addiction. Drug users are not usually gang boys. Often they become adult, criminal, drug-users. Juvenile addicts are products of urban, slum areas and have lower-class backgrounds. They are recruits from the groups that have the most marked feelings of low status, lack of opportunity and inability to face stressful situations. The families of drug users are relatively conventional, but close parent-child ties are missing.

Gibbons described this type as "double failures," in that they had failed and retreated from both conventional and delinquent pursuits. This, of course, is Ohlin and Cloward's point of view discussed previously. However, Gibbons goes further than most sociologists would in the further description of this type as suffering from deep-seated inadequacy feelings. This is very close to the psychiatrist's label, "inadequate personality," which is often applied to addicts by analysts.

Proposed Treatment. Gibbons advised group therapy, individual psychotherapy and a milieu-management program similar to that of Synanon.

VII. *Overly Aggressive Delinquent*—defined as "lone-wolf" offender who engages in apparently meaningless assaults upon peers, adults and animals, but who rarely engages in property offenses for gain. Overly-aggressive delinquents see themselves as "picked-upon" victims of a hostile environment. They are defiant, sensitive and suspicious offenders who begin committing assaultive and violent acts before adolescence. They are frequently found in child guidance clinics. Many continue in aggressive behavior beyond adolescence and become inmates of adult correctional institutions where their adjustment is poor. These delinquents come from a cross-section of the social classes. Severe parental rejection is characteristic of their family backgrounds. Many have lived in several different family groups, in foster homes and in orphanages. Hostile and socially inept, they do not seek peer relationships. Moreover, peer groups steer clear of them. Overly-aggressive delinquents have many contacts with the police, child guidance clinics and correctional machinery, to which they exhibit hostility. They are described as unsocialized aggressive personalities with the implication of sociopathy.

Proposed Treatment. Gibbons reasoned that, first of all, these offenders should be forcibly controlled, i.e., prevented from injuring themselves or others. Subsequently, residential, individual psychotherapy is recommended. Group therapy is not indicated for this unsocialized aggressive type.

VIII. *Female Delinquent*—defined as the girl who comes to

official attention for sexual reasons. Promiscuous girls who associate with a number of "wild" boys and who engage in visible and promiscuous sex acts with a number of male companions are likely to be adjudicated delinquents. Delinquent girls associate with each other and with delinquent male companions; however, they neither form gangs nor possess a delinquent subculture. Girls of this type do not define themselves as delinquents, but they are aware that they have problems. They manifest hostility toward their parents, whom they describe as lacking in affection. In a quest for substitute affection and understanding, they become involved in sex activities with male associates which involves them in further difficulty because they are then labeled as sex deviants ("easy lay"). Actually, with the exception of their problem of affectional relations with others, most delinquent girls are well socialized and have normal personality structures. They come from several social classes. Family tension marks their background, and relationships with one or both parents are impaired. Girls of this type have frequent contacts with the police and correctional personnel, which they define as negative. Most delinquent girls, even those institutionalized, eventually marry and make good adult adjustments.

Proposed Treatment. Group therapy, individual therapy and family therapy are recommended. Therapists, ideally older women, would serve as mother-substitute figures.

IX. *"Behavior Problem" Delinquent*—defined as a shy and withdrawn, "lone-wolf" offender who suffers from deep-seated personality difficulties—"neurotic" or "pre-psychotic" syndromes. Delinquent acts of such offenders are bizarre and seem to be triggered by hidden motivations, e.g., arson, assault and deviant sexual acts. They conceive of themselves as "different" from others, but not delinquent. Their attitudes without the sexual sphere are conventional. Many of these offenders end up in guidance clinics, psychiatric facilities, mental hospitals and, in some cases, correctional institutions. Behavioral difficulties continue into adult life. Prognosis in short is negative. These offenders are not class-linked. Many peculiar and abnormal patterns of parent-child interaction are obtained in their family backgrounds, e.g., seduction interaction patterns with parents, parental repression, etc. Depth psychotherapy administered by clinical psychologists and psychiatrists aimed at deducing the hidden sources of deviant motivational patterns is recommended as treatment.

On the basis of our present etiological and treatment knowledge of juvenile delinquents, Gibbons offers an excellent typology. He made careful distinctions between different types on the basis of delinquent-role behavior, thereby evading the error of attempting to distinguish between delinquents on all dimensional levels. Gibbons established that delinquent types vary from each other in some ways, but not in all. Delinquent types share some attributes with each other and with non-delinquents. Delinquents in some dimensions are different from non-delinquents. Most important, Gibbons made use of *offense pattern* as a significant dimension in differentiating offender types. This dimension has been unfortunately ignored by most typologists.

Some might criticize with some justification his failure to include an explicit, definitional, personality dimension in his analysis. He did define and deal with several personality attributes throughout several definitional dimensions; this was the case especially in two dimensions of self-concept and attitudes. Additionally, Gibbons made use of personality attributes in his discussion of patterns of treatment, treatment typology. In fact, Gibbon's typology is based on a social-psychological approach rather than a restricted, sociological frame of reference. This the author finds extremely refreshing.

The author would question only one of Gibbon's delinquent types, Type II—Conflict Gang Delinquent. The criticism that ensues is qualified and is aimed only at a part of Gibbon's construct. This type may be equated with Yablonsky's *Violent Gang*. The activities of conflict gangs are probably more serious and persistent than Gibbons supposes. Their structure approaches the "near-gang" type rather than the tight, cohesive peer group. Gibbons probably underestimates the importance of sociopathic leaders and sociopathic core members in the formation and perpetuation of this type of gang. Members of conflict gangs probably evince more pronounced hostile, aggressive and anti-social attitudes than Gibbons reported. Since it appears that many conflict gang members have sociopathic personalities, it is unlikely that many of them settle down and adjust as adults. On the contrary, many boys of this type end up in adult correctional institutions where their pattern of violence and maladjustment continues.

TYPOLOGIES OF ADULT OFFENDERS

The materials in the first section of this chapter illustrate that the literature is replete with various endeavors at juvenile delinquent typologies. However, there have been fewer attempts at a construction of adult offender typologies, though several sociologists, including Reckless, Clinard, Tappan and Cressey, have called attention to the necessity of research in this area.[15] Certainly there is a need for further research on specific types of adult offenders because many juvenile delinquents do not mature into adult criminals and since some adult criminals do not have juvenile delinquent records.

In a generally descriptive manner, the sociologist has dealt with several classifications of adult offenders in criminology textbooks: professional criminals; non-professional criminals; habitual offenders; occasional offenders; organized offenders; alcoholics; drug addicts; prostitutes, etc. Cavan has probably offered the most inclusive textbook typology of adult offenders: professional, organized, habitual, white collar, causal, and other offenders who live in the noncriminal world; seriously maladjusted, etc.[16] These types are discussed both as distinct behavior systems with their own philosophy, codes and practices and in their relationship to other parts of the social structure. A frame of reference accompanies each offender type. Unfortunately, no research design or methodology is available to test this typology. Furthermore, Cavan's typology needs refinement in that there are sub-types of offenders within its broad categories of offender types. Additionally, distinctions between types are not always made clear. Bloch and Geis postulated a similar classification which suffers from similar weaknesses plus the dearth of an adequate frame of reference.[17]

Two decades ago, Lindesmith and Dunham employed a continuum in an inclusive criminal typology, the two polar extremes of which are the "social criminal" and the "individualized criminal."[18] They stated that the socialized criminal is one who commits crimes that are supported and prescribed by his culture. He acts in close collaboration with other persons and is dependent on them for the continuation of his criminal career. The individualized criminal, on the other hand, acts for reasons that are personal and private. He commits his offenses alone and, in theory, is a stranger to others who commit similar crimes. His criminal act is not an acceptable form of behavior in his social milieu. The socialized criminal is likely to be a normal person. The individual criminal, at odds with his primary groups, seems likely to be a person whose criminality is symptomatic of deep psychological pressures.

The findings of three psychologists, in a study of sixty-two institutionalized, delinquent boys, aged fourteen to eighteen, in Northern California in 1961, support Lindesmith and Dunham's two polar types.[19] Thirty-nine boys had always been social, and eighteen had always been solitary in their official delinquencies. A statistical analysis showed that the solitary delinquent came from a higher socioeconomic level as measured by an adaptation of the Warner Index, was of higher intellectual ability (Wechsler Adult Intelligence Scale, WAIS) and was more psychologically maladjusted (based on the Minnesota Multiphasic Personality Inventory). Differences on the MMPI scales Hs, D, Hy, Pd, Pt, and Sc were significantly different beyond the .01 level of confidence.

Research reports unfortunately are not available on criminal types falling between the two poles of Lindesmith's and Dunham's typology. In the preceding California study, four subjects were eliminated from analysis because examination showed them to have mixed (solitary and social) delinquent careers. Clearly, other identifying dimensions of criminal behavior beyond "social" and "individualized" criminal behavior must be added to this kind of typology if it is to lend itself to empirical verification.

Clinard has recently attempted to amplify Dunham's continuum thesis on the basis of what he calls social processes and behavior systems. Offenders in his typology are classified according to the degree to which they make a long-term career out of crime. At one end of his continuum Clinard placed the criminally insane and at the other end the professional criminal. In between he ranged extreme sex deviates, occasional offenders, homosexuals and prostitutes, habitual petty criminals, white-collar criminals, those with ordinary criminal careers, organized criminals and professional criminals. Several criminal sub-types were subsumed within three broad categories. Clinard utilized the following definitional dimensions: social roles; identification with crime; conception of self; pattern of differential association with others; progression in crime; and the degree to which criminal behavior has become a part of the life organization.[20] His classification system was based on secondary sources and descriptions of offenders found in the literature. Though appearing plausible, Clinard's scheme needs empirical testing. Additional definitional dimensions of analysis are also called for, e.g., a personality dimension.

Currently, Clinard is refining a classification system in terms of criminal behavior systems. The following broad, tentative outline indicates the direction of his schema: personal violent crime; political crime; occupational crime; public order crime; gang delinquency; conventional property crime; organized crime; and professional crime.

Arthur V. Huffman has recently suggested a social-psychological behavior pattern typology similar to a classification system originally proposed by Donald Clemmer when he was on the State Criminologists' staff at Illinois.[21] Huffman adds a formula to be used in his classificatory process:

$$C = \frac{S \& P}{R}$$

C (criminal behavior) = S (total situational factors, i.e., environmental, sociological, exogenous factors) and P (personality factors, i.e., criminogenic temperament, character and intelligence components affecting behavior) + (the individual's resistance to criminal behavior). His behavior pattern scheme follows.

I. *No Apparent Criminal Pathology* (usually law-abiding, well-integrated individuals who do not accept antisocial mores).

A. Deprivational—e.g., law-abiding citizen who steals to provide food for his family.

B. Provocational—e.g., the individual who, under extreme pressure from his group of peers, commits a crime.

C. Accidental—e.g., the individual who runs over and kills a child on a bicycle.

II. *Personality Demoralization* (a delinquency-area type whose behavior pattern is primarily influenced by rejection of the generally accepted standards of conduct. The delinquent conditioning and attitudes are firmly rooted, stemming from a delinquent subculture, family, gang or other social group with which the offender identifies. Classification in this group does not rule out the presence of some personality disorganization, but it does imply that the primary factor is demoralization rather than personality disorganization).

A. Highly advanced—e.g., the professional offender against property who has developed skillful criminal techniques and who has internalized an entrenched criminal philosophy—advanced robber, clever burglar, smooth confidence man, the capable counterfeiter, skilled embezzler, operator of criminal syndicates, such as hot-car ring and drug trafficking. He is rarely legitimately employed.

B. Marked—e.g., the would-be professional criminal who possesses the entrenched criminal philosophy, but for some reason has not developed the sophisticated technique of the true professional. Criminal offenses, arrests, convictions and institutionalizations are frequent. He is also prone to violence. Part of the time he is legitimately employed.

C. Occasional—e.g., the situational offender with low criminalistic tendencies but with low resistance to these tendencies. Strong predispositions and/or precipitating criminogenic factors must be present in the total situation before he resolves the conflict between a relatively strong id, ego and superego or resistant force. This offender is usually regularly legitimately employed. He is likely to blame society for placing temptation in his path.

III. *Personality Disorganization* (inmates whose criminogenic behavior reactions are associated with some type of personality disorganization. The characteristic pattern of behavior of this group are related to endogenous forces—psychological rather than sociological. The personality disorganization is not severe enough to constitute mental illness, legally speaking).

A. Personality Pattern Disturbances—e.g., non-professional offenders with fixed personality structures.

    1. Inadequate personality.
    2. Schizoid personality.
    3. Cyclothymic personality.
    4. Paranoid personality.

B. Personality Trait Disturbances—e.g., non-professional offenders who are unable to maintain emotional equilibrium and independence.

    1. Emotionally unstable.
    2. Passive-aggressive.
    3. Compulsive.

IV. *Sociopathic Behavior Reaction* (the classic sociopath who commits all sorts of criminal and antisocial acts).

Though Huffman claims no empirical research to back up this scheme he states its purpose as follows:

> An effort to explore the possibilities of distinguishing fundamentally different patterns of behavior which could likewise be differentiated in terms of the general situations under which each type develops.

With his first two major categories, I (No Apparent Criminal Pathology) and II (Personality Demoralization), he has made a stab in this direction. However, the categorization of the robber, burglar, confidence man and the embezzler under one basic type (Personality Demoralization, Highly Advanced) is questionable. The findings of other scholars reveal major differences among these different offenders. Huffman's categorization here is not discriminating. With his two psychological categories there is no effort in this direction. He lists a group of psychiatric categories with no attempt to explain under what conditions and in what situations people who suffer from these maladies come to engage in certain antisocial and criminal patterns of behavior. Finally, Huffman's formula $C=\frac{S \& P}{R}$ does not seem to be objectively measurable. How does one determine R (criminal resistance)?

Gibbon's criminal typology, recently published along with his delinquent typology discussed previously, marks the most ambitious attempt at the classification of adult offenders by any sociologist. The criminal typology was based upon an earlier work by Gibbons and Donald L. Garrity with slight modification.[22] The typology consists of fifteen patterns of adult criminal behavior drawn from a research of the literature. Nine types have careers of property crime, and six constitute personal offenders. Gibbons does not claim that his typology is inclusive, but rather that it represents a middle ground between gross systems of differentiation and categorical systems employing larger numbers of types. The dimensions of analysis were the same as those employed in the juvenile delinquent typology; however, five of the adult types were described as an abridged form. All types were accompanied by treatment suggestions.[23]

I. *Professional Thief*—defined as the offender who participates in a highly skilled nonviolent form of crime, including confidence games, shoplifting, pocket-picking, circus grifting and other kinds of professional thieves. Never numerous, these professionals are disappearing on the American scene. Very few are found in prison because of their cleverness in avoiding arrest. Thieves become thieves by differentially associating with thieves. Though little is known about the backgrounds of potential professional thieves, it is likely that cab drivers, bellhops and bartenders may be the types of people most often recruited into professional theft. These occupational types have frequent contacts with the underworld. A certain personality type, "budding grifter," characterized by verbal skills and manipulative skills is likely to be recruited into the practice of professional theft. Deep-seated personality problems are infrequently found among this group.

Proposed Treatment. Group therapy, along with a systematic frustration of their "con-politician" behavior. Their manipulative behavior in prison should not pay off. Longer sentences are also recommended. Parole planning should guide this type of offender toward law-abiding occupations where his manipulative role-playing skills would be utilized and acceptable, e.g., auto salesman.

II. *Professional "Heavy" Criminal*—defined as the offender who engages in highly skilled, full-time, lucrative, property crime, i.o., armed robbery, burglary and other direct assaults upon property. These criminal activities are carried on as a team or mob operation inviting division of labor. Professional heavies define themselves as professional criminals and are satisfied with their criminal life style. They view the police as adversaries who have their work to do. Efficient police are respected; inefficient police are scorned. Hostility toward police is not marked. Professional heavies have negative attitudes toward conventional work roles. These offenders are products of the urban, lower class, and most of them are predatory gang delinquents grown up. They learn their particular criminal skills from older professionals. They continue in crime until middle age, when many retire into noncriminal occupations. As adults, their type has minimal contacts with the police, courts and correctional institutions.

Proposed Treatment. No specific treatment is advocated. Fortunately, according to Gibbons, professionals ultimately "reform" themselves by retiring from criminality because at a certain age they decide the hazards of crime are too great. Reportedly, they take up safer lines of work. Gibbons suggested that professional crime could be partially repressed by "legislative" and law-enforcement tactics which would increase the risks of detection and apprehension.

III. *Semiprofessional Property Criminal*—defined as the offender who tries to carry on crime as an occupation despite limited criminal skills. Such criminals engage in armed robbery, holdups, burglaries, larcenies and direct assaults upon personal or private property. Semiprofessionals at times operate as loners and at times in small groups of crime partners. The implication is that semiprofessionals are not usually organized in mobs. These offenders conceive of themselves as criminals and as people who have few alternatives to criminal behavior. They view themselves as victims of a corrupt society in which all occupational roles constitute rackets. As "system blamers" they relieve themselves of guilt feelings. Semiprofessionals are more hostile toward the police, courts and correctional agents than are professional criminals because of their frequent contacts with such agencies. They comprise a major part of the adjudicated offender population. They also generally evince bitter and resentful attitudes toward their parents, social agencies and legitimate institutions. These offenders, like the professionals, are predatory gang delinquents grown up. Unlike the professionals, they accumulate extensive arrest histories, and many of them spend a sizeable part of their early adult years in correctional institutions. Frequent contacts with law-enforcement machinery and correctional agents reinforce their prevailing negative attitudes. Rehabilitative efforts are generally unsuccessful. They continue in crime into middle age, when many retire into legitimate occupations. Personality-wise, they are not emotionally maladjusted. Their feelings of resentment, hostility and bitterness are the result of involvement in deviance rather than the cause of it. Some of these offenders have personality problems, but they are not causally related to their criminality.

Proposed Treatment. Intensive group therapy in the various correctional situations, probation treatment with small case loads centering around group therapy, compulsory involvement in group therapy in prison, concentrated group therapy treatment immediately prior to release from prison, the limited use on a voluntary basis of halfway houses, milieu management (complete therapeutic environment) in small institutions (100 offenders or less). Treatment proposals for this group are obviously similar to those suggested for Predatory Gang Delinquents.

IV. *Property Offender "One-time Loser"*—defined as the unskilled loner without previous delinquent or criminal record who commits a single, serious property crime, e.g., grand theft. Such offenders are often arrested and placed on probation. They are prosocial in attitude and for the most part have lived conventional, law-abiding lives. They define themselves as noncriminals. Should they go to prison they are regarded as "square Johns." They make good institutional adjustments and generally law-abiding adjustments in the community following release. One-time losers come from several social classes but most commonly from the lower-middle class. They are semiskilled or skilled working-class people who are products of stable and conventional family backgrounds. Though they might rationalize away their offense as atypical and not "too bad," they admit that they have broken the law toward which they manifest respect. Personality-wise, they are normal.

Proposed Treatment. Probation with minimal supervision; those institutionalized should be confined in minimum security correctional facilities and isolated from offenders with criminalistic attitudes; group therapy immediately prior to release from prison as a form of pre-release orientation.

V. *Automobile Thief and Joyrider*—defined as the adult version (usually young adult) of the juvenile delinquent Type V (Automobile Thief, Joyrider). Most members of this category who are incarcerated succeed on parole and thenceforth lead law-abiding lives.

VI. *Naive Check Forger*—defined as unsophisticated, recidivistic check passer (NSF) without delinquent history or otherwise criminal background. These offenders do not define themselves as criminals and attempt to rationalize away their offenses as minor infractions. They verbalize prosocial attitudes toward work roles and legal social institutions; however, they manifest a pattern of occupational and marital difficulties prior to their involvement in forgery. Frequently they express bitterness and resentment regarding those difficulties. Lone-wolf check forgery begins in adulthood after these offenders have been isolated from stable social ties. Law-enforcement machinery and the courts tend to be quite lenient with these offenders; e.g., many are at first handled unofficially, then placed on probation and finally incarcerated. Since check passers are repeaters in crime, many of them end up in correctional institutions. Offenders in this category are generally products of respectable middle-class backgrounds. Their family backgrounds are adequate, and they do not associate with delinquents or other offenders. Many are employed as white-collar workers. They do not suffer from personality aberrations.

Proposed Treatment. Group therapy to build up a fund of acceptable solutions to problems which these offenders have heretofore responded to by writing checks; "shock therapy" in terms of a jail or institutional commitment early in their check-passing careers; client-centered individual therapy for those on probation.

VII. *White-collar Criminal*—defined as a person in business and corporate organizations who violates state and federal regulatory statutes. White-collar offenses are usually prosecuted by Federal administrative agencies, e.g., Interstate Commerce Commission, Federal Trades Commission, Securities Exchange Commission, Attorney General's Office. Courts of equity frequently dispose of these cases because of the difficulties of criminal prosecution. White-collar offenders are aware of the fact that they are violating regulatory statutes, but they consider these violations necessary in the transaction of business. They withdraw legitimacy from the legal regulations and operate on the basis of business ethics. White-collar offenders are normal, conventional people who learn definitions of the situation favorable to the violation of the law in their everyday business activities. They define themselves as law-abiding individuals. Very few of this type are ever adjudicated criminals.

Proposed Treatment. Vigorous and consistent law enforcement is recommended for this type. Regulatory agencies should ferret out these violators. Many should be tried in criminal courts. Those convicted should receive stiff fines and prison sentences.

VIII. *Professional Fringe Violator*—defined as a member of a legitimate profession who utilizes professional skills in the commission of crimes, e.g., doctors who perform criminal abortions, lawyers who employ illegal practices in the practice of law. These offender offenses involve two persons: the offender and his patient or client. They regard themselves as law-abiding persons and not as criminals. They work and live in a noncriminal world. Though they acknowledge the illegal nature of their criminal acts when caught, they rationalize away these acts in a way which permits them to retain a noncriminal image of themselves. They have prosocial attitudes, begin their illegal acts late in life, are infrequently detected or prosecuted. They are products of the middle class and have been reared in adequate homes from the economic as well as the emotional viewpoint. Contacts with the police, courts and correctional agents leave a neutral impact. Personality-wise, they are normal.

Proposed Treatment. No treatment *per se* is recommended, because these offenders are normal, prosocials. Correctional agents can best help them with post-release adjustment, e.g., finding suitable jobs in which their talents may be utilized pending the return of their revoked licenses.

IX. *Embezzler*—defined as an offender who violates a position of trust by stealing large sums of money from employers, usually through alteration of business records. Operating as a loner, the embezzler attempts to keep his illegal activities a secret from employers, associates and his family. Embezzlers define themselves as noncriminals, and they build up strong rationalization for their illegal acts when apprehended; e.g., "they were only borrowing money which was to be replaced." They possess conventional, prosocial attitudes and do not have delinquent or criminal records. Embezzlers are products of respectable middle-class backgrounds. Very few of this type are committed to prison. Many are dealt with informally by their employers or by bonding agencies. Those who are adjudicated and sentenced to penal institutions make good adjustments. In prison they are "square Johns" who associate with other "square Johns." They rarely are involved in further criminal acts. Embezzlers have normal personalities. Frequently, embezzlers have "non-share-able" problems which seem to precipitate criminal acts, e.g. drinking problems, women problems, expensive recreational problems, standard of living problems (living beyond means).

Proposed Treatment. No treatment is required for these normals. In penal institutions they should be isolated from contacts with criminalistic inmates. The problem of finding these offenders a job in line with their educational backgrounds and experience at release constitutes another adjustment problem.

X. *Personal Offender, One-time Loser*—defined as an offender involved in a serious, violent crime, e.g., murder, negligent manslaughter, serious assault. Frequently, these violent acts are "victim-precipitated" and involve spouses, relatives or close friends. Long-term tension and antagonism between perpetrator and victim usually precede the criminal assault. One-time losers define themselves as noncriminals, and they exhibit prosocial attitudes. They are "square Johns" in prison. Most personal offenders of this type have no extensive delinquency or criminal record. Some have been involved in a pattern of minor offenses, e.g., drunkenness and wife-beating. They serve long sentences. On release they live law-abiding lives. Personal offenders come from all social classes; and their family backgrounds appear adequate. The conjugal family backgrounds of these offenders are often marked by tension and violence, e.g., wife beating. Personal offenders have not had juvenile delinquent or criminal companions. Institutional experience has little if any effect on these individuals. Personality-wise, they are normal.

Proposed Treatment. No treatment is recommended for these normals. In prison they should be segregated from antisocial inmates. They require help from parole officers upon release, e.g., help with post-adjustment difficulties.

XI. *Psychopathic Assaulter*—defined as the adult counterpart of the delinquent pattern VII (Overly Aggressive Delinquent). Such offenders are members of a recidivistic group of offenders who commit a variety of offenses against property and persons. Unnecessary violence usually accompanies their offenses. Psychopathic assaulters are the products of the same causal backgrounds as delinquents of Type VII. In correctional institutions they are known as "outlaws" or "gorillas." They are feared by other inmates. Their asocial attitudes and violent acts result in administrative segregation, i.e., placement in maximum security cell blocks where many of them serve out their sentences.

Proposed Treatment. Gibbons recommended that these offenders be incarcerated in specialized institutions. Treatment attempts should parallel that of the "overly aggressive" delinquent.

XII. *Violent Sex Offender*—defined as offender who violently attacks female victims. The assaults are characterized by extreme and bizarre violence, often culminating in homicide. Abnormal sex acts against the victim may be involved. These violent sex assaults are two-person crimes between a victim and an offender. Victims are generally strangers to the offender. Violent sex offenders define themselves as noncriminals, but they are aware that they are "different" from other people. They possess conventional attitudes beyond the sexual sphere. Most violent sex assaulters have no delinquent or criminal history. They are usually apprehended for their offenses and spend long periods of time in prison. These offenders come from no particular social class. Family backgrounds are characterized by a family pattern of repressive sexual notions, seductive mother-son interaction, etc. Contacts with correctional agents are neutral.

Proposed Treatment. Gibbons recommended psychotherapy.

XIII. *Nonviolent Sex Offender* (Rapo)—defined as the offender involved in exhibitionism, child molesting or incest where violence is seldom employed. The victim of exhibitionists and child molesters may or may not be known to the offender. Nonviolent sex offenders define themselves as noncriminals. Many of them deny, despite strong evidence to the contrary, their offenses. They have prosocial attitudes beyond the sexual sphere and are without delinquency or criminal records for other types of offenses. Nonviolent sex offenders are frequently caught and serve long prison terms. Many of them repeat nonviolent sexual offenses after release or parole. These offenders come from no particular social class. Family background experiences have rendered them timid and retiring personalities. The faulty adult marital situation of these offenders more than anything else seems to causally link with their sex offenses. Long-term sexual inadequacy frequently precedes involvements in sex crimes. Especially is this the case with exhibitionists and child molesters. The husband is usually dominated by a more aggressive spouse. The conjugal family situation is somewhat different in cases of incest. The wife is sexually cold to her husband and gives tacit encouragement to her husband's incestuous relationships with one or more daughters. The police, correctional agents and prison inmates share extremely negative views of these offenders. Within correctional institutions these offenders are extremely stigmatized. This means that these offenders have a "self-image" of themselves as abnormal; however, they resort to rationalization or denials of guilt. Personality-wise, they are timid, suffer from feelings of sexual inadequacy, are insecure and are victims of sex-role conflict.

Proposed Treatment. Client-centered therapy, individual psychotherapy and group-therapy.

XIV. *Nonviolent Sex Offender* (Statutory Rape)—defined as adult males who participate in sexual intercourse with minor females. The female "victim" is a voluntary participant. Statutory rapists define themselves as law-abiding citizens. They exhibit prosocial attitudes, and do not have previous records of delinquency or crime. They make excellent probation and parole adjustments. In prison they are "square Johns." These offenders are products of several classes. Their family background and peer group association are normal. Contacts with defining agencies are neutral. They constitute a group of normals personality-wise.

Proposed Treatment. No treatment is recommended. Probation rather than incarceration is indicated. These offenders should be isolated from antisocial inmates if imprisoned.

XV. *Narcotic Addict* (Heroin)—defined as belonging to three sub-types: (a) medical addicts; (b) those addicted in adulthood through participation in some noncriminal, deviant subculture, e.g., jazz musicians; and (c) the adult counterparts of the delinquent Type VI discussed previously. Though using narcotics as a consequence of different causal processes, these sub-types become similar, often engaging in habitual drug use. Beyond the possession, use and sale of narcotics, wide-range property offenses are engaged in by adult addicts who are motivated by the need of cash with which to purchase drugs. Female addicts generally resort to prostitution in order to maintain their expensive habits. Drug-addict offenders usually carry out illegal acts as loners. They view themselves as criminals by virtue of a personal vice, drug addiction. They rationalize away their habit as "really not criminal," and view themselves as victims of an unjust legal system. They scorn conventional work roles, social institutions in general and "squares." Habitual drug use becomes a way of life characterized by repeated commitments to correctional institutions or hospitals, release and relapse. Treatment attempts are unsuccessful. Drug addicts are not products of any particular social class. The family backgrounds of addicts vary. Medical addicts and deviant subculture addicts, e.g., jazz musicians, seem to come from conventional backgrounds. Adult addicts who become users as juveniles are products of disordered family settings. With the exception of medical addicts, most addicts initially become involved in drug use in interaction with addicted peers. Drug addicts practice mutual aid and support each other with rationalization for their habits. The addict's contacts with defining agencies reinforces his feelings of being a social outcast from conventional society.

Proposed Treatment. Gibbons recommended for this group similar treatment to that suggested for juvenile narcotics users— long-term milieu management patterned after Synanon. Drug addicts need continuous support from a subculture of "clean" former drug-users to prevent relapse.

Gibbon's typology of adult offenders lacks the preciseness and consistency of his juvenile delinquency typology. Four categories, V, VI, IX and XIV, may be identified by legal labels and each indicates one offense pattern. Six categories are broad, including several different patterns of crime. These are I, II, III, VII, VIII. One category makes use of a personality label, XI. Category I, Professional Thief, comprises a strange collection of bedfellows: short con men; long con men; shoplifters; thieves; and pocket-pickers. Though certainly similar in some dimensions, it is likely that variations among these sub-types preclude their categorization under one label. The dumping together of burglary and robbery as sub-types in both the professional heavy criminal and the semiprofessional property criminal is questionable. The burglar rarely resorts to violence, whether he be professional or nonprofessional. In fact, his *modus operandi* is entirely different from that of the robber. Again, the separation of the White-Collar Criminal from the Professional Fringe Violator makes little operational sense since both, by Sutherland's definition, are White-Collar Criminals. It could also be argued that the construct "White-Collar Criminal" is a misnomer. Gibbons defined the White-Collar Criminal category as comprising those persons in business and corporate organization who violate state and federal regulatory statutes. Violators of this type are usually processed by governmental agencies or in civil courts; therefore they are not adjudicated as criminals. Gibbons, as Sutherland before him, seems to be saying these violators *should* be processed by criminal courts and adjudicated criminals. Since most so-called White-Collar Criminals are in fact not criminals, such a type has no place in a criminal typology. Should the definition of White-Collar Criminal be limited to only those offenders (violators of state regulatory statutes) who were in fact adjudicated criminals in criminal courts, the construct would be legitimate.

Gibbons, though a sociologist, was not afraid of including personality attributes in his analysis of several types of offenders. His conclusion that Semiprofessional Property Criminals and

Personal Offender, One-time Losers have normal personalities seems questionable to the author. It is likely that many recidivistic, Semiprofessional Property Offenders who spend a considerable part of their lives in penal institutions are sociopathic personalities. Some One-time Losers who commit violent crimes probably have deep-seated emotional difficulties. Many people, including offenders, live through stressful and highly emotionally charged situations without resorting to violence. The resort to extreme violence in a stressful situation marks only one alternative. Certainly there are others. Persons who resort to violence are likely to have different personalities from those who choose some other recourse of action.

Though Gibbons made no claim of complete coverage in his typology, several additional criminal types could have been included: draft dodgers; traitors; saboteurs; tax evaders; serious traffic offenders; civil-rights violators; etc. Perhaps, ideally, his greatest error of omission lies with the following offender types: gamblers (several sub-types including the "numbers man" and the "bookie"); non-addicted drug traffickers; illicit liquor traffickers; business and labor racketeers; illegal loan sharks, syndicated criminals; prostitutes; pimps; fences; petty thieves; vagrants; and drunkards. Admittedly, research materials on all of these excepting the last three types are limited. Moreover, offenders within many of these categories are not easy to come by for research purposes in or out of prison. These types do exist in correctional institutions, and some of them have been studied in a limited way and reported in the research literature.[24]

Despite the minor errors of omission and commission as defined by the author, Gibbon's typology of adult offenders represents the most systematic, plausible and inclusive classification schema to date. He has performed the necessary and monumental task of delineating a series of theoretically relevant criminal types based on empirical models found in the research literature. Additionally, Gibbons recommended specific patterns of treatment or control for all of his criminal types.

Some of the most significant and fundamental research by sociologists in the field of criminal typology has been done on specific patterns of criminal behavior. Certain types of professional criminals have been delineated along with their characteristic social backgrounds, *modus operandi*, attitudes, self-definitions, family patterns, group organization and criminal associations. There is also much known about their behavior in prison and after release. Several specific criminal types have also been researched, e.g., the white-collar criminal, "Black Market" violators, confidence men, auto thieves, naive check forgers, embezzlers, robbers, drinkers and assaulters, drug addicts, numbers writers, jack rollers, jack-of-all-trades offenders, murderers, assaulters, rapists, burglars and grand larcenists.[25] Sociologists have also classified prison populations into types. The reference group and social-type typologies of Schrag, Sykes, Clemmer and Hayner comprise significant contributions in this area.[26]

Schrag has demonstrated that four sets of inmate role patterns exist in the prison community: (a) "square Johns" or prosocial inmates; (b) right guys or antisocial inmates; (c) outlaws or asocial inmates; and (d) politicians or pseudo-social inmates. These role patterns are important in understanding inmate behavior within prisons. Moreover, Schrag, who has collected data on the pre-prison experiences of prisoners, has exhibited that offenders playing specific role types are products of a different constellation of background experiences. Sykes found a series of role patterns similar to those of Schrag, e.g., real men, merchants, toughs, rats, gorillas, center men, ball busters, hipsters. The findings of Schrag and Sykes show that prison inmates may be categorized into homogeneous types on the basis of three dimensions: criminal backgrounds; social experiences; and social-psychological characteristics.

The material in this chapter concludes the author's critical review of several typologies representing various approaches to criminal typology. The succeeding chapters deal with his typological attempts.

REFERENCES

1. COHEN, ALBERT K.: *Delinquent Boys, The Culture of the Gang.* Glencoe, The Free Press, 1955; COHEN, ALBERT K., and SHORT,

James F.: Research in delinquent sub-cultures. *Journal of Social Issues, 14*:20-36, August, 1958.

2. Reiss, Albert J., Jr., and Rhodes, Albert Lewis: The distribution of juvenile delinquency in the social class structure. *American Sociological Review, 26*:720-732, October, 1961.

3. Cloward, Richard A., and Ohlin, Lloyd E.: *Delinquency and Opportunity, A Theory of Delinquent Gangs.* Glencoe, The Free Press, 1960; Cloward, Richard A.: Illegitimate means, anomie, and deviant behavior. *American Sociological Review, 24*:164-176, April, 1959.

4. Ohlin and Cloward: *Delinquency and Opportunity,* pp. 161-178.

5. Miller, Walter B.: Lower class culture, as a generating milieu of gang delinquency. *Journal of Social Issues, 14*:5-19, August, 1958; Preventive work with street corner groups: Boston delinquency project. *The Annals of the American Academy of Political and Social Science, 322*:97-106, March, 1959; Implications of urban lower class culture for social work. *The Social Service Review, 33*:219-236, September, 1959.

6. Tappan, Paul: *Crime, Justice, and Correction,* pp. 170-174, 181-183.

7. For criticisms of the Delinquent Sub-Culture Approach see Bordua, David J.: A critique of sociological interpretations of gang delinquency, as found in Delinquent subcultures: Sociological interpretations of gang delinquency. *The Annals of the American Academy of Political and Social Science, 338*: 120-136, November, 1961; Kitsuse, John I., and Dietrich, David: Delinquent boys: A critique. *American Sociological Review, 24*:213, April, 1959.

8. Yablonsky, Lewis: *The Violent Gang.* New York, Macmillan, pp. vii-xiii, 101-110, 146-169, 195-221, 222-234, 1962.

9. Schepses, Erwin: Boys who steal cars. *Federal Probation, 25*:56-62, March, 1961.

10. Clinard, Marshall B., and Wade, Andrew L.: Toward the delineation of vandalism as a sub-type in juvenile delinquency. *Journal of Criminal Law, Criminology, and Police Science, 48*:494-499, January-February, 1958.

11. Reiss, Albert J., Jr.: Sex offenses of adolescents. In Cavan, Ruth S. (ed.): *Readings in Juvenile Delinquency.* New York, J. B. Lippincott, pp. 225-237.

12. CHEIN, ISIDOR: Narcotics use among juveniles. *Social Work,* *1*:50-60, April, 1956.

13. HILL, MOZELL: The metropolis and juvenile delinquency among Negroes. *Journal of Negro Education, 28*:277-285, Summer, 1959.

14. GIBBONS, DON C.: *Changing The Lawbreaker: The Treatment of Delinquents and Criminals.* Englewood Cliffs, New Jersey, Prentice-Hall, 1965, pp. 74-97, 228-252.

15. RECKLESS, WALTER C.: *The Crime Problem,* pp. 324-325; CLINARD, MARSHALL B.: Research frontiers in criminology, pp. 110-122; CLINARD, MARSHALL B.: *The Sociology of Deviant Behavior,* pp. 200-229; TAPPAN, PAUL: *Crime, Justice, and Correction,* pp. 74-82, 1-13; SUTHERLAND and CRESSEY: *Principles of Criminology* (6th ed.), pp. 237-238.

16. CAVAN, RUTH SHONLE: *Criminology* (3rd ed.). New York, Thomas Y. Crowell, 1962, pp. 96-220.

17. BLOCH, HERBERT A., and GEIS, GILBERT: *Man, Crime, and Society.* New York, Random House, 1962, pp. 135-404.

18. LINDESMITH, ALFRED H., and DUNHAM, H. WARREN: Some principles of criminal typology. *Social Forces, 29*:309-311, March, 1941.

19. RANDOLPH, MARY H., RICHARDSON, HAROLD, and JOHNSON, RONALD C.: A comparison of social and solitary male delinquents. *Journal of Consulting Psychology, 25*:293-295, August, 1961.

20. CLINARD, MARSHALL: *Sociology of Deviant Behavior,* (rev. ed.). New York, Holt, Rinehart, and Winston, 1963, pp. 210-290.

21. HUFFMAN, ARTHUR V.: The behavior patterns of criminals. *The Journal of Social Therapy,* 8:15-33, 1st Quarter, 1962.

22. GIBBONS, DON C., and GARRITY, DONALD L.: Definition and analysis of certain criminal types. *Journal of Criminal Law, Criminology, and Police Science, 53*:27-35, March, 1962; see also ROEBUCK, JULIAN B.: A criticism of Gibbon's and Garrity's criminal typology. *Journal of Criminal Law, Criminology, and Police Science,* 54:476-478, December, 1963.

23. GIBBONS: *Changing the Lawbreaker,* pp. 97-128; 253-282.

24. PETERSON, VIRGIL W.: The career of a syndicate boss. *Crime and Delinquency,* 8:339-354, October, 1962; ROEBUCK, JULIAN: The Negro numbers man as a criminal type. *Journal of Criminal Law, Criminology and Police Science,* 54:48-60, March, 1963; TYLER, GUS: *Organized Crime in America.* Ann

Arbor, University of Michigan Press, 1962; *Third Interim Report of the Special Committee to Investigate Organized Crime in Interstate Commerce.* Washington, The Government Printing Office, United States Senate, Report No. 307, 1951; BLOCH, HERBERT A., and GEIS, GILBERT: *Man, Crime, and Society.* New York, Random House, 1962, pp. 216-251; JOHNSON, EARL JR · Organized crime: Challenge to the American legal system. *Journal of Criminal Law Criminology and Police Science,* 53:399-425, December, 1962; LINDESMITH, ALFRED R.: Organized crime. *The Annals of the American Academy of Political and Social Science,* 217:119-127, September, 1941; Organized Crime, *Crime and Delinquency,* 8: October, 1962.

25. SUTHERLAND, EDWIN H.: *The Professional Thief.* Chicago, University of Chicago Press, 1937; MAURER, DAVID W.: *The Big Con.* New York, Bobbs-Merrill Company, 1940; MAURER, DAVID W.: *Whiz Mob.* Gainesville, Florida, American Dialect Society, 1955; JENKINS, RICHARD L.: *Breaking Patterns of Defeat.* Philadelphia, Lippincott, 1954, pp. 136-158; CLINARD, MARSHALL B.: *The Black Market.* New York, Rinehart, 1952; WATTENBERG, WILLIAM W., and BALISTRIERI, JAMES: Automobile theft; A "favored group" delinquency. *American Journal of Sociology,* 57:575-579, May, 1952; SCHEPSES, ERWIN: The young car thief. *Journal of Criminal Law, Criminology, and Police Science,* 50:569, March-April, 1960; LEMERT, EDWIN M.: An isolation and closure theory of naive check forgery, pp. 296-307; LEMERT: The behavior of the systematic check forger, pp. 141-149; LOTTIER, STUART: A tension theory of criminal behavior. *American Sociological Review,* 7:840-848, December, 1942; RIEMER: Embezzlement; pathological basis, pp. 411-423; ROEBUCK: The Negro armed robber as an offender type, pp. 21-27; ROEBUCK and JOHNSON: The Negro drinker and assaulter as a criminal type, pp. 21-33; AUSUBEL: *Drug addiction;* ROEBUCK: The Negro numbers man as an offender type; SHAW, CLIFFORD R.: *The Jack Roller.* Chicago, University of Chicago Press, 1930; ROEBUCK and JOHNSON: The Jack-of-all-trades offender, pp. 172-181; CALDWELL, MORRIS G.: Personality trends in the youthful male offender. *Journal of Criminal Law, Criminology and Police Science,* 49:405-416, January-February, 1959.

26. SCHRAG, CLARENCE A.: *Social Types in a Prison Community.* Unpublished M.A. thesis, University of Washington, 1944; Leadership among prison inmates. *American Sociological Review, 19*:37-42, February, 1954; SYKES, GRESHAM M.: Men, merchants and toughs: A study of reactions to imprisonment. *Social Problems, 4*:130-138, October, 1956; SYKES, GRESHAM M.: *The Society of Captives: A Study of a Maximum Security Prison.* Princeton, Princeton University Press, 1958; CLEMMER, DONALD: Leadership phenomena in a prison community. *Journal of Criminal Law, Criminology, and Police Science, 28*:851-872, March-April, 1938; CLEMMER, DONALD: *The Prison Community.* Boston, Christopher, 1940, re-issued by Rinehart, 1958; HAYNER, NORMAN S., and ASH, ELLIS: The prisoner community as a social group. *American Sociological Review, 4*:362-369, June, 1939; HAYNER, NORMAN S., and ASH, ELLIS: The prison as a community. *American Sociological Review,* August, 1940, pp. 577-583.

Chapter V

AN ARREST HISTORY TYPOLOGY OF FELONS

THE WRITER was interested in developing an inductive criminal typology based on the ideas expressed in the last section of the first chapter of this work. The primary, envisioned function of his typology was in terms of explanatory theory rather than in terms of diagnostic systems to be used in treatment. However, subsequent material will demonstrate that treatment suggestions are considered. The author's typology was based on the following assumptions:

1. The study of patterned behavior is the chief province of the behavioral scientists and of the criminologists who are concerned with the etiology of human behavior.

2. Persons who are officially adjudicated criminals or delinquents are frequently ones who are involved in recidivistic and serious acts of law violation. Adjudicated offenders provide the most adequate base for criminal typologists' study samples.

3. Among adjudicated offenders there are variations in the type and intensity of the criminal or delinquent role. These include variations in offense behavior as well as related social-psychological characteristics. Some offenders have a self-image as a criminal or delinquent. Others do not. Some offenders conceive of themselves as professional criminals. Others do not.

4. Many offenders close on certain types of criminal activity during their career spans, albeit at one time or another they might commit several different types of crime. Stable patterns of criminal behavior are accompanied by uniform social-psychological characteristics; i.e., certain social and psychological types close on certain patterns of criminal activity.

5. Behavioral and social-psychological changes may occur dur-

ing the development of specific criminal career spans; however, these changes are limited and identifiable.

6. Criminal behavior has many causes. The sociological and psychological approaches (in combination) to criminal etiology are currently the most fruitful approaches. The sociological-psychological process that leads to one specific type of criminal career includes several causal variables and differs from that process which leads to another type of criminal career. The search for the causes of crime in general are fruitless. The search must be directed toward the causes of specific criminal patterns.

7. Criminal typologies must include the explicit use of legal nomenclature and give special emphasis to criminal careers. The accessible official data concerned with official criminal histories exist in terms of legal nomenclature, i.e., arrests and convictions by criminal charges; and the criminal code contains more specific, hence operational definitions of criminal behavior than any set of nonlegal categories.[1]

The writer analyzed several specific offender types found in a prison population in terms of an arrest history typology. The sample of subjects studied consisted of four-hundred offenders selected at random from 1,155 Negroes who entered the District of Columbia Reformatory, Lorton, Virginia, between January 5, 1954, and November 8, 1955. The typology was based on the following criteria: (1) the presence of criminal patterns in offenders' criminal histories as determined by arrest patterns; (2) the levels of *modi operandi* found in the official criminal records; (3) social and personal correlates of the criminal patterns;[2] and (4) qualitative clinical impressions.

The data concerned with the arrest histories were obtained from an examination of the offenders' official arrest histories. Levels of *modi operandi* were determined from the research interviews, court records and from District Attorney's Reports.

Data pertaining to dimension 3 "social and personal correlates of the criminal patterns," were defined in terms of thirty-four social and personal characteristics which were obtained from the institutional folders and research interviews. These thirty-four attributes were selected from the following areas: (a) family background, including interpersonal relations obtaining in parental families; (b) neighborhood and area background; (c) school background and school adjustment; (d) work background and attitude toward work; (e) indices of personal disorganization, i.e., drug addiction, alcoholism, inveterate gambling, vagabondage, residential mobility; (f) military adjustment; (g) marital status; (h) indices of juvenile delinquency. Three continuous properties, age, I.Q. and Stanford Achievement Test grade median, were also included.

Data on qualitative clinical impressions were obtained by the author in the research interviews, from psychological profiles drawn by a resident clinical psychologist (Ph.D.) and from medical records developed by District of Columbia Department of Corrections Physicians. This dimension included an assessment of the offender's social-psychological personality type based on interview reactions, personality characteristics, attitudes, self-concept and physical and mental health. (For the development and rationale of the social case history schedule, the instrument on which the preceding four sets of criteria were recorded, see Appendix B, pp. 247-286.

METHOD

The arrest patterns were ascertained from longitudinal study of the known criminal offenses charged to individual offenders as revealed in their arrest histories. A type theory in which criminals are differentiated according to a single (usually most recent) offense has an extreme disadvantage because offenders show some variability in their offenses.[3] Labeling a man an "armed robber type" on the basis of his most recent crime, even though he has had a long previous history as a con man, is unlikely to lead to any large amount of useful knowledge.

By contrast, the present typology was based on the configuration of total known arrests for various criminal charges. The arrest history, a longitudinal measure of behavior, allowed the investigator to observe the existence of a fixed pattern of criminal behavior, if any such pattern existed. An offender whose official arrest history showed nine robbery charges out of a total of twelve arrests may be taken as a hypothetical case. Classifying similar sequences of arrests on other charges, e.g., assault, drunkenness, housebreaking, etc., made it possible to assign individual criminals to criminal pattern categories.

One of the basic assumptions underlying this typology and the research that emanated from it was that arrest patterns would indicate a particular pattern of behavior or criminal career. If noncriminals manifest a pattern in their legal activities, then the logic of contemporary behavioral theory leads us to assume that the illegal activities of the criminal must also manifest an identifiable pattern. This typology was designed to classify criminals in terms of illegal careers as revealed in cumulative arrest histories. The most frequent charge or charges in the total arrest history of the subject was the basis for classification. The charges appearing in the later phases of the criminal's arrest history were given greater weight, since later entries would reflect more accurately the current state of his criminal development than would those entries occurring in his earlier arrest history.[4]

It is certainly legitimate to question, as has been done by criminologists, the validity of differentiating between criminals on the basis of legal rather than behavioral categories. If legal criminal categories were only legal categories, any criticism would certainly be justified. However, studies by the author show that a considerable number of behavioral differences exist between groups of individuals with different arrest patterns, while the backgrounds of individuals within a specific category of arrest patterns have a good deal in common.[5] Thus, arrest patterns appear to be behavioral, as well as legal, categories of offenders. The fact that significant differences exist between arrest-pattern groups seems sufficient reason to follow this approach to criminal typology further.

Of course, this index, because it is a product of official records, does not account for all the crimes committed by the subject in his criminal career. No offender is apprehended for every crime he commits; and, of course, the offender may not be guilty of all the crimes he is charged with. However, the principal advantage in the use of arrest records stems from the fact, as Sutherland and Cressey (among others) have noted, that the further one gets away from a criminal's arrest history, the more obscure and distorted become the facts of his criminal activities.[6] Certainly, one would hesitate to use the offender's own story about his past offenses as a primary and exclusive typological criterion. Researchers have noted the reluctance of many offenders to divulge their unknown unofficial criminal activities. In any event, *the offenders' stories about their unreported criminal activities during the research interviews indicated an unofficial pattern of crime parallel to their official arrest history pattern.*

Other academic criminologists have made a limited use of the arrest histories of certain offender types for purposes of illustration and interpretation,[7] while institutional caseworkers and parole and probation officers have also made use of the arrest history in discussing criminal careers and in developing the case histories of offenders. The police have recognized the importance of arrest history analysis. Some criminals often concentrate on one type of crime and, in fact, may specialize on a certain technique, or *modus operandi,* within this type. The technique may be significant in determining the direction of police investigation. In many instances, in fact, the police in large cities have combined or cross-filed their *modus operandi* files with their "rap sheets," in a rough attempt at classifying by criminal type those who have been arrested. Most large law-enforcement agencies have appropriately titled spaces on the reverse side of their fingerprint blanks for noting the specific techniques used in the commission of each specific crime.[8] Given a filling-station holdup by a lone-wolf bandit wearing a stocking over his face, the police investigator may well check his "m.o. file" and then begin to check up on the whereabouts of criminals who specialize in this form of activity.

An analysis of the four hundred arrest histories, based on the frequency of criminal charges occurring in each, permitted the grouping of all cases into four general classes.[9]

1. *Single Pattern.* This label was attached to an arrest history

which showed a high frequency of one kind of criminal charge. In order for a history to be classified as a single pattern, it had to satisfy one of the following conditions: (a) It had to show three or more arrests, all of which were for the same charge; or (b) an arrest history which contained at least four arrests for a given charge and additional arrests for other charges, was divided into three sections and qualified for a single pattern if at least one of the four or more arrests for a given charge appeared in the last section of the arrest history, and if the charge constituted at least 33 per cent of those charges which occurred in the last two sections of the arrest history.

Obviously, not all numbers are divisible by three. When the number of arrests could not be divided into three equal sections, the latter sections were given more weight. Following are four examples of how the patterns were arrived at.

An arrest history with an incidence of four arrests was divided into three sections—1, 1 and 2. The first arrest (that arrest appearing first on an offender's rap sheet) constituted the first section, the second arrest the second section and the last two arrests the third section. If all four arrests were for robbery, this arrest history would show a single pattern of robbery. If all four arrests in this instance were not for one criminal charge, the arrest history would show "mixed pattern."

An arrest history containing five arrests was divided into three sections—1, 2 and 2. The first arrest constituted the first section, the second and third arrests the second section and the fourth and fifth arrests the third section. Hypothetically, if the charge for the first arrest was robbery, the second arrest housebreaking, and the third, fourth and fifth arrests robbery, we would have a pattern of robbery.

An arrest history containing seven arrests was divided into three sections—2, 2 and 3. The first two arrests constituted the first section, the next two arrests the second section and the last three arrests the third section. Hypothetically, if the charges for the first two arrests were for housebreaking, the third for robbery, the fourth for housebreaking and the last three for robbery, a pattern of robbery is demonstrated.

An arrest history with ten arrests was divided into three sections—3, 3 and 4. The first three arrests comprised the first section, the fourth, fifth and sixth arrests the second section and the seventh, eighth, ninth and tenth arrests the third section. Hypothetically, if the charge for the first arrest was assault, the second arrest disorderly conduct, the third arrest drunkenness, the fourth arrest drunkenness, the fifth arrest assault, the sixth arrest drunkenness, the seventh arrest assault, the eighth arrest petty theft, the ninth arrest drunkenness and the tenth arrest assault, this would constitute a double pattern of drunkenness and assault.

2. *Multiple Pattern.* An arrest history of two or more single patterns derived by the procedures set forth in Item 1 above.

3. *Mixed Pattern.* An arrest history of three or more arrests in which none of the charges formed a frequency pattern as defined above ("Jack-of-all-trades").

4. *No Pattern.* An arrest history of only one or two arrests. This is a residual category of those offenders with insufficient arrests to warrant analysis.

The final result was a typology of thirteen criminal patterns, eleven of which include distinct legal categories.[10]

Of the four hundred cases studied, the following chart shows the number of cases found for each of the thirteen patterns.

Criminal Pattern	*Number*
1. Mixed pattern (Jack-of-all-trades offender)	71
2. Double pattern of larceny and burglary	64
3. Single pattern of narcotic drug laws	50
4. Triple pattern of drunkenness, assault and larceny	43
5. Double pattern of drunkenness and assault	40
6. Single pattern of robbery	32
7. No pattern[11]	32
8. Single pattern of gambling	16
9. Single pattern of burglary	15
10. Single pattern of sex offenses	15
11. Single pattern of fraud[12]	10
12. Single pattern of auto theft	8
13. Single pattern of forgery and counterfeiting	4

Given the arrest history typology, the next step was to investigate the relationship between the various classes of criminals and thirty-four social and personal characteristics which were obtained for each inmate from institutional records and scheduled interviews. Comparisons were made for each of these characteristics (chi-square statistic when cell frequencies permitted) with the arrest pattern. Each pattern was compared with the remainder of the sample, and each pattern was compared with all other patterns in reference to these thirty-four variables. Additionally, three continuous properties, age, IQ, and Standard Achievement Test grade median scores were used for comparative purposes in terms of the medians of their respective distributions. No test of significance was applied to the difference between means and medians because it was reasoned that the characteristics in question were of descriptive rather than analytical character. The data concerned with levels of *modi operandi* and qualitative clinical impressions were also used for comparative purposes in a qualitative manner.

It is evident then that this typology utilized a legal, sociological and psychological approach. It combines a modified categorical system of classification (arrest pattern category) with a flexible multi-dimensional system of classification (see criteria 2, 3 and 4 on page 98). The classification of offenders into arrest-pattern categories is specific and categorical. Dimensions 2, 3 and 4 are variable.

Subsequent chapters are concerned with the social-psychological profiles of six of the above criminal patterns: Single Pattern of Robbery; Single Pattern of Narcotic Drug Laws (Drug Addicts); Single Pattern of Gambling (Numbers Men); Single Pattern of Fraud (Confidence Men); Double Pattern of Drunkenness and Assault (Drinker-Assaulter); Mixed Pattern (Jack-of-all-trades Offender). The remaining seven patterns are less systematically described.

REFERENCES

1. For a description of arrest history sources and legal labeling procedures see Appendix A, pp. 242-246.
2. In point of time, the data on the social and personal characteristics

were obtained first to preclude any bias that might result from pre-knowledge of the arrest-history patterns.

3. GILLIN, JOHN LEWIS: *The Wisconsin Prisoner: Studies in Criminogenesis.* Madison, Wisconsin, The University of Wisconsin Press, 1946, for purposes of analysis, classified a number of incarcerated offenders into general criminal categories; e.g., sex offenders, property offenders and murderers on the basis of a single (conviction) charge.

4. In addition to the question of frequency of charge, consideration was given to the role of intervals between charges. A preliminary investigation of the sample revealed a remarkable homogeneity in the length of these intervals. Only ten out of the four hundred arrest histories exhibited an interval of five or more years between arrests, (omitting, of course, time spent in incarceration).

5. ROEBUCK, JULIAN B.: The Negro drug addict as an offender type; Roebuck and Cadwallader: The Negro armed robber as a criminal type: The construction and application of a typology," pp. 21-26. See also Roebuck: *A Tentative Criminal Typology of 400 Negro Felons.* Unpublished study for the District of Columbia Dept. of Corrections, 1955.

6. SUTHERLAND, EDWIN H., and CRESSEY, DONALD R.: *Principles of Criminology* (6th ed.), pp. 32-36.

7. RECKLESS, WALTER, *op. cit.*: pp. 87-95, 119-128, 154-177; Tappan, *op. cit.*: pp. 122-130, 138-140, 149-150, 153-154, 166-167, 204-205, 226-229.

8. FITZGERALD, MAURICE J.: *Handbook of Criminal Investigation.* New York, Greenberg, 1951, pp. 119-125.

9. In determining criminal patterns (arrest-history patterns) the writer derived a chronological arrest history on each of the four-hundred cases from the official arrest records. Legal nomenclature was adhered to, including the offense categories found in the criminal codes of the District of Columbia, the various states, and the U. S. Code.

10. For a definition of these legal categories see Appendix C, pp. 287-289.

11. Residual categories of cases with less than three arrests.

12. This F. B. I. classification covered the pattern of confidence game charges found in all the records.

Chapter VI

THE ARMED ROBBER[1]

R OBBERY is an offense in which force or a real threat of force is used to deprive the victim of money or property. In some instances, bodily injury is involved. It is, at the same time, a property offense and an offense against the person. Robbery differs from embezzlement, forgery, larceny and many other property offenses in that the perpetrator physically confronts and dominates the victim. Subterfuge is not a part of this "heavy" crime. Some robbers have been romanticized as courageous, frank, direct and deliberate offenders, as opposed to the despicable petty thief. Bell, in discussing crime as an American way of life, points out that the American hero has been the hunter, cowboy, frontiersman, soldier, naval hero and, in the crowded slums, the man with a gun who acquired by personal merit and courage what was denied to him by complex orderings of a stratified society. Bell, however, recognizes that the man with the gun has lost much of his glamour with the evolvement of the "industrial, non-heavy" rackets. According to Bell, as the American businessman became "civilized" and less "buccaneering," so did the man with the gun. In any event, many robbers interviewed by the writer have verbalized a romantic stereotype of themselves, i.e., alluded to themselves as "honest thieves" who go forth and directly take what they want.[2]

Robbers may be amateur or professional, solitary or organized. The behavior included in this criminal category ranges from "mugging" and "heist" in the street or home through hijacking and bank robbery. Weapons may or may not be used.

Based on data reported to the police during the first quarter of 1964, armed robbery constituted 59 per cent of the overall offenses, while 41 per cent was strongarm mugging. Robbery comprised 4 per cent of the Crime Index Offenses in 1963. The national arrest rate for robbery in 1963 was thirty arrests for each 100,000 population. The robbery rate (those reported to police) since 1958 has increased 12 per cent. Robbery is primarily a big city offense. The highest arrest-rate-age group in 1963 was found in the 20 to 24 year old age group. In 1963, street robberies made up about 53 per cent of all robberies in cities, chain store robbery, 2 per cent of total robberies, bank robbery, 1 per cent of total robberies. Of all robberies reported to police in 1963, 39 per cent were solved by the identification and arrest of the offender.[3]

Previous comparative studies of robbers have indicated the following results: Robbers are more frequently single, migratory, narcissistic, intelligent, quick-witted and emotionally maladjusted than are other offenders as a group; they also more frequently lack family attachments and possess insecure feelings about recognition; their IQ's and criminal style (amateur or professional) vary with their social-class background.[4]

THE ARMED ROBBER AS A CRIMINAL TYPE

The statistical analysis showed that the thirty-two subjects, characterized by a pattern of arrests for armed[5] robbery, differed widely from the other 368 offenders in twenty-two of the thirty-four social and personal characteristics studied. These differences were significant at the .01 level. An additional six were significant at the .05 level, making a total of twenty-eight characteristics in which the differences were deemed significant when measured by chi-square.[6]

The robbers were a comparatively young group of offenders with a median age of thirty. They approached average intelligence; the median IQ was 90, and the Stanford Achievement Test grade median was 5.0, while for the remainder of the sample the median age was thirty-three, the Stanford Achievement Test grade median was 5.0, and the median IQ was 86.

The armed robbers were reared in slum neighborhoods where unfavorable home and area conditions prevailed more frequently than for the men in the rest of the sample. They grew up more frequently in several homes which were marked by criminality, desertion, conflict, and inadequate parental supervision. Public assistance was the rule, their families being known to several social agencies over long periods of time. Their childhood experiences were unsettled as a consequence of frequent moves to foster homes and the homes of relatives. Their mothers entertained various paramours in the home situation, and their sisters were often prostitutes. Their fathers were generally heavy drinkers who displayed little interest in them. Frequently, their parents and siblings had misdemeanor as well as felony-sentence records. More frequently, the mother figure was the dominant parental figure, a migrant from the South and a domestic servant. In a home marked by conflict, parental supervision by either parent was at a minimum. A pattern of maladjustment since early childhood was easily discernible in their home, school and community backgrounds. They more frequently expressed hostility to their father figures. They were more often disciplinary problems at home and school, and a higher proportion of them were truants and "home runaways." They worked more frequently at street trades during childhood and adolescence, and more of them had had delinquent companions. More of them were adjudicated juvenile delinquents, members of juvenile delinquent gangs, committed as juveniles, experienced police contacts prior to age eighteen, associated with adult criminal companions as adolescents. They were less frequently addicted to drugs or alcohol than the other offenders.

Internal statistical comparisons, comparisons with each of the other patterns, when cell frequencies permitted, demonstrated the robbers to be more similar to the offenders within the patterns of Double Pattern of Larceny and Burglary and Mixed Pattern than with offenders in any other groupings. They were more frequently (statistically significant) disciplinary problems at school and members of juvenile delinquent gangs than the offenders in these two patterns; they also more often had police contacts and criminal companions, prior to age eighteen.

The interviews revealed a disorganized home background shot

through with conflict and economic and emotional deprivation. Their responses indicated qualitative as well as quantitative differences in their homes when compared with the other men in the sample.[7] The robbers talked more about such physical violence in the home as corporal punishment, fights with brothers, sisters and father, than did the men in the other criminal patterns. One of the robbers commented:

> There was always a battle going on. My younger brother wanted everything. I had to fight him every week to keep him in place. The old man would come home drunk as hell and start kicking people around. When I got fourteen, I poked him once or twice. The nothing used to smack my mother too.

They had run away from home frequently and found what they felt to be more satisfying group attachments in "street corner society." Upon reaching their middle teens, they generally left home and shifted for themselves, usually living in rented rooms in cheap boarding houses. These remarks were typical:

> With all the hell at home and half hungry too, I stayed on the street most of the time. I run with a bunch of boys, who I had fun with. We shot pool and run up and down, you know. We got money too, you know; we had our ways.

An early patterning of: stealing from their parents, from school and on the street; truancy and suspension or expulsion from school; street fighting; association with older delinquents and juvenile delinquent gang memberships was usually evident in their social backgrounds. When compared with the men in the other criminal categories, it was found that there was more destruction of property in their delinquent activities, and there were more frequent fights with schoolmates, male teachers and delinquent companions. There was a higher incidence of "mugging" and purse snatching. They had more often been the leaders of delinquent gangs, and they claimed they were leaders because of their superior size and physical strength. This quotation from one of the robbers was typical:

> I soon found out the man who was boss got the most bread (money). Well, I was the biggest and strongest, so I just knocked off the top boy and took over. If they didn't go my way, I clipped them that's all.

These men more frequently carried and used weapons of violence as juvenile delinquents.

> Sometimes you gotta carry some heat to put the pressure on. Some people won't get up off that money less they see you are ready. The studs I ran with, Jack, had to have some kind of heat . . . knife, gun, blackjack or something.

Criminal progression appeared to occur at a more rapid rate with an early trend toward crimes of violence—from petty thefts and playground fights to the rolling of drunks and homosexuals and on to holdups with such weapons as pistols and knives.

As adults, these men constituted a group of juvenile delinquents "grown up" who remained in slum areas free of family-group ties. In discussing their criminal companions, these offenders indicated a broad knowledge of the underworld but no close ties with it.[8] Their close affiliations were with former juvenile delinquent companions with whom they had served time as juveniles and as adults. These companions were usually robbers and were referred to as "rap partners."

> I never did nothing with no pimps . . . dudes with no heart. I run with the studs I know from way back, studs I had done a bit with. We know what we want, and we know how to get it. We learned the hard way, but we was ready.

They scoffed at their criminal acquaintances who were nonviolent property offenders, particularly check forgers and confidence men. These offenders lacked nerve, physical courage and strength, according to the robbers. They represented themselves as brave, daring men who took what they wanted in a straightforward way.

> You got heart, you can get that bread in a hurry! Course you got to figure the angles. These pimps and con men ain't nothing. Those suckers are punks on the street just like they are here. Holler at one and see him keep getting up.

The arrest histories of these offenders showed a mean of 18.2 arrests. Sprinkled through the arrest histories were a scattered assortment of assault and sex charges, and occasionally drunkenness and disorderly arrests; however, the pattern of robbery was clear-cut. Most of the non-property arrest charges were for crimes against the person.

The District Attorney's Reports on all crimes for which these offenders had served under felony sentence revealed a robbery *modus operandi* at various levels of operation. Fifteen of the thirty-two incorporated at least five of the following procedures in their *modus operandi*. (a) There was a definite target of operations where there was reasonable assurance that a large sum of cash was available. (b) The target was carefully "cased" at least three weeks in advance. (c) At least one practice run was made. (d) A careful and detailed timetable was established. (e) There was a getaway car and a special driver. (f) There was a "gun man" and an accomplice for the inside job. (g) There was a lookout man. (h) There was a definite leader. (i) There was a prearranged agreement for the division of the money, and a definite time and place was planned for this part of the operation. (g) There was a plan of escape to follow the robbery. Six of the thirty-two operated as "loners" holding up individuals at the point of a gun or knife. Six operated with one accomplice. Two simply knocked the victim down and relieved him of his money by physical force.[9]

As a group, the robbers appeared to be physically strong, athletic in body build and in very good health. They gave the impression of being five to ten years younger than their chronological age and they made very few somatic complaints.[10] They seemed to be repressing a great deal of restless, physical energy. They verbalized well in a glib, aggressive and breezy fashion. Their vocabularies revealed them to be a group of street-wise toughs who were quite familiar with the criminal argot. At times during the interviews they gave the impression of being friendly, gay and cooperative. At other times they reacted in an aggressive and hostile manner. Frequently, they responded to the writer's questions with a question attempting to "personalize" the interview. This was particularly the case when the interview probed in the area of their relationships with their parents. They were extremely self-centered, and nearly every sentence uttered made use of the first person singular. They impressed the interviewer as being emotionally cold in their relationships with others. Generally, they were sharply critical of other people, including relatives and friends. They criticized established social institutions such as the family, marriage, the church, the economic system, the courts and law enforcement machinery. They took great pride in their individualism.

The robbers expressed no clear-cut long-term goals, and their remarks indicated a preoccupation with the immediate present. The plans they did mention in regard to the future were vague and whimsical. They rationalized away their past difficulties by placing the blame for their mistakes on others. They expressed bitterness toward police and the courts for their present sentence. Most of them insisted that they were not technically guilty of their present charge and over one half of them asked the interviewer questions about the legal writs which they were working on. They demonstrated little insight into the nature of their past difficulties and expressed little desire for any modification of their own personality. Throughout the interviews they spoke of physical violence as the best possible means to settle any and all difficulties.[11]

In summary, the armed robbers were a group of hardened, antisocial recidivists, the products of disorganized homes and slum neighbors where they come in contact with criminal norms and activities at an early age. Rejected and ill-supervised in homes charged with emotional conflict, they entered street corner society early—between the ages of six and nine. Case histories showed a pattern of unadjustment at home, school and in the community. They had usually been gang leaders prone to violence and the destruction of property. Perhaps their size, physical strength and excess energy had something to do with their leadership role as juveniles. Twenty of them had been amateur boxers. As adults they sought out criminal companions of a similar type, that is, other robbers. They took real pride in their criminal style—the taking of property by force or threat of force. Most of them had developed some skills and a *modus operandi* in their criminal activities. Criminal progression was accelerated in the careers of the robbers. As a group, these offenders comprised a more homogeneous category personality-wise than did any other criminal-pattern group, with perhaps the exception of the Drug Laws Offenders and the No Pattern Offenders. All of them exhibited a clearly delineated pattern of armed robbery.

INDICATORS FOR A MULTI-DISCIPLINARY APPROACH WITH ARMED ROBBERS

Assuming that the findings on the above armed robbers have some reliability; i.e., if replication (studies) on other groups of armed robbers would yield similar results, what are the indicators which would call for a multi-disciplinary approach to this criminal type? The constitutionalists would note the physical strength and restlessness of these men which may have been translated into a violent leadership role from early boyhood. The constitutionalists might compare the somatotype of this group with other criminal types. Since all of these men had serious behavior problems dating to early childhood and, since twenty-five of them had been diagnosed as psychopathic personalities, the constitutionalists might search for a common organic defective base, for example, an EEG profile. They would also note the frequency of criminality and antisocial behavior among the parents and sibs of the robbers which might lead them to probe into the backgrounds of more remote relatives.

The psychologists and psychiatrists would take cognizance of the fact that these men were of average intelligence, that they experienced punishing and unrewarding experiences from early childhood with their parents and sibs, that their reactions to frustration were of the acting-out violent type. Through and by objective and projective personality tests and detailed psychiatric interviews, the psychologists and psychiatrists might be able to sift out a refined personality type for the armed robber.

The sociologists would be interested in probing deeper into the following findings: the robber's early association with juvenile delinquent companions and juvenile delinquent gangs; residence in delinquency areas; dearth of proper parental supervision; commitments to juvenile institutions; consciousness of kind as armed robbers; reference group identification with armed robbers; criminal progression; leadership roles in gangs; socioeconomic class and opportunity structure.

The legalist and correctional administrator would probably envision offenders of this type as serious recidivists who would not be good probation and parole risks.

In reference to treatment considerations, these offenders pose a very difficult problem. Little success, if any, has actually been accomplished in the past with such types. Psychiatrists and clinical psychologists generally recommend close custody and firm supervision for them in a penal setting.

It has been the writer's prison experience that offenders of this type are thoroughly antisocial. Moreover, they are generally disciplinary and custody problems; they thrive on conflict, excitement and trouble. Peace and tranquility appear to disturb them. Fights, knifings and aggressive homosexual attacks are usually attributed to them. Physically vigorous, restlessly energetic and rebellious, they are "natural" trouble makers in a penal setting.

Perhaps offenders of this type should be incarcerated in specialized close-custody institutions, where their particular problems could better be met. Certainly their presence in reformatories calls for more stringent custody measures than are necessary for well over half of most inmate populations. If they were isolated in specialized institutions, various *experimental methods* of treatment could be attempted with them by research-minded psychiatrists and clinical psychologists. It is certain that their absence from the general type of reformatory or prison where many of them are presently incarcerated would make possible a let-up of custody measures, a less tense atmosphere and an institutional setting more in keeping with treatment techniques than now exist. Under present prison conditions, which as a rule do not provide for the segregation of these men, they are permitted too much freedom of movement among members of the general population. Predatory, aggressive and at all times potentially violent, they often intimidate other offenders. In the writer's opinion, they should be housed in cell

TABLE I

COMPARISON OF SINGLE PATTERN OF ARMED ROBBERY OFFENDERS WITH ALL OTHER OFFENDERS

Selected Social and Personal Attributes	Armed Robbers (N=32) N.W.C.*	All Others (N=368) N.W.C.	Sign of X^2	Selected Social and Personal Attributes	Armed Robbers (N=32) N.W.C.*	All Others (N=368) N.W.C.	Sign of X^2
Reared in more than one home	25	136	.01	Weak parental family structure	29	185	.01
Mother figure southern migrant	29	145	.01	No parental family ties	25	257	N.S.
Mother figure domestic servant	31	269	.01	Reared in urban area	32	302	N.S.
Dependent family	30	266	.01	Reared in slum area	32	219	.01
Family broken by desertion	15	125	.05	Living in slum when arrested	30	271	.05
Demoralized family	27	169	.01	History of school truancy	29	174	.01
Criminality in family	25	146	.01	Disciplinary problem at school	30	158	.01
Mother figure dominant	26	193	.01	Street trades as juvenile	28	175	.01
Inadequate supervision—father	19‡	177‡	.01	No marital ties	29	259	.05
Inadequate supervision—mother	29	253	.05	Juvenile delinquent companions	31	205	.01
Conflict in family	19	215	N.S.†	Member delinquent gang	31	111	.01
Overt hostility toward father	18	153	.01	Adjudicated juvenile delinquent	30	147	.01
Overt hostility toward mother	6	73	N.S.	Committed as juvenile	29	117	.01
Disciplinary problem at home	18	101	.01	Police contact prior to age 18	32	189	.01
History of running away	27	158	.01	Criminal companions as juvenile	31	132	.01
Inveterate gambler	18	152	N.S.	Drug addict	1	68	.05
Problem drinker	9	184	.05	Positive attitude toward work	8	145	N.S.

*Number with characteristic.

†Not significant.

‡Based on those with fathers.

blocks, where firm and consistent discipline could be imposed at all times. At no time should they be permitted to become inmate leaders, nor should they be placed in sensitive or prestige jobs where they can connive and exert their selfish negative influence.

REFERENCES

1. ROEBUCK, JULIAN B., and CADWALLADER, MERVIN L.: The Negro armed robber as a criminal type: The construction and application of a typology. *Pacific Sociological Review, 4*:21-28, Spring, 1961.
2. BELL, DANIEL: Crime as an American way of life. *The Antioch Review, 13*:131-154, June, 1953.
3. *Crime in the United States—Uniform Crime Reports,* 1963. Issued by J. Edgar Hoover, Director, Federal Bureau of Investigation, U. S. Department of Justice, Released July 20, 1964, pp. 13-15.
4. TAPPAN, PAUL: *Crime, Justice, and Correction,* pp. 226-229.
5. These offenders were designated armed robbers because all of them used weapons in their *modus operandi.*
6. See Table I, p. 115.
7. In addition to the statistical findings reported here, considerable qualitative evidence was gathered from interviews to support and extend the quantitative study. This material is summarized below.
8. They knew by name and criminal specialty the numbers operators, the heads of gambling houses, the operators of the afterhours clubs, the operators of the houses of prostitution and the bootleggers. They did not associate with these criminals nor did they engage in their type of criminal activities.
9. DEBAUN, EVERETT: The heist: The theory and practice of armed robbery. *Harper's, 200*:69-77, February, 1950. This article, by an armed robber, gives an extended description of the *modus operandi* of this type of criminal that agrees in every detail with the findings presented here.
10. All of these thirty-two men were found to be organically sound and in general good health by an examining physician of the District of Columbia Department of Corrections.
11. The Admission Summaries in their official dossiers showed that

during past and present incarcerations twenty-five of these men had been diagnosed as psychopathic personalities by psychiatrists and clinical psychologists. All of them had been disciplinary problems at one time or another in a correctional institution. The MMPI scale 4 scores (pd) showed all of these 32 men to have T scores above 75. No other criminal category scored as high on this scale.

Chapter VII

THE DRUG ADDICT[1]

DRUG ADDICTS (opiate addicts) generally become offenders in two ways: (a) by the possession, purchase, sale or transfer of narcotics, i.e., direct or indirect violations of state or federal narcotics acts; or (b) by the commission of property crimes for economic rewards which are then used in the purchase of drugs. Sociologists and psychiatrists have noted that the drug addict as an offender type cannot be defined as a criminal in the traditional sense of a robber, auto thief, burglar, murderer, etc.[2] Generally, he is conceded to be a criminal only by virtue of a personal vice, similar in a sense to the alcoholic. Unlike the alcoholic, however, the addict's vice is a criminal act, regardless of the social consequences. His behavior, as distinct from that of the traditional criminal, may not involve a victim, except, of course, the user himself. When the addict's vice leads to traditional, non-drug-law offenses, he is rarely found to be a serious offender against person or property; nor is he often found among the organized criminals, racketeers or professional thieves. His property crimes usually consist of unsophisticated thefts, burglaries and forgeries.[3] Additionally, since narcotic drugs are depressants, addicts are rarely involved in sex offenses and other offenses against the person, e.g., assault, armed robbery, murder.[4]

The relationship between addiction and traditional crime remains unclear. Some studies show that criminality precedes the use of drugs in the individual addict's criminal career; others claim criminality occurs only after addiction.[5] Certainly the criminal career, if any, is an ordinary one in either case. Personality-wise, psychologists have emphasized the strong dependency needs and feelings of inadequacy of the addict. Psychiatrists and psychologists have found addicts to be emo-

118

tionally immature, passive, hedonistic and withdrawn. Some scholars point out that it is not clear whether the personal disorganization exhibited by addicts is the cause or effect or unrelated to the presence of addiction. Sociologists deprecate the significance of personality factors in the etiology of addiction and concentrate on the social process leading to the use of drugs.[6]

Societal reaction to the drug-addict offender is ambivalent and generally varies on a continuum between two extreme positions: the addict offender is a weak-willed, morally and physically debilitated dangerous criminal who should be removed to prison for a long period of time; or the addict offender is a sick person who needs medical treatment. Some holding the latter view recommend outpatient treatment including the use of "substitute" drugs. According to this view, the use of drugs has no deleterious effects on personality nor does it induce criminal tendencies.[7]

In any event, following addiction, the primary criminal motivation of the drug-addict offender does not appear to be economic gain nor the need to express aggression, but rather a physiological and psychological compulsion that demands satisfaction. Thus, if the addict's motivation differs from that of non-addict offenders, then it can be expected that he may possess social and psychological characteristics that distinguish him from other offenders.

Statistics on narcotic drug laws offenders are fragmentary. The Federal Bureau of Narcotics reported 47,489 active addicts in 1962.[8] Out of a total of 4,259,463 arrests in 1963, 20,760 arrests were for narcotic drug laws offenses.[9] Offenders who violate narcotic laws more frequently than any other offense group repeat the same type of crime (narcotics violations).[10]

THE DRUG ADDICT AS A CRIMINAL TYPE

The statistical analysis showed that the fifty subjects, characterized by a pattern of arrests for narcotic drug laws offenses,[11] differed from the other 350 offenders in twenty-eight of the thirty-four social and personal characteristics studied. Twenty-seven of these differences were significant at the .01 level, and one at the .05 level.[12]

The drug offenders were comparatively a young group (median age—25) of fairly literate offenders (S.A.T. grade median 8.6) of average intelligence (median IQ—100).

The statistical analysis revealed that in many ways their early family, school, and community backgrounds and adjustments were more favorable than those of the other offenders. They were reared less frequently in slum neighborhoods. They were more often products of one home situation, and the home was less commonly marked by criminality, conflict, demoralization and parental desertion. Less frequently were their mothers migrants from the South and domestic servants. More often they were products of families which enjoyed strong ties. As further evidence of this familial milieu, these drug addicts less frequently expressed hostility toward their fathers, and they were less often disciplinary problems either at home or in school. Additionally, fewer of them were school truants and "home runaways." They worked less frequently at street trades during childhood and adolescence, and fewer of them had had delinquent companions. Furthermore, they were less often found to be members of juvenile delinquent gangs; fewer of them had been adjudicated juvenile delinquents; and a smaller proportion of them had been picked up by police prior to their eighteenth birthdays. A higher proportion of them (86 per cent) had adult criminal companions as adolescents. This factor was probably quite significant in their becoming drug addicts, as these adult companions were, for the most part, themselves addicts. As adults they were less frequently drinkers or gamblers.

Internal comparisons demonstrated the drug addicts to be more similar to the offenders found in the No Pattern group (a residual category of thirty-two men who had fewer than three arrests and whose lives were not organized around criminal activities) than to offenders in any other category. The addicts, however, more frequently had dominant mother figures and received inadequate supervision by both parents than did the No Pattern offenders.

Probably the most important factor in the background of these offenders was maternal dominance. A higher proportion of them grew up in families where the mother was the dominant parental figure (82 per cent). The father figure seemed to have been quite indifferent to them, and in most cases he was dominated by the mother. Consequently, his presence and authority accounted for little in the family milieu. Quite frequently he spent long periods of time away from the home situation. As a typical addict commented:

> My old man was from nowhere, man. I seldom saw him. When he was home he sat in the corner and read the paper or something. Mama had to take care of things. She told us all what to do . . . The old man walked the chalk too when she spoke. I don't know where he went. Probably out with some chick drinking or living it up.

From the inmates' comments during the interviews, the maternal figures appeared to be strong-willed and mentally-alert perfectionists who overprotected and over-indulged the offender at every turn. She often set high goals for the offender, who was usually her favorite child. During his formative years, she selected his limited number of playmates, many of whom were girls. This domination probably shielded the addict from the normal scuffles of boyhood. This is sharply portrayed by the following addict's comment:

> My mama, man, was a tight woman on me. She insisted I come home right after school. I wasn't allowed to run no streets, man. If I got in a fight, she raised hell. She didn't want me to play sports. Guess she was afraid I would get hurt. I didn't care much anyway. I enjoyed my spare time with her. She knew what was right for me.

Many of them stated that the mother encouraged them to participate in passive activities, e.g., reading, music, drawing and art. As a consequence, they spent a good share of their leisure time during childhood in the home isolated from neighborhood play groups. These remarks from one offender were typical:

> Mama didn't go for no rough stuff. She was hard, but she knew what was right. I got interested in music and art because she encouraged me. You know, she was refined. She wasn't like these hip bitches in the street.

It is likely that this maternal pattern accounted for the statistically significant infrequency of these men as disciplinary
problems at school and at home when compared with the other
men in the sample.

On the other hand, their adulthood maladjustment in all
probability reflected their isolated status as drug addicts. At the
time of their arrests they were, for the most part, slum dwellers
cut loose from conjugal group ties. Only nine had marital ties,
though forty-nine had been married at one time or another.

Their remarks in the personal interviews demonstrated that
heroin was the "prime mover" in their lives. They lived a hand
to mouth existence in cheap rooming-houses where they were
isolated from the majority of their former contacts with non-users,
including their wives, children and relatives (with the exception
of the mother). This isolation was apparently self-imposed to
allow escape from detection, proximity to drug sources and other
addicts and avoidance of the censure and reform attempts of
relatives or other well-wishers.

They had an excellent command of the criminal argot, and, as
expected, they used the slang expressions generally identified
with drug addicts. Though not closely identified with the organized underworld, their remarks indicated a greater criminal
sophistication than possessed by others in the sample, with
perhaps the exception of the professional gambler. While they
were reluctant to discuss their criminal companions and their
criminal activities, all of them admitted to the use of heroin with
other drug addicts. They insisted that they engaged in theft
and in the traffic of drugs in order to supply their drug needs.
A typical quotation illustrates their attitude toward theft:

> My heart wasn't in it, but what could I do? I couldn't make $30.00
> a day. If I didn't get drugs I got sick, so I hustled in some way.
> Usually I hustled alone.

All of them insisted that they were not "true" drug peddlers, and
they showed marked bitterness at being so identified. As one
addict stated:

> By no stretch of the imagination am I a peddler. What the hell does
> the court treat me like one for? I was only trying to do a sick friend a

favor when I copped the caps. I know how it is when I need to cop. You know you got to have it. Have you ever seen anybody sick? They punish me because I'm sick.

Approximately half of these men were jazz musicians who played in local night clubs. All of this group claimed that they were introduced to heroin by "fellow musicians," and they asserted that more than half of the musicians they knew used heroin or marijuana. As one fairly articulate musician commented:

> All the musicians I knew were well acquainted with drugs. Most of them used drugs in one form or the other . . . usually marijuana or heroin. A few cats didn't partake, but man they were regular fellows. I mean man they understand if the other cats 'took off.' The ones who didn't 'cool it,' drank the 'hot stuff' (whiskey) It was more or less understood you had to get 'your kicks' some way. Man, all musicians are sensitive and crazy. Playing long hours in clubs gets to be a drag. You need a kick to keep you cool. The trouble is when you get hooked you don't make enough money legit to buy the white stuff (heroin). You got to hustle.

Though their arrest histories were quite extensive (an average of nine arrests per man), few arrests were for offenses other than narcotic drug laws violations. Other violations were for non-violent property offenses, e.g., shoplifting, petty larceny and housebreaking. These acts apparently stemmed from their need to secure a personal supply of drugs. Forty-three of these offenders had never been arrested prior to their first use of drugs.

The District Attorney's Reports provided strong evidence that charges for the sale of narcotics were rarely motivated by gain *per se*. Frequently, an addict became involved in a situation (technically defined in law as a sales situation) while acting as "contact man" between purchaser and the peddler from whom his own personal supply came. (The addict could be sure of at least a one-way cut!) This was the typical situation leading to a sales charge. In the few cases of sales charges where the offender actually possessed a supply for sale, they were found to be "small-time" street peddlers who sold drugs in order to earn money to support their own habits. They generally picked up a small supply of drugs at certain intervals. Usually they knew only the first name of the seller, and they had no idea of his drug source. The "pick-up" spots were frequently changed, and therefore they had difficulty in purchasing drugs. In short, they did not appear to be on the inside of a "true" peddler's organization. They were merely tools of the organized peddler in that they actually made street sales, and in so doing rendered themselves potential "fall guys." Five of the fifty men had tie-ups with a dope ring which imported heroin from outside the District of Columbia and distributed to street peddlers. Though professional in the sense that they lived from money made by selling drugs, they were not simon-pure drug wholesalers; they dispensed drugs to addicted street peddlers, and they personally transported drugs from other areas into Washington, D.C. Such obvious action does not attest to their status as "true" professionals.

As a group they appeared to be frail (small-boned) and less muscularly developed than the men in the other criminal patterns. They expressed many somatic complaints, chief among which were the following: nervousness; sinus trouble; weak heart; headache; ulcerated stomach; and poor blood circulation. Moreover, they claimed that these conditions antedated their drug addiction. The medical records disclosed that only six of these men were not organically sound: four were arrested cases of tuberculosis; one suffered from a severe case of asthma; one had a heart murmur.

They had excellent verbal ability; their vocabularies were quite impressive in relation to their formal education. Soft spoken and nonaggressive in speech and general demeanor, they tended to intellectualize their problem of addiction. By and large they were introspective, passive and withdrawn, rarely expressing interest in active sports such as hunting, fishing, baseball and boxing. On the other hand, they were generally interested in reading, movies, writing and especially in listening to music. For this group of men, the association of drugs and music constituted a way of life which for many other types of offenders was represented by an association of alcohol and women. As one addict commented:

Man, I like to shoot a pill or two . . . then rear back and relax after I put on some of that crazy jazz like, say Sonny Stitt (well-known musician) . . . Man . . . progressive jazz grooves me. Drugs and plenty crazy music was what I lived for.

Rarely did they speak of close friends, and when they did, their remarks suggested acquaintanceships rather than friendships. They voiced a preference for socializing with one or two male companions rather than with a larger group. Object relations to others appeared weak. A strong identification with the mother figure was expressed. They evinced affected, superior attitudes. Egocentric and lacking in self-criticism, they pretended to be quite satisfied with themselves as they were. They presented themselves in the interviews as victims of circumstances over which they had no control. One sensed a certain fatalism and resignation prevalent among them. They expressed very little interest in, or respect for, the opposite sex, with the exception of their mothers. Wives, girl friends, and former women companions were of no major concern. In movement and in speech they manifested what seemed to be a strong feminine component, though none were overtly homosexual. Illustrative of their lack of sexual interest is this comment by one inmate:

> Man, women have never done too much for me. They are all the same anyway. When I was high—and man, I stayed high—I didn't want no women. Course I have gone ahead with the thing if one insisted—you know, I was a man, but the kick from the drugs was the thing. Women want too much of your time. I had to hustle. Now if a broad could help me get some money or cop some drugs . . . well, you know, I went along with the happenings if I was able to. One way or the other I tried to satisfy the chick if she had some bread (money).

They abhorred violence of any kind, as exemplified by this characteristic statement:

> Man, these thugs are nothing. I wouldn't dirty my hands on them. You got to move people with your mouth. Just know what to say out of your mouth. Violence of any kind is for ignorant people. Only fools fight. Who wants to be a hero?

In summary, then, the addicts, unlike the other offenders, were criminals by virtue of their personal vice, drug addiction. As a group they were younger, more literate and more intelligent than the offenders in most other patterns. They came less frequently from disorganized family backgrounds, and their childhood adjustments in school, at home and in the community were such as to call less frequently for formal sanctions. They were less frequently involved in serious delinquencies which called for their adjudication as juvenile delinquents. On the other hand, they more frequently had adult criminal companions prior to their eighteenth birthdays. When engaged in delinquent or criminal activity they were more frequently "loners." They were reared by dominant mothers who kept them at home during their formative years and who probably had much to do with rendering them what appeared to be "passive-dependent" personality types. During their adolescent and young adult years they were introduced to heroin by addict companions, and, for the most part they were not delinquent prior to their addiction. All of them stated that listening to jazz music was their chief means of recreation. Popular musicians who are known addicts were their heroes. Just what jazz music had to do with their addiction process is not known, but certainly there was a relationship. Other students of the addict have cited a relationship of drugs to jazz music.[13]

It may be that their personality type rendered them susceptible to the opiates. The state of euphoria produced by the opiate drugs is described in the literature as a peaceful, dreamy and tranquil nirvana. This state is the antithesis of dynamic action. All these men abhorred alcohol, known to be somewhat of a personality irritant. The individual intoxicated on alcohol usually craves action and boisterous group entertainment. The drug addict, on the other hand, gets his "kicks" in a passive manner by listening to music or by daydreaming. Moreover, psychiatrists who have attempted therapy with both drug addicts and alcoholics have noted the difficulty involved in switching the drug addict to alcohol or the alcoholic to opiates.[14] During the research interviews, the drug addicts expressed a great distaste for alcohol. Forty claimed they never had liked alcoholic beverages. Five claimed they had never used any. On the other hand, the "problem drinkers" expressed a similar distaste for opiates, although several stated they had experimented with heroin at one time or another.[15] These claimed it did nothing for them. The following quotations from the interviews illustrate this point:

Drug addict: Man, the joy-juice (alcohol) never did nothing for me. I never liked the stuff. I tried it a few times before getting hooked. That stuff makes you sick and wild. Why cats use that stuff I can't understand. It tears you up.

Problem drinker: Drugs! No, I don't go for the stuff. I shot a little H (heroin) once or twice along the way, but I got only sick and sleepy. I want something to make me feel peppy, not something to knock you out. That stuff takes your nature away.

Be this as it may, pressed for the need of funds with which to purchase drugs, the addicts turned to illegal methods. Legitimate work did not pay enough to support their habits. In order to escape police detection and secure a ready supply of drugs, they isolated themselves in slum areas, away from relatives and "square" acquaintances, where they associated with addicts and petty criminals. Their possession and use of drugs and the petty offenses they engaged in to secure a ready supply of drugs rendered them vulnerable to police apprehension. Not one was found to be a racketeer or gangster. In short, they made up a group of petty, habitual offenders.

INDICATORS FOR A MULTI-DISCIPLINARY APPROACH WITH DRUG ADDICTS

The constitutionalists, by somatotyping, could validate or invalidate the impression that drug addicts are different in physical build and temperament than other types of offenders. They might also be able to find a physical-biological-chemical base which would explain the drug addict's preference for and dependence on the opiates rather than alcohol. The psychologist and psychiatrist would close on for further study the apparent passivity and dependency of this group, their interpersonal family relationships with a dominant mother and a weak indifferent father, their lack of interest in women, their tendency to intellectualize their problems at highly verbal levels, their apparent femininity, and their weak object relations with others. The sociologists would wish to study further the addicts' association with adult addicts prior to their addiction, their delinquent and criminal history prior to and antedating addiction, the addiction process, the relationship of certain occupational pursuits, and career patterns with addiction, e.g., the jazz musician.

Legalists and correctional administrators should be aware of the fact that there is no ready explanation of drug addiction, and, in fact, the etiology of drug addiction is in an even more confused state than that of criminal behavior in general. Probably the Federal Government has provided for the most intensive study and treatment of incarcerated drug addicts. The Government maintains two institutions for drug addicts, one at Fort Worth, Texas, and the other at Lexington, Kentucky. The Lexington Institution, known as the U.S. Public Health Service Hospital, was opened in 1935. At present it is overcrowded, and as a consequence many drug addicts arrested in the District are committed to the D.C. Reformatory, which is not set up for the treatment of this type of offender, though their numbers increase here each month.

There are four definite reasons why drug addicts should not be committed to institutions similar to the D.C. Reformatory.

First, there is no specific treatment available for these offenders. Since they are actually criminals by virtue of a personal vice, addiction to narcotic drugs, they probably should be housed in a hospital-type situation similar to that of the U.S. Public Health Service Hospital at Lexington, Kentucky, where specialized medical and psychiatric treatment for drug addicts is provided. The writer is aware that relapse is the rule rather than the exception for addicts who have been treated at Lexington. In fact, it is common knowledge that no treatment for drug addiction has met with glowing success anywhere. However, it is in specialized hospitals like the one at Lexington, Kentucky, that various treatment methods are experimented with and where research in reference to opiate addiction, causation and treatment is in progress. Psychogenic, organic and biochemical theories of addiction and treatment are being tested there. Individual and group therapy, for whatever they are worth, are available under the auspices of trained psychiatrists and psychologists, many of whom have dedicated their careers to the study of drug addiction. Certainly the needs of the drug addict are better understood there than in ordinary penal settings.

Second, the addict in a general penal setting comes in contact with a group of seasoned criminals of many different types. A ready-made learning situation is presented to him, where he may assimilate specific criminal techniques and the antisocial attitudes that many times accompany these techniques. Moreover, the knowledge that he is serving time under felony sentence in a penitentiary or reformatory may operate to change the addict's conception of himself and his role. Under such conditions he may actually come to conceive of himself as a criminal. The writer has known several drug addicts now serving time at the D.C. Reformatory for a crime other than a narcotic-drug-laws offense—a crime which required some specialized criminal technique, *viz,* forgery, burglary, counterfeiting, etc. These addicts were previously committed there on narcotics-drug-laws charges. Some of these men have stated that, during a previous commitment, they learned these techniques from friends among the inmate body who were not addicts. In fact some of these men were returned to this institution with non-addict, co-defendants whom they had met on a previous commitment.

Third, drug addicts may impart favorable impressions of narcotics to inmates who are not drug addicts. This may make for future drug addiction among other types of offenders. The writer noted that drug addicts in this penal setting are quite vociferous; not only are they smooth, polished talkers, but they can be quite persuasive. One could not pick a more adept group of teachers in one sense of the word. Essentially nonviolent in personality type, they tend to manipulate others in a passive, intellectualistic manner. Unfortunately, quite a few of these incarcerated drug addicts accept their addiction as an established fact for which they claim not to be sorry. These men tried to rationalize their use of drugs in the interview situation. A few quotations extracted from the interviewees illustrate this point:

Everyone has to get his kicks one way or the other; mine are drugs.

Drugs are better for me than alcohol, and you know most people drink.

I am not hurting anybody else when I use drugs.

Drugs relieve the strain and I can play better music for a longer period of time with them.

It has been proven drugs do not weaken you physically; they don't hurt me.

If there were no laws against drugs everything would be O.K., etc. . .

The writer has heard from non-addict offenders that these same rationalizations are used by the addicts in their "bull sessions" with other inmates.

A few addicts boast of their addiction. These claim to be a select group who know the greatest thrill that life can bring—drugs. These men can and do give all sorts of arguments in favor of the use of the opiates. They refer to themselves as "cool cats" and to the non-addict as a "dumb square." They pretend to conceive of themselves as sophisticated, worldly-wise individuals, who live in a more colorful world than non-users.

Whether or not the above responses are rationalizations and defense mechanisms for feelings of insecurity or something else, they are responses. It is likely that they fall on other ears than those of the present writer. Certainly drug addicts are talkers; and certainly some of them describe their claimed state of ecstasy and euphoria to other non-addict offenders.

The New York Reformatory for Women at Bedford Hills, New York, for instance, has maintained for years a policy of separating the drug-addicted women from the rest of the reformatory population, most of which comes from New York City. The basis of the separation is that the addicted inmates so glamorize the use of drugs that they motivate the non-users of drugs toward drug use ("You haven't had it unless you've had the needle.") This administrative experience testifies to the fact that the transmission of pattern, desire and appropriate attitude in reference to the opiates takes place in association within the confines of a penal institution.[16]

Fourth, the mixing of offenders who are drug addicts with offenders who are not addicts in the same penal setting poses administrative and custodial problems. The presence of a group of addicts calls for closer custody measures. The drugs in the hospital have to be carefully watched and administered; and materials in the kitchen have to be carefully checked. More stringent controls of visiting and mail procedures are also demanded. The employment of inmates on "outside the wall" jobs necessarily is curtailed. In short, there has to be an over-all tightening up of security measures to prevent the addict from securing a source of drugs. These measures many times fall on the non-addicts as well as the addicts.

The author has personally experienced some of these tightening up procedures. Many times they curtail to some extent the therapy attempts of the case worker with the non-addict offender. It has been his further experience to note that some drug addicts will go to extremes (violating many regulations) in an attempt to secure a supply of drugs. If and when evidence of drugs is found within an institution, a general "tightening up" of security measures ensues. Suspicion is cast in many directions, and for a time a heavy atmosphere prevails for everyone. These administrative reasons alone should preclude the mixing of drug addicts and non-addicts in the same penal setting.

The writer has no treatment solution for the drug addicts examined in this study. As has been explained, he thinks that drug-addict offenders should be committed to hospitals similar in type and orientation to that found at Lexington, Kentucky. The Government could construct more institutions of this kind for drug addicts who are seriously interested in treatment for their vice.

In regard to the search for causation in this field, an important facet of research undoubtedly has been overlooked. The few drug addicts who have conquered their personal vice, as established by three to four years of abstention, have received very little if any attention. It could be that a study of the social backgrounds of these individuals, past and present, including their addiction and their process of abstention, their personality configuration, their blood chemistry and organic processes and their mental processes, etc., would prove fruitful in the quest for causation and treatment. The "whys" and "hows" of such ab-

stention as shown by these individuals in successfully breaking
the drug habit may be of value.

In recent years there has been a growing interest in the
therapeutic methods of Synanon. Synanon was founded in 1958
as a private orgnization of former drug addicts. There are at
present Synanon Houses in Santa Monica and San Diego, California, Reno, Nevada, and Westport, Connecticut. The organization and the selection of persons for admission are autocratic,
though to some degree Synanon members are self-governed.
Treatment is envisaged in three stages. Stage I—Admittance
procedures require the addict to "fight his way in." The would-
be member must demonstrate a sincere interest in joining a
drug-free society. Withdrawal from drugs (cold turkey) occurs
in the presence of Synanon members. The new member initially
is derogated by peers as a "sniveling, whining dope fiend from
the gutter." The addict is indoctrinated against drugs and assigned to a low-status position where he participates in general
housekeeping chores. Stage II—As the resident matures and
gathers insight and strength, he graduates to a stage during
which he works outside of a Synanon House and returns in the
evening. Stage III—In this final stage the former addict lives
outside a Synanon and returns for occasional meetings.

Members are required to subordinate individual desires to the
group norms. Group cohesion is maintained through and by
the manner of admitting new members, the status system,
family-like ceremonials, mutual activities in the maintenance of
Synanon Houses, and group discussions. Holidays, birthdays,
and anniversaries are celebrated in a family manner. Contacts
with former acquaintances from the outside world are prohibited. Synanon becomes a major reference group of the
members and offers empathy and a sense of belonging. The
former addict is subjected to constant assessment by his peers
so that he begins to see himself from the perspective of others.
Social class status and responsibility increase with each successive stage. Residents are encouraged to cease talking about
hustling and drug use and instead to discuss music, art, literature, and philosophy. Group therapy sessions patterned after

TABLE II

COMPARISON OF OFFENDERS WITH A SINGLE PATTERN OF NARCOTIC DRUG LAW OFFENSES WITH ALL OTHER OFFENDERS

Selected Social and Personal Attributes	Drug Offenders (N=50) N.W.C.*	All Others (N=350) N.W.C.	Sign of X²	Selected Social and Personal Attributes	Drug Offenders (N=50) N.W.C.*	All Others (N=350) N.W.C.	Sign of X²
Reared in more than one home	6	155	.01	Weak parental family structure	16	198	.01
Mother figure southern migrant	9	165	.01	No parental family ties	18	264	.01
Mother figure domestic servant	29	271	.01	Reared in urban area	47	287	N.S.
Dependent family	33	263	N.S.†	Reared in slum area	29	222	.05
Family broken by desertion	4	136	.01	Living in slum when arrested	34	267	N.S.
Demoralized family	8	188	.01	History of school truancy	12	191	.01
Criminality in family	6	165	.01	Disciplinary problem at school	5	183	.01
Mother figure dominant	41	178	.01	Street trades as juvenile	16	187	.01
Inadequate supervision—father	28	168‡	.01	No marital ties	41	247	N.S.
Inadequate supervision—mother	45	237	.01	Juvenile delinquent companions	17	219	.01
Conflict in family	10	224	.01	Member delinquent gang	6	136	.01
Overt hostility toward father	9	162	.01	Adjudicated juvenile delinquent	5	172	.01
Overt hostility toward mother	7	72	N.S.	Committed as juvenile	4	142	.01
Disciplinary problem at home	3	116	.01	Police contact prior to age 18	14	207	.01
History of running away	8	177	.01	Criminal companions as juvenile	43	120	.01
Inveterate gambler	7	163	.01	Drug addict	50	19	.01
Problem drinker	3	190	.01	Positive attitude toward work	15	138	N.S.

*Number with characteristic.

†Not significant.

‡Based on those with fathers.

those of Alcoholics Anonymous reportedly enable the addict to gain insight into his problems. They also serve as emotional outlets.[17]

The effectiveness of this program in the third stage is not clear. Population statistics on the members of Synanon in the various stages are unknown. Relapse figures are unavailable. Synanon maintains an anti-attitude concerning outside, professional, research evaluation. Rehabilitation in the usual sense of the word (getting the addict back into the larger community as an autonomous, conforming individual) is not among Synanon's primary objectives. Synanon, rather, appears to be an in-grown protective community—an end in itself rather than a means. There is no compulsion for addicts to move out of the drug-free community. It is likely that the addict functions without drugs only as he stays at Synanon.[18]

Despite the preceding limitations, for a selected group of addicts, Synanon provides a haven far superior to any program utilized for drug addicts to date. Certainly, Synanon does not constitute a universal panacea. The study of and the utilization of some of Synanon's methods might prove useful to official and other private agencies and programs in their treatment efforts with drug addicts.

REFERENCES

1. ROEBUCK, JULIAN B.: The Negro drug addict as an offender type. *Journal of Criminal Law, Criminology, and Police Science*, 53:36-43, March, 1962.
2. RECKLESS, WALTER C.: *The Crime Problem* (2nd ed.). New York, Appleton-Century-Crofts, Inc., 1955, pp. 353-356; PESCOR, MICHAEL J.: A statistical analysis of clinical records of drug addicts. Suppl. 145, Public Health Reports, 26, 1938; KARPMAN, BENJAMIN: Laws that cause crime. *American Mercury*, 23:74, 1931.
3. LINDESMITH, ALFRED R.: Dope fiend mythology. *Journal of Criminal Law, Criminology, and Police Science*, 40:199, 1949; KOLB, LAWRENCE: The drug addiction muddle, *Police*, 1:57, 1957.

4. TAPPAN, PAUL: *Crime, Justice and Correction,* pp. 165-167.
5. CAMPBELL, ROBERT J.: Etiology and personality factors. In BIER, WILLIAM C., (ed.): *Problems in Addiction.* New York, Fordham University Press, 1962; BRILL, LEON: Agency treatment. In BIER, WILLIAM C. (ed.): *Problems in Addiction.* New York, Fordham University Press, 1962, pp. 227-229; JOHNSON, ELMER H. *Crime, Correction, and Society.* Homewood, Illinois, The Dorsey Press, 1964, pp. 293-304.
6. JOHNSON, ELMER H.: *Crime, Correction and Society,* pp. 295-297.
7. HOWE, HUBERT S.: An alternative solution to the narcotics problem. *Law and Contemporary Problems,* 22:132-137, winter, 1957.
8. SCHUR, EDWIN M.: *Narcotic Addiction in Britain and America.* Bloomington, Indiana, Indiana University Press, 1962, pp. 44-45.
9. *Uniform Crime Reports,* 1963, p. 111.
10. *Uniform Crime Report,* 1963, p. 111.
11. All fifty were heroin addicts, as attested to by a medical examination conducted by a D.C. Department of Corrections physician.
12. See Table II, p. 133.
13. WINICK, CHARLES: The Use of Drugs by Jazz Musicians. *Social Problems,* 7:240-253, Winter, 1959-1960.
14. MEERLOO, JOOST, A. M.: Artificial ecstasy. In PODOLSKY, EDWARD (ed.): *Encyclopedia of Aberrations, A Psychiatric Handbook.* New York, Philosophical Library, 1953, pp. 195-206.
15. "Problem Drinkers" as found in the criminal category, Double Pattern of Drunkenness and Assault.
16. RECKLESS, WALTER C.: *The Crime Problem,* p. 137.
17. VOLKMAN, RITA and CRESSEY, DONALD R.: Differential association and rehabilitation of drug addicts. *American Journal of Sociology,* 69:129-42, September, 1963. YABLONSKY, LEWIS. *The Tunnel Back: Synanon.* New York: Macmillan, 1965.
18. STERNBERG, DAVID: Synanon House—a consideration of its implications for American correction. *Journal of Criminal Law, Criminology and Police Science,* 54:447-455, December, 1963.

Chapter VIII

THE NUMBERS MAN[1]

NUMBERS game operators are usually defined as lottery law or policy violators. They are defined by themselves, the police, the underworld and the betting public as numbers men, and therefore they are so designated in this book. The numbers game, a variant form of policy, is a special type of *lottery* which constitutes a notorious form of gambling among Negroes in the large metropolitan areas of the Eastern Seaboard and the Midwest. Some have claimed that the numbers game has a certain integrative function for the Negro community, furnishing much of the content of casual conversation, imparting temporal structure to the day and offering a sense of participation in a community-wide institution.[2] It has a widespread patronage among the lower-income and working classes, especially in Negro residential areas. Although only small amounts are generally involved in individual bets, many Negroes who play the game regularly can ill afford to lose. One survey shows that during 1960, almost three out of every eight persons who gambled in this country played the numbers. It is estimated that these 32,000,000 Americans, of whom 14,000,000 were women, wagered the sum of five billion dollars in an effort to hit a lucky number.[3] The numbers game constitutes professional organized crime. It represents the only such area, at present, that Negroes have participated in in large numbers at the higher echelons of organization.

The numbers player bets one cent upward on a three digit number (any combination of numbers from 000 to 999) which he notes on a "slip" and turns over to a "numbers writer," a street numbers bookie (with his wager commonly from ten cents to a quarter), who in turn passes it on to a "pick-up man," and it finally reaches the counting office (the "bank" or "drop") of the numbers ring. At the drop, clerical workers check and tally each individual numbers slip and wager and sift out the slips bearing the winning combination, which is usually determined from pari-mutuel totals at a certain race track. The total payoff figures for the three, five and seven races may be used, or any combination of prices in any three designated races. The last dollar numeral before the decimal is used. The last three digits of the daily total amount bet may also be designated the winning combination. Odds, though varying from one city to another, are usually in excess of 1000 to 1 that any particular combination of three numbers will turn up. The operators pay a winner from 500 to 800 to 1.[4]

THE NUMBERS MAN AS A CRIMINAL TYPE

Statistical comparisons showed that the sixteen men in this group differed from the remainder of the sample on twenty-six of the thirty-four selected social and personal attributes; eight differed at the .05 level and eighteen at the .01 level.

The numbers men were a comparatively older, more intelligent and more literate group of offenders. Six were between thirty and thirty-nine; four, forty to forty-nine; three, over fifty; two, twenty-five to thirty; one, under twenty-six (median age 38). According to the Lindner-Gurvitz Revised Beta IQ Test, twelve were of average intelligence, and four were of above average intelligence (median IQ, 105). Their median Stanford Achievement Test grade level was 8.1. For the remainder of the sample the median age was thirty-three, median IQ 86, and S.A.T. grade median, 5.0.

Statistical comparisons revealed that the men in this pattern less frequently grew up in slum neighborhoods. They were more often products of strong family structures in which close ties were the rule; i.e., divorces, desertions, abandonments and separations were less frequent, and more often the family relationships were characterized by intimate, affectionate ties. They were less often from families in which other members had criminal records and less often from economically dependent or demoralized families; e.g., comparatively, arrest, jail, and prison records among family members were rare; economic aid from welfare agencies was uncommon; and the excessive use of alcohol, the use of opiate drugs and the engagement in prostitution, adultery and incest by family members was unusual. They came significantly more often from patriarchal homes, as opposed to the typical matriarchal home of most other offenders; e.g., the father played the dominant role in interpersonal relations with his spouse in decision-making during family-crisis situations and in disciplining children. They were more frequently products of homes unmarked by emotional conflict where adequate supervision by both parents was typical. Supervision of their childhood activities was generally firm, considerate and consistent. Conversely, the men in the remainder of the sample frequently grew up in families characterized by emotional conflict where supervision by parents was usually lax. Hostility toward the father figure was expressed less frequently by this group. Contrariwise, a high proportion of the other offenders repeatedly expressed enmity, antagonism, resentment and dislike for their fathers. This hostility seemed to stem from a basic lack of admiration and respect for a rejecting parent.

The childhood and adolescent adjustments of the numbers men (as measured by the researcher's criteria) were far superior to those of the men in the remainder of the sample. They were less often disciplinary problems at school; i.e., they were rarely in trouble for fighting, stealing, insubordination, sex delinquency and the destruction of school property, in contrast to many of the other offenders. A lower proportion of them were school truants and "home runaways." They worked less often at street trades, and they had fewer juvenile delinquent companions. Only one was a member of a juvenile delinquent gang; only one was committed to an institution for juvenile delinquency; and only one had adult criminal companions before age eighteen (these companions were numbers men). As adults, they were more often married (usually, they said, happily). They were less often problem drinkers. Not one was a drug addict. On the negative side, a higher proportion of them were inveterate gamblers.[5]

A qualitative examination of this group indicated a stable family background relatively free of emotional conflict, economic deprivation and physical violence.[6] These remarks from one numbers man about his parental family were typical:

> My father worked at the post office as a mail clerk. He retired a few years ago. My mother worked in the government at one time as a clerk. You know, she typed. When us children came along she quit and stayed home. There were times when things were tight but we managed. We didn't bother with no welfare. We had enough to eat and wear. We had to go to school and keep clean. Also Sunday School. We didn't run the streets either. We stayed at home when we were not at school or at the playground. The old man brought his check home at the end of each month and we all shared alike. He didn't drink it up or live it up with the chicks. He wore the pants in the family, but he wasn't rough. You know he didn't cuss and slap everybody around. He was good to my mother. All in all we had a happy home. If we got out of line they (parents) mostly talked to us and made us stay in the house for a day or two. I never got but two whippings.

In discussing their infrequent juvenile delinquent activities, not one mentioned housebreaking, strong-arm activities, robbery. Involvement in sporadic, unplanned pursuits such as petty thefts from grocery stores were mentioned. Their friends were free of police and juvenile court contact. Accounts of this kind were common:

> I had no use for gang boys. Most of them were thugs who lived in the bottom. They never was my kind. I scuffled around with some of them at school. You know, I was no sissy, but I gave them plenty of traveling space and they just left me alone. Sure, I stole a few things as I went through life. I guess everybody does. You know, like a toy or something. I sure had no habit of stealing. My buddies were good boys. We didn't get in trouble with the teachers and we steered clear of cops.

It is of note that these men between the ages of seventeen and eighteen began drinking beer, gambling at cards and dice and engaging in sexual intercourse with schoolgirl companions. These activities were generally conducted surreptitiously and rarely led to parental attention or police action. As one offender asserted:

> Well I always wanted to be a sport. You know wear sharp clothes and have a good time with the chicks. I guess you would say I always had a desire to live high on the hog. About seventeen or eighteen I started

to really make out with the girls. I was a good dancer, and I knew how to dress. I also had a good line. I could sweet talk them into anything. Well, if you call messing around with the girls delinquent I was one. I liked to shoot craps and play poker a little too. I drank some beer at parties and mostly when I danced. I didn't talk about this at home. The folks would have raised a howl. All the other boys in the neighborhood did the same thing though. Some of them are school teachers and lawyers now. Some of them write numbers too.

Conversely, the onset of delinquent activities among the men in the other criminal categories who were delinquents generally occurred in pre-adolescence. Their activities—not as masked as those of the numbers men—more frequently resulted in formal community and police action. Their offenses more often involved stealing, the destruction of property and violence.

Though the numbers men grew up in non-slum areas, they claimed that their family members and neighborhood acquaintances were tolerant of the numbers game.

My folks were respectable, law-abiding people. None of them went to jail. They knew about the numbers. Man, everybody knows about the numbers. My mother and father use to play a number now and then. My sister, who went to college, was married to a numbers man. Everybody in the neighborhood knew what the number was each day whether they played one or not. Everybody knew too when somebody hit (won). Of course my folks didn't like no craps or poker playing. At home we use to joke about dreaming up a good number to play.

In reference to later community adjustment, all of these men had strong primary group ties. Eleven maintained strong ties with their first primary group, the parental family; thirteen experienced strong marital ties; the remaining three sustained stable relationships with a paramour.

Their difficulties as adults stemmed from gambling. Though professional gamblers with some understanding of odds and the laws of chance, these men spent much of their leisure time betting at the racetrack, prize fights, poker games and at various other major sports events throughout the Northeast. Betting on horses was their chief recreation. They earned their money from "marks" (numbers players), and at the same time they were "marks" themselves at the race track. Their reactions to this anomaly are illustrated by these comments:

Money that comes easy, goes easy. Money you win from gambling moves around like ice on top of a red-hot stove. But you know horse racing is the sport of kings. I got to have some fun, you know. Then too, I don't gamble all of the money I make from the numbers away.[7]

A sizeable portion of their time was spent with attractive young women whom they euphemistically alluded to as "slick chicks," "fine broads," "foxes," and "party girls." They wined, dined and socialized with these women at two plush cocktail lounges situated in a Negro commercial section of Washington, D.C. They passed these girls around among themselves at what they termed "respectable time intervals" (3-6 months). Many of these "playmates" worked in a numbers ring as clerical workers. At times they were actually "kept women," who accepted their roles as companions and sex partners. These remarks were characteristic:

These chicks as a rule were for real. I mean they would never squeal. They knew we were in the life, and with us they knew they got the best of what there was to get like entertainment, clothes, perfume, booze. Everybody knew who was going with who. The fruit basket would turn over now and then and we would change partners in a nice way, but we didn't get upset and jealous. It was the life. You know we lived it up. We were gentlemen. No girl had to worry about us beating her up or pushing her around. You know many men do slap women around. They understood we were married. They never called us at home. In fact we were all good friends. Some of the chicks worked for us as clerical help.

Their leisure-time nexus of gambling and women seemed to constitute prescribed role playing:

Well, you know in my business you have to be a sport and a spender. You got to have front. You have to impress the public that you are a man in the know who knows how to live it up. You got to wear sharp clothes, hang out in the best places, set up the boys and girls at the bar with drinks. And you know, give the chicks a break. When these suckers see you swinging out now and then with a fine broad they know you have some money, and they figure they can play their numbers with you safely. This is a competitive business. Of course it's not too hard on me to play the game. My wife understands this. She's been with me now ten years. She isn't going anywhere. Of course she is not happy when I go out and blow a chunk (money) after a big run, but I have to do that. At that time I have to prove I can stand the run.

Their statements demonstrated that the numbers game was a regular, day-by-day occupation and that they were interested in upward mobility in an activity which called for differential responsibility and skills at various levels of performance. As one numbers man reported:

I've made my living by the numbers for years. I started out working for a 'numbers writer' twenty years ago as a 'runner.' He died two years later. I had worked hard and had played him square. The big boy ('numbers backer') knew I knew the territory and everybody in it. He also knew I was a pleasant, fast talker and a hard worker who could put on a front. I know to keep my mouth shut when necessary. I could shoot the breeze with the customers about most anything they wanted to talk about . . . you know, sports, gambling, women, even politics. He knew I could also keep my hand out of his bag (steal the backer's take). Five years later he made me a 'pick-up man.' You see I had a head for figures. I could estimate the normal take in most areas of the city. It was hard for a 'writer' to hold out on me cause I knew what the people bet in his area. A few years later the big boy's 'head man' was 'busted' (arrested) at the drop and then I got my big break. He called me up to help supervise the drop. Three of us fought it out for 'head man' for two years. The competition was keen. I had to be nice to everybody there though I knew some were gunning for me. I really had to be a politician and learn more about numbers too. You know, a little bookkeeping and percentages. I also had to get to know the strong and weak points of workers. I had to learn when to recommend hiring and firing certain people. It takes a certain kind of head for figures and a certain kind of personality for numbers. You got to be careful who you hire. You can't afford to hire a 'willy' (country boy). You got to pick a man with some class who knows what's happening, and who knows how to dress and talk right. You got to stay away from gorillas (strong armers) unless you are hiring a bouncer. Finally I made a 'head man.' After the big boy *was* finally busted I took over as a backer. Not everybody makes it. You can get froze at any level. I was lucky, and I guess I got more class than most people.

Though all these men made their living primarily from numbers, ten of them claimed that at one time or another they had invested money as "silent partners" in what they referred to as legitimate enterprises—bars, liquor stores, tourist homes, poolrooms and used car lots. Five said they owned rental property. The capital for these business ventures was invariably made from numbers. Their general attitude toward legitimate business, money, and the numbers game may be adduced from the following expressions of one numbers man:

> What good is a lot of money less it's put to use? Stepping out into business was just like another gamble to me. Many Negro businessmen in this town got their start from working at numbers. Some retire, some don't. If it wasn't for numbers some people wouldn't have jobs and homes. I went into numbers for the same reason other people go into teaching or medicine or anything else. I noticed some outstanding successful people in the game. They attracted me so I went in.[8]

None of them claimed any association with other aspects of the organized underworld, though they were quite familiar with the criminal argot. They asserted only a newspaper knowledge of other underworld activities and admitted to no more than a nodding acquaintance with offenders outside the gambling fraternity. Their criminal companions were usually other numbers men, though they admitted to some association with other types of gamblers, e.g., owners and operators of gambling houses, race-track bookies, boxing, football and baseball bookies, and "house" card and dice dealers:

> I associated with my own kind. Now and then I went to the racetrack or had a drink with some of the dice and card players. One or two were pretty good guys. Now and then I had a drink with old Charlie, a cardsharp, and with Bill who runs a crap table. Those hoodlums, like muggers, heist men and housebreakers were not my kind of people. They were in another world. They are nothing but scum.

These men were members of different gambling rings varying in number of personnel from fifteen to one hundred, and they identified themselves as gamblers with a definite status among their kind. One commented:

> I have been in business for years as a gambler. The police have known me and everybody who works for me for years. I am hard to catch. All of the Negroes in D.C. know about me and my organization. You and everybody else knows about me from the newspapers. I'm a numbers man and I'm not ashamed of it. I started as a numbers runner. I worked hard and was honest. I never reneged on a bet. I got respect from my own kind. I got a $50,000 house, a wife and two nice kids. This is my first bust in thirty years. How much money you got? I got a few 'big' ones (one thousand dollar bills).

The interview material suggested that fifteen of these men were products of the Negro middle class. All were reared in non-slum neighborhoods by respectable parents; twelve graduated from high school; three attended college; ten stated that one or more of their siblings had attended college; twelve stated that their wives attended college; fourteen claimed that their parents had steady, non-laboring jobs; and all mentioned friends and family connections among professionals and semiprofessionals. The admission summary materials and the visiting and correspondence records supported these statements.[9] The men presented themselves as respectable, middle class people who were churchgoers, homeowners, and fathers.

Perhaps, though products of the Negro middle class, these men who lived in the noncriminal as well as the criminal world could best be described as middle and upper class "shadies." But no less a scholar than E. Franklin Frazier lends support to their claim of respectability. He contends that "playing the numbers" has become respectable among members of the Negro middle class and that some members of Negro "society" derive their incomes from the numbers. He claims further that the Negro middle class is also being recruited from the successful underworld Negroes who have gained their money from numbers and that the sporting and criminal elements are acquiring a dominant position among Negroes.[10]

Regardless of their class position in the Negro community, these men were criminals because they engaged in an illegal racket. They evinced in the interviews the "fast buck" philosophy of the "angle boy" and the professional criminal and expressed negative feelings about all law enforcement machinery, especially the police. Moreover they seemed to have rationalized away their specific form of criminal activity. Gambling to them did not constitute "real" criminal behavior. These assertions by one interviewee were typical:

> Why don't the cops spend their time on these hoodlums and leave us numbers men alone. All we do is provide opportunity for people to gamble. You can't stop gambling. We provide a service for which we deserve some return. Hell, we pay 800 to 1 odds. Everybody has

his angle. Take you, you got your racket. You probably will write a book. The police have theirs. They will take a red hot stove (accept bribes). Trying to do away with crooked cops is as easy as dipping all the water out of the Atlantic Ocean with a saucer.

All claimed that the gambling ring for which they worked retained a criminal lawyer on a permanent basis. It is interesting to note that their court records revealed that only four different lawyers (three Negro and one white) were involved in the sixteen different court cases.[11]

Though, according to their reports, the various numbers rings in which they worked competed with each other for personnel and for betting customers, there was no evidence of syndicated numbers activity. On the contrary, the data indicated that the leaders (numbers backers) were local products. There appeared to be a feudal system (minus a king) including several rings, each maintaining its own organizational pattern and its own base of operations and each possessing an individual set of employees. Additionally, the process of mutual aid as well as competition was evident in the relationships among these various rings:

Anybody can move with no trouble from one backer to another if he is a good man. Backers hire out from under each other, and they don't get mad about it. That's the game. We don't worry about no violence or syndicate business. D.C. is just not that kind of town. All the backers I know are local yokels like me. They just worked upon their own. If somebody gets in your bag (steals from the ring) too much he just gets fired. You may get another backer. Then you steal too much again and get caught, well, have somebody stick a fork in you, for brother you are done. You are through. You see these backers know each other and help each other. What one knows all knows. Say a man wants to bet $100 on a number. That's too much. Sure, I'll take his bet all right, but the backer will call up and lay part of it off to other backers. He might keep $25 and then lay $25 each off to three others. That way if the number comes up the run isn't so bad on any one backer. Again, if one backer gets a big run he can call four or five other backers and borrow some bread (money) to cover the bet if he's short. They all scratch each other's backs. In this business it's live and help live. One backer gets too smart and tries to cut the big fat hog (attempts to hog all the business by playing lone wolf), the others cut off his water in time (force him out of business). Backers also tip each other off if they hear about police raids.

The arrest histories of these men were comparatively brief (mean: 5.2 per man), and the overwhelming number of their arrests were for lottery law charges. There were a few disorderly conduct charges, usually connected with the presence of the offender in a house dice or card game or in a numbers-counting office and an occasional intoxication charge. Other types of charges were rare. Criminal progression was not in evidence; the arrest histories generally began and terminated with lottery law violation charges.

The District Attorney's Reports on all crimes for which these offenders had served felony sentences showed that these men were engaged in professional gambling. A study of the *modus operandi* of these offenders disclosed their membership in a gambling ring where planning, organization, leadership, chain of command, skills and techniques and a division of labor were in evidence. Each ring was headed by a "numbers backer." Included in these organizations were head men or "lieutenants," "pick-up men," "numbers writers," clerical workers, "look-out men," "numbers runners" and "bouncers."[12] Four of the sixteen men under study claimed to be "numbers backers;" four were numbers backer's "lieutenants;" two were "pick-up men;" and six stated they were "numbers writers."

The numbers men appeared to be in good health and made few somatic complaints. Medical examinations showed that twelve were organically sound, one had diabetes, one had a hyperthyroid condition, and two suffered from mild heart murmurs. They reacted to the interview situation in a friendly and cooperative manner. There were no obvious diagnostic signs of neurosis, psychopathy or psychosis.[13] They appeared to be extroverted and outgoing personalities, who verbalized well at a highly literate level. Neither verbal aggression nor verbal passivity was noted. These men expressed strong emotional ties with friends and family members. Comparatively speaking, they appeared to be sophisticated in reference to the criminal as well as the noncriminal world. Though not regular church attenders, they expressed a strong religious orientation of an orthodox type.[14] They were well poised, confident and self-satisfied. In short, they seemed to relate well and to have well-integrated personalities.

These offenders, unlike the majority of the other offender types, grew up in "adequate" home situations unmarked by weak family structure, faulty parental supervision, demoralization, criminality or economic dependence. Personal vices—alcoholism and drug addiction—were not in evidence, and they were relatively free of personality deviations. Moreover, they were not juvenile delinquents (officially speaking) grown up. Despite these favorable factors, they became professional criminals in the fullest sense.[15]

What peculiar constellation of background and personality characteristics disposed them to this and not to other patterns of criminal behavior? The full answer to this question is not known. However, their developmental histories offer some hypothetical clues in this direction. They grew up in home and neighborhood situations which were quite tolerant of the numbers game racket. Parents, friends and acquaintances played numbers. In fact, some of their neighbors and in-laws were numbers men. In a sense they were reared in a cultural milieu where the numbers game constituted a community institution which, though illegal, was not defined as "really criminal." In late adolescence they adopted an adult recreation pattern of drinking, gambling and dancing which they did not conceive of as reprehensible or illegal. Sexually precocious, they began dating early and engaging in promiscuous heterosexual relations. The role of the "sport," the "smoothie" and the "big spender" which was tied in with their early recreation pattern intrigued them. They became interested in "sharp clothes," expensive tastes and what they called "high living." They were surreptitious in these activities because of their desire to please "conventional parents." They avoided juvenile delinquents and juvenile delinquent gang activity. Fighting, stealing, and violence were defined as behavior outside of their life style. They were especially concerned with remaining clear of arrest and police contacts. In a sense they conceived of themselves as what Walter C. Reckless has called "good boys."[16] As young adults they admired the numbers men with whom they came in contact through family and neighborhood acquaintances. They considered some of these racketeers to be outstanding successes in their field. Material success and the way of life of the numbers man that went with this success appealed to them. Consequently they rationalized away the illegal aspects of the numbers game and entered it as a "business pursuit."

This rationalization was probably not too difficult. Perhaps the urban Negro middle class has in part accepted the numbers man. Perhaps he is acceptable because of his money. Material wealth is undoubtedly a great determinant of social status among members of a minority group who are at the bottom of the economic ladder, who have not been stratified into functional social classes until quite recently and who are discriminated against and segregated. In these circumstances the social class lines of urban Negro are probably fluid. It must also be remembered that the Negro middle and upper classes are much smaller in base and less economically secure than are the white middle and upper classes.[17]

Treatment prospects with such a group of offenders do not appear heartening. Perhaps when the urban Negro comes to be less spatially separated and socially isolated from the remainder of the community, and when his middle and upper class membership increases in size, economic base and security, the numbers man will come to be viewed for what he is, a racketeer. Perhaps then the moral indignation of the Negro community will fall upon him, and all supports for his claim to respectability will be removed. Horace Cayton, co-author of *Black Metropolis* and a noted authority on Negro life in Northern cities, supports this point of view.[18]

In prison, the numbers men were generally tractable, pleasant and courteous inmates who were usually liked by other inmates as well as by prison employees. They accepted their time philosophically, and they did not seek special favors. The prison term was viewed as an occupational hazard. In the prison setting they made themselves as unobtrusive as possible. As a rule they were not interested in status within the inmate subculture. Neither "peddler-connivers" nor prison toughs, they seemed to approximate in type the "real man" construct suggested by Gresham Sykes—the dignified, composed inmate who does not exploit others and who is able to endure the hardships of incarceration.[19] Their short sentences (usually three years) and their strong primary group ties on the outside perhaps militated against preoccupation with prison status. On the other hand, they subscribed to the principle that every man has his price, that all occupations are rackets. They saw little use for and they avoided such therapy programs as group counseling, group therapy, and individual therapy. The institution's religious and educational programs were of no interest to them. They appeared to have crystallized their social values and the attitudes which underpinned their specific form of criminal behavior—a behavior which appears to have strong support among their peer groups in "free" society.

The sample of offenders used in this study is admittedly small, and the claim is not made that it is representative of all Negro numbers men throughout the United States. The assumption is made, however, that some common elements in social background and personality configuration exist among Negro numbers men. The confidence man is a confidence man whether he resides in Philadelphia, Boston, Washington, D.C. or elsewhere. In the same sense, so is a numbers man. Though the numbers game varies slightly from one locale to another, its *modus operandi*, as practiced among Negroes, is fairly well standardized. More research needs to be done on this specific type of criminal behavior and on the men who participate in it as operators. No definitive work is extant on such a group of offenders to this writer's knowledge. It is hoped that this research may pave the way for further research in reference to the etiology of the Negro numbers man.

INDICATORS FOR A MULTI-DISCIPLINARY APPROACH WITH NUMBERS MEN

The numbers men did not appear to have any relevant indicators for the constitutionalists. The psychologists and psychiatrists would be interested in the personality type which could adjust to the criminal as well as the noncriminal world without guilt feelings, and which could rationalize away criminal behavior as really not being criminal. The sociologists might wish to probe

TABLE III

COMPARISON OF SINGLE PATTERN OF NUMBERS GAME VIOLATORS WITH ALL OTHER OFFENDERS

Selected Social and Personal Attributes	Numbers Men (N=16) N.W.C.*	All Others (N=384) N.W.C.	Sign of X^2
Reared in more than one home	3	158	N.S.†
Mother figure southern migrant	3	171	N.S.
Mother figure domestic servant	13	287	N.S.
Dependent family	6	290	.01
Family broken by desertion	2	138	N.S.
Demoralized family	1	195	.01
Criminality in family	1	170	.01
Mother figure dominant	2	217	.01
Inadequate supervision—father	3§	193	.05
Inadequate supervision—mother	4	278	.01
Conflict in family	3	231	.01
Overt hostility toward father	2	269	.01
Overt hostility toward mother	1	78	N.S.
Disciplinary problem at home	2	117	N.S.
History of running away	3	182	.05
Inveterate gambler‡	16	154	.01
Problem drinker	2	191	.05

Selected Social and Personal Attributes	Numbers Men (N=16) N.W.C.*	All Others (N=384) N.W.C.	Sign of X^2
Weak parental family structure	0	214	.01
No parental family ties	2	280	.01
Reared in urban area	9	325	.01
Reared in slum area	1	250	.01
Living in slum when arrested	0	301	.01
History of school truancy	2	201	.01
Disciplinary problem at school	3	185	.05
Street trades as juvenile	3	200	.05
No marital ties	3	285	.01
Juvenile delinquent companions	5	231	.05
Member delinquent gang	1	141	.05
Adjudicated juvenile delinquent	4	173	N.S.
Committed as juvenile	1	145	.05
Police contact prior to age 18	1	220	.01
Criminal companions as juvenile	1	162	.01
Drug addict	0	69	N.S.
Positive attitude toward work	11	142	.01

*Number with characteristic.
†Not significant.
‡Nonprofessional gambling.
§Based on those with fathers.

further into the legitimate and illegitimate avenues of upward mobility available to such offenders, into the numbers game as a semi-legitimate institution within the urban Negro's community structure, into the "tie-in" of the police with this racket, into the numbers game as a professional, criminal behavior system. They might also ask the questions: How do they select this criminal career? How are they selected? What factors and attributes militate for success or failure in this criminal career?

The legalists and correctional administrators must view numbers men as dedicated professional criminals. Present sentencing procedures in most jurisdictions are extremely lenient for this type of offender. As a rule, they are not good probation and parole risks. Attempts at rehabilitation appear dim for these men, since they appear to have deep-seated crystallized criminal values. Moreover, their criminal behavior appears to have strong support among Negroes of all social classes in free society.

Generally, these professional gamblers are model prisoners. To the writer's knowledge, not one "numbers man" has been reported for a serious violation of prison regulations during his sentence at the D. C. Reformatory. They are tractable, pleasant and courteous inmates. They usually competently fill clerical positions as inmate clerks. They are generally liked by other inmates as well as by prison officials. Contrary to what would be expected of the professional criminal, they do not seek special favors. In short, they make "good" adjustments in prison, where they make themselves as unobtrusive as possible. As other professional criminals, they subscribe to the principle that "every man has his price," that all occupations are rackets. In short, they are what is generally referred to in prison slang as "angle boys." For these reasons they should be separated (housing and work details) from nonprofessional criminals in the prison setting.

REFERENCES

1. ROEBUCK, JULIAN: The Negro numbers man as a criminal type: The construction and application of a typology. *Journal of Criminal Law, Criminology and Police Science,* 54:48-60, March, 1963.

2. McCall, George J.: "Symbiosis: The case of hoodoo and the numbers racket." *Social Problems, 10*:368-370, Spring, 1963.

3. Scarne, John: *Scarne's Complete Guide to Gambling.* New York, Simon and Schuster, 1961, p. 164.

4. For a history of the numbers game among Negroes, see Drake, St. Clair, and Cayton, Horace R.: *Black Metropolis* (Vol. II). New York, Harper and Row, Torchback Edition, 1962, pp. 470-494. For an account of the extent and method of operation of this gambling racket, see Davie, Maurice R.: *Negroes in American Society.* New York, McGraw-Hill, 1949, pp. 422-425; Kefauver Report. Washington, Government Printing Office, U. S. Senate, Report No. 307, 1951; Jacoby, Oswald: The forms of gambling. *Annals of the American Academy of Political and Social Science, 269*:39-45, May, 1950; Morehead, Albert H.: The professional gambler, *Annals of the American Academy of Political and Social Science, 269*: 81-92, May, 1950; Sprigle: *Inside the Rackets,* Pittsburgh Post-Gazette, July 10, 1950, p. 1, cols. 1-2.

5. See Table 3, p. 150.

6. Drake, St. Clair, and Cayton, Horace R.: *Black Metropolis,* pp. 546-549. Note the respectable, middle-class backgrounds of many Negro numbers men.

7. These remarks revealed an adage of the professional gambling fraternity that the gambler wins at the game that is his specialty, only to lose money at another man's game. See Morehead, Albert H.: The professional gambler. *Annals, 269* May, 1950. For a psychological explanation of this phenomenon see Bergler, Edmund: *Tensions Can Be Reduced to Nuisances, A Technique for Not-Too-Neurotic People.* New York, Liveright Publishing Corporation, 1960.

8. Drake, St. Clair, and Cayton, Horace R.: *Black Metropolis,* pp. 486-494, found that Negro numbers men often invested in legitimate business in Chicago, e.g., taverns, shoe stores, food marts, and real estate. Moreover, many numbers men considered themselves to be race leaders. Warner, W. Lloyd, Junkeb, Buford H., and Adams, Walter A.: *Color and Human Nature.* Washington, D.C., American Council on Education, 1941, pp. 20-21.

9. All these men had received numerous friendly letters and visits from Negro professional and business men while incarcerated.

Some of their family members and friends have married into the Negro professional and business classes.

10. FRAZIER, E. FRANKLIN: *Black Bourgeoisie: The Rise of the Negro Middle Class in the U.S.* Glencoe, Illinois, The Free Press, 1957, pp. 127-213.

11. The white attorney, a well-known local criminal lawyer, was referred to jokingly by this group under study as the "Great White Father." While the research was in progress, this paternal figure died. He was sorely grieved both inside and outside the institution. Relatives and friends of the men under study viewed his remains and sent flowers. As one numbers man remarked, "An institution has passed on."

12. The numbers backer finances the operation, suffers the "hits" (numbers players' wins) and receives the profits. He selects and pays the personnel of the gambling ring, employs the legal talent, acts as chief planner, and symbolizes in his leadership role the security and strength of the organization. The backer's lieutenant supervises the personnel and the operation at the drop. The pick-up man moves from one designated spot in the city to another at certain hours of the day to pick up the money and numbers slips from individual numbers writers which he in turn delivers to the drop. He also delivers the winnings from the "hits" to the numbers writers. Lookout men report any ascertainable police surveillance or activity in reference to any phase of the organization's operation. Numbers runners are employees of a numbers writer who pick up small bets in a given numbers writers' area. Bouncers work as watchmen, bodyguards, and, janitors at the drop.

13. According to Minnesota Multiphasic Personality Inventories, which were interpreted by a D.C. Department of Corrections clinical psychologist, only one score of the total 144 subscale scores was above 70. These scores would compare favorably with those of a noncriminal group.

14. Five were Baptists, five were Methodists, two were Presbyterians, and four were Roman Catholics.

15. Three other criminal categories approached the status of professional criminals in certain respects; however, they were less skilled in their criminal activities and less well organized. They represented for the most part institutionalized offenders

(having served time frequently in correctional institutions as juveniles and as adults) who were much less successful in their criminal pursuits—Single Pattern of Robbery, Single Pattern of Burglary, and Single Pattern of Fraud.

16. RECKLESS, WALTER C., DINITZ, SIMON, and MURRAY, ELLEN: Self concept as an insulator against delinquency. *American Sociological Review*, 21:744-746, December, 1956.

17. FRAZIER, E. FRANKLIN: *Black Bourgeoisie*, p. 47. For a more recent historical overview of Negro social classes, see KAHL, JOSEPH A.: *The American Class Structure*. New York, Rinehart, 1957, pp. 233-248.

18. Interview with Horace Cayton, July 18, 1961. Mr. Cayton says that it is increasingly difficult for the Negro numbers man to mingle socially with members of the Negro middle and upper classes. He claims that there have always been certain elite Negro circles which numbers men could not crash, though he agrees that there has been some penetration of the middle and upper Negro social classes by numbers men.

19. SYKES, GRESHAM M.: Men, merchants, and toughs: A study of reactions to imprisonment. *Social Problems*, 4:130-138, October, 1956.

Chapter IX

THE DRINKER AND ASSAULTER[1]

Drunkenness and the Relationship of Alcohol to Crime

ALCOHOL has several connections with crime which for the most part may be divided into four levels. (a) Persons may become criminals as a consequence of breaking laws on the production, storage, packaging, distribution, sales and advertising of alcoholic beverages. (b) Persons may become violators of regulatory laws prescribing where, when and under what circumstances alcohol may be purchased and consumed. (c) Persons may become violators through behavior that is defined as public drunkenness. (d) Persons may be involved in criminal acts excluded in the preceding three levels as a consequence of the use of alcohol. Frequently, association between degrees of intoxication and such offenses as assault, murder, sex violations against the person, theft, burglary, and check passing are reported in the literature.[2] There is no full agreement at this level, i.e., the direct or indirect relationship of the influence of alcohol on these types of crime. Drinking may be parallel to, rather than the cause of, criminality. Drinking beyond control and crime may reflect inadequacies of personality.[3]

The author's concern is with violators at levels c. and d. *Uniform Crime Reports* consistently reveals that arrests for drunkenness make up the largest arrest group category.[4] They generally constitute in excess of 35 per cent of all arrests. Moreover, intoxicated persons are frequently charged with misdemeanors closely associated with and including drunkenness, e.g., driving while intoxicated, disorderly conduct and vagrancy. Various studies indicate that one half of the persons committed to our

155

jails are drunks, and half of all jail time is served by drunks.[5]
A California study revealed that during 1955 the total bookings
in California city jails numbered 472,202. Of this number, 52.8
per cent of the total, 249,312, were drunk bookings. During the
same year, 42.4 per cent of the bookings in the fifty-eight county
jails were drunk bookings.[6] Many offenders convicted and incarcerated on drunkenness charges are known alcoholic recidivists
who serve continual periods of time in jails and workhouses.

Studies of the chronic drunkenness offender frequently show
him to be a product of lower-class background. His educational
and job achievement is low. Generally he has had marital difficulties. Between the ages of thirteen and thirty, he has often
been involved in criminal activity of a varied and unsuccessful
amateurish type. Between thirty-five and forty his behavior
becomes less felonious and his use of alcohol more and more
excessive. Arrests for drunkenness increase in frequency.[7]

In reference to level d, Robert V. Seliger has pointed out that
evidence so far is insufficient for definitive conclusions on
whether alcohol inhibits or releases aggressive drives.[8] Certainly
there is an agreement among authorities that alcohol relaxes and
impedes critical judgment and control. Assault resulting in death
is probably the felony most highly correlated with alcoholic use.
Wolfgang found a significant association between violent homicide and presence of alcohol in the offender in a study of 588
homicides occurring over a five-year period in Philadelphia. It
was observed that in 374 (64 per cent) of the 588 cases, alcohol
was present in the homicide situation. In fifty-four (9 per cent)
of the 588 homicides, alcohol was present in the victim only, and
in sixty-four (11 per cent) of the total homicides, alcohol was
present in the offender only. Also significant was the fact that
of the 374 cases in which alcohol was a present factor nearly
seven tenths were those involving the presence of alcohol in
both the victim and the offender.[9] In Columbus, Ohio, the urine
of 882 persons arrested during or immediately after the commission of a felony over a two-year period was analyzed to
determine alcohol concentration. Findings showed that 64 per
cent of the felons were under the influence of alcohol to an

extent sufficient enough to reduce their inhibitions (0.10 per cent or more of urine alcohol was the criterion). Crimes of physical violence were most frequently associated with intoxication. Eleven displayed such a concentration of alcohol for every one who was sober in crimes of cutting and stabbing. Statistics show figures of: eight to one in the carrying of concealed weapons; ten to one in non-felonious assaults; four to one in shootings and murders. Property crimes were much less frequently related to drinking.[10]

Dr. Ralph Banay has estimated that 25 per cent of the total number of offenders he studied at Sing Sing Prison demonstrated a close or direct causal relationship between their crimes and alcoholism. He found marked differences when intemperance was related to the type of crime committed. The highest percentages of both intemperance and intoxication were found for those guilty of sex crimes, assaults, burglary and homicides.[11] In a recent California study consisting of 2,325 newly committed male felons entering the Department of Corrections Reception Centers, it was found that the proportion intoxicated during the commission of the crime for which they were arrested varied with the type of crime committed—50 per cent for auto theft, 37.8 per cent for murder and manslaughter, 37.7 per cent for assault, 37.5 per cent for sex offenses and 34.9 per cent for forgery and passing bad checks. Twenty-nine per cent of the 2,325 prisoners interviewed claimed that the use of alcohol had been a problem prior to incarceration.[12]

ASSAULT

The *Uniform Crime Reports* divide assaults into two groups: (a) aggravated assault and (b) other assaults.[13] In 1963, there were an estimated 147,800 serious assaults with intent to kill or commit serious injury in the United States. The national aggravated assault rate has increased 16 per cent since 1958. Two thirds of the offenses in 1963 involved either persons within the same family unit or otherwise acquainted persons. In this respect, aggravated assault resembles murder. Geographically, the aggravated assault rate was highest in the Southern states and in large standard metropolitan areas. The high arrest rate age group was for twenty to twenty-four-year-old males. Persons under eighteen years of age represented only 14 per cent of the total arrests for this offense. It is known that aggravated assault is an under-reported offense and, moreover, because of the relationship between the assailant and the victim, there is comparatively little prosecution for this offense. For simple assault (other assault), which is not considered in computing the *Crime Index,* there were 145 arrests per 100,000 population in 1963. A frequent cause for police arrests, simple assault arrest rates were higher in the larger cities of great density of population.[14]

Probably the most significant study of assault and assaulters to date is that of F. H. McClintock in the Metropolitan Police District of London for the decade 1950 to 1960.[15] The author selected from Criminal Statistics, under the heading of "Indictable Offenses of Violence Against the Person," those offenses which he determined involve an element of personal violence. Those offenses selected for detailed examination were classified by the author according to legal criteria into five classes: I. homicides and attempts; II. felonious woundings; III. malicious woundings (misdemeanors); IV. assaults for rape and other sexual offenses accompanied by violence; and V. possession of firearms and other offensive weapons. Felonious woundings and malicious woundings and assaults accounted for over 90 per cent of the indictable crimes of violence recorded by the police in the Metropolis for 1950, 1957 and 1960. A series of spot maps (1950, 1957 and 1960), including locales of indictable crimes of violence and residences of assailants and victims, demonstrated that crimes of violence occurred overwhelmingly in the inner divisions of the Metropolitan Police District which were characterized by densely populated slum conditions. The outer suburbs toward the green belts remained virtually free from violent crimes. The increase in crimes of violence was confined throughout the decade to those districts with a high incidence of violent crime at the beginning of the decade.

From recordings of indictable crimes of violence by the police

(police files) and individual criminal records, an analysis was attempted of the circumstances in which each indictable crime (1950, 1957 and 1960) was committed. Findings revealed that "attacks" in and around public houses, cafes and streets accounted for nearly one half of all recorded crimes of violence: violence resulting from family and domestic disputes—one third; attacks on police and civilians—12 per cent; sexual assaults 6 per cent; and miscellaneous attacks (on prison officers, injury from criminal negligence, attacks by persons of unsound mind)—2 per cent. During the decade there was a rise in all types of violent crime (almost doubled in all legal categories); however, a greater-than-average increase occurred in violent street attacks. Excluding attacks on police, in more than one half of the crimes, the offender and victim were known to each other prior to the offense. The proportion of attacks on strangers was highest in sexual attacks and in attacks on the street. The majority of crimes of violence were committed among working-class people in slum neighborhoods. Three fourths of the victims of crimes of violence were males; 70 per cent of the victims were between the ages of twenty-one and fifty. The assailants were almost all males (94 per cent) and two thirds of them were over twenty-one. During the decade under study, the proportion of victims and assailants under twenty-one increased significantly. More than seven in ten of the attacks were by one offender on one victim. Firearms were rarely used. More than one half of the assailants used no weapon and attacked by punching and kicking. The number of victims killed, those who suffered permanent disablement or disfigurement, and those detained in the hospital for more than a month comprised only 3 per cent of the total victims. Most of the crimes of violence were not committed in conjunction with other crimes but rather reflected violent patterns of social behavior indigenous to the area of residence and social class of the victims and assailants. Violent sexual crimes, attacks on police, and hooliganism increased in the decade, but they continued to constitute a very small percentage of the crimes of violence. The author found that crimes of violence were more frequently cleared by arrest and resulted in conviction than offenses against property. Street attacks by strangers and hooligan behavior by juveniles had low "cleared-up" and conviction rates.

In an endeavor to assess the social backgrounds of offenders convicted of crimes of violence in the metropolis during the years 1950, 1957 and 1960, an analysis was made of those charged and convicted of indictable crimes of violence and those charged with an indictable crime of violence but convicted of a non-indictable assault only. Eighty per cent of these offenders had no previous convictions for crimes of violence. Half of them had prior records of nonviolent offenses. Twenty per cent of the nonviolent recidivists, however, had engaged in previous indictable violence or aggressiveness for which they were not convicted, e.g., fighting while drunk, intimidation and attacking citizens, disturbances in public places and gang fights. Moreover, a large proportion of them were found to be aggressive or unstable in disposition. A great deal of this aggressiveness was associated with heavy drinking.

McClintock discovered a hard-core group of violent recidivists (violent offenders with three or more violent offenses in their records). Their past records included serious property offenses, malicious damage, sex offenses, borstal training, four or five prison sentences, frequent short-term sentences, fights or assaults in public houses while intoxicated, attacks on police, serious attacks on strangers and neighbors and a long record of unreported acts of violence. Their violence was of an unplanned type. They constituted three sub-groups: (a) those with long records of property offenses who repeatedly used violence in order to escape from the police; (b) heavy drinkers who became aggressive after a few drinks; and (c) offenders with a pattern of aggression and tough behavior as a way of life. A five-year follow-up of violent recidivists convicted in 1950 showed that 60 per cent were reconvicted. More than one half of these reconvictions were for violent offenses. Violent offenders in general were frequently single, divorced or separated, unskilled, residents of high crime areas living away from home. Irish and Negro immigrants accounted for a high proportion of them.

Intoxication was frequently associated with their crimes of violence.[16]

THE DRINKER AND ASSAULTER AS A CRIMINAL TYPE

The forty offenders in the double-arrest pattern of Drunkenness and Assault (with the two offenses usually occurring concomitantly) when statistically compared with the remainder of the sample, revealed differences in twenty-six of the thirty-four personal and social characteristics tested.[17] Twenty-five were significant at the .01 level, one at the .05 level.

The men in both groups—the forty in the double-pattern and the 360 in the remainder of the sample—were literate (Stanford Achievement Test grade median of pattern group—5.8, of remainder—5.2), young (median age of pattern group—30.7 years, of remainder—30.4 years) and of average intelligence (median IQ for pattern group—93.8; for remainder—89.1).

Statistical comparisons revealed that the men in the double-pattern group came less often from demoralized families, from families in which other members had criminal records or from homes with weak or absent family ties, either during their childhood or at the time of the study. Rather, they came significantly more often from patriarchal homes, as opposed to the typical matriarchal home of most other offenders. However, the father's supervision, too harsh or erratic, was considered to be inadequate more often than for the remainder as a whole, whose supervision by the father was too lax. Supervision by the mother figure was also inadequate (too lax). Perhaps these double-pattern offenders showed significantly more conflict in the home because they maintained close ties.

Men in this pattern group were also significantly more often disciplinary problems in school, but appeared more willing to face their problems since they were also less often runaways from home or truants from school. They were less often reared in a slum environment, worked less frequently in street trades, had fewer police contacts before age eighteen and were less often adjudicated juvenile delinquents. With regard to this last, they had fewer delinquent companions, were less often members of a juvenile delinquent gang and had criminal companions less frequently before age eighteen.

As adults, members of the pattern group expressed more positive attitudes toward work, were more often married (usually, they said, happily) and maintained family ties more closely than did the men in the remainder of the sample. Not one was addicted to opiate drugs. On the negative side, they were found to be more frequently inveterate gamblers and problem drinkers when compared with the rest of the sample.

The internal comparison data demonstrated that offenders in this group were most similar in background to those in the residual category of No Pattern. Offenders in the No Pattern category differed in the area of parental supervision and in their response toward this supervision. The No Pattern offenders were much less prone to drinking, violence and gambling.

A qualitative examination of this pattern group revealed a peculiar constellation of background characteristics that may have disposed them to this and not to other patterns of criminal behavior. For the most part, they were first generation (35 of them spent a part of their childhood in the rural or small town South) city dwellers who grew up in a family setting in which the parents adhered to the patriarchal values of the rural South. The family was dominated by a rigid, self-righteous father who at times was severe in his disciplinary measures and at other times erratic. Corporal punishment, though not brutal in type, was the rule. A strong flavor of Baptist fundamentalism was present, as was an insistence on Sunday School and churchgoing (38 attended Sunday School and church regularly as long as they remained at home; 35 of them remained at home through the twenty-first birthday). Gambling, drinking, card playing and dancing were frowned upon. These verbatim remarks were typical:

> My father, man was a holy-joe. He should've been a preacher. Mama was long on that religious kick, too. We had to go to church. The old man laid the belt on me when he caught me wrong—lying, fooling around, out late at night. He allowed no card playing, dancing or

drinking. Quiet, one of those serious kind. He knew he was the rightest man in the world next to Jesus Christ. I had to work at home too, and the dishes . . .

Though holding up a rigid moral code, the father at times would permit transgressions, pretending that he did not know the code was being violated. On other occasions, he would resort to corporal punishment in an attempt to enforce it. As one inmate stated:

> As much as he hated liquor, I know he smelled it at times after a dance. He wouldn't say nothing. Then again he might smell me and tear me up!

The mother generally subscribed to the father's values and disciplinary methods, though at times she was surreptitiously permissive in an attempt to attenuate the strictness of the father. At other times, she also resorted to corporal punishment. Though these men spoke of verbal clashes with their parents during the formative years, there seemed to have been little overt rebellion in the home. These statements were typical:

> My folks were good people. They were too light on me. I didn't go along with a lot of the old man's trash. You know, it just had to be taken by me, though. Guess my mama caused me to. She loved him and wanted me to do what he said. I talked back to him once in a while. That was all.

All of them claimed respectable parents, and they made a point of mentioning this several times throughout the interviews. They seemed proud of their fundamentalistic backgrounds.

Twenty-eight of these men were expelled or suspended from school for one or more of the following conduct violations: fighting with other male students; fighting with male teachers; gambling; and insubordination to male teachers. All of them spoke of difficulty with their parents and with teachers in reference to frequent fights with neighborhood companions and schoolmates. Though expressed in several different ways during the interviews, their rationalization for fighting was generally in terms of the principle: "Nobody will ever push *me* around." They had resorted to physical violence from childhood in order to solve their personal problems of adjustment. As one inmate stated:

> I had to fight all my life. Them slum bums thought I was weak because I had clean clothes. They want to take my stuff . . . push me around. I always had to show them suckers I was a tough man too. I stripped my reverse gears long time ago. In street fighting it's best to have some heat for protection. You know, like a gun or knife. Cold steel backs them up.

They evinced a preoccupation with physical courage; and they mentioned again and again the necessity for *fighting* and violence as a method of self-preservation. Readiness to fight, according to them was a masculine proclivity, a necessary element in the temperament of every "real man." The possession of a knife at all times was a must. In a sense, they may be viewed as juveniles, as street and playground "warriors." The necessity of defending themselves, as well-dressed, "good" boys, from their more delinquent peers at school provided a socially useful, rewarding outlet for aggressive impulses that could not be vented in the home.

In discussing their juvenile delinquent activities, these offenders indicated involvement in sporadic, unplanned activities usually associated with street fighting, drinking, gambling and sex relations with girls of their own age. These enterprises did not generally involve juvenile gang behavior. Remarks of this kind were frequent:

> I didn't go for no gang stuff. All that stealing only would get me in jail. I didn't want to be told what to do by no group of thugs. But if somebody wanted to shoot some craps or play some cards then I was ready. Of course you have to fight sometime when you gamble or they will take your money. I knew some gang guys. We got along O.K. I just didn't go along with their hustle. I rather be with the girls—you know, dancing, drinking and living it up. I even tried some H once but it didn't do nothing for me but put me to sleep. Who wants to sleep? Those junkies ain't nothing. I stayed away from them.

In reference to their community adjustment as adults, the qualitative materials revealed that these men were well integrated in primary groups. Twenty of the twenty-five who were married were living with their wives at the time of their incarceration. The thirteen who were single and the two who were divorced maintained a stable relationship with a girlfriend or a paramour. A high proportion of them maintained intimate contacts with their parental family. Most of them had had regular work histories, and thirty expressed positive attitudes toward legitimate work in the future.

On the negative side, a high proportion of them (28), were inveterate gamblers. The remaining twelve claimed that a good part of their leisure time was spent in gambling and that they had financial problems as a result. All were problem drinkers and had served at least one misdemeanor sentence for drunkenness. Their choice was whiskey; they abhorred wine, which they considered the drink of the alcoholic, "the wino." Although they thought, in a vague way, that alcohol was at the bottom of many of their problems, they did not think of themselves as alcoholics. Their pattern of violence as juveniles continued into adulthood:

> When I get to drinking, I really don't take nothing from nobody. A man steps on my toe or they go to get smart . . . man, he's got me to whip. I clean him up. Guess I shouldn't drink so much.

Most of their fighting which led to assault charges took place in bars, with male drinking acquaintances and in gambling games with their peers. To repeat, they all carried knives, which were the weapons of their choice. They displayed little respect for the policeman, who to them was "the man" who snooped into their private lives—a "kill-joy." The following comments were common:

> Cops ain't from nowhere! All they do is prance around with these sticks and guns. Take them off, they got no heart. They busy bodies. Why they so busy about drinking? They ought to be after those muggers and housebreakers. I don't hurt nobody. All I want to do is gamble and drink a little. When somebody call them for protection, they likely to lock him up with everybody else.

Their discussion of their gambling activities showed them to be "marks" of the professional gambler. They played dice and poker in gambling houses and in "floating" house dice and poker games where they faced "house odds." Most of them spent from twenty to thirty dollars per month on numbers. Not one had ever worked as a professional gambler or for a professional gambler. Moreover, they had no set group of gambling companions; rather, they moved individually from one gaming group to another. As a typical inmate stated:

Man, I didn't have no gambling buddies. Every man is for himself.
I didn't care who the studs were. The game would be in somebody's
basement one night and then the next night it might be in a back
room of a stick hall (pool room). Of course the guys who run the
tables usually wound up with the money, but it was fun anyhow. Sure
I rubbed elbows with some fellows more than once, but that didn't
make me no difference. You go to get friendly with those suckers and
they want to borrow your money. They was all really strangers to me.
I went in alone, and I left alone.

The arrest records of this group were comparatively long
(mean average arrests per man, 15), but few property charges
were evident. Rather, intoxication and assault charges appeared
with regularity and often concurrently. There was no evidence
of criminal progression. Sprinkled throughout these arrest histories were a few charges for the possession of concealed weapons,
disorderly conduct, "suspicion" and gambling; however, the
pattern of drinking and assault was clear-cut. Most were serving
time on an aggravated assault charge; however, simple assault
charges appeared more frequently in their arrest histories than
did aggravated assault. The District Attorney's Reports and the
research interviews demonstrated that these men were not professional criminals and did not conceive of themselves as having
criminal careers. They had come in contact with professional
gamblers and bootleggers in a rather segmental fashion and had
been the "marks" of these professionals rather than their cronies—
a kind of contact that probably exists for a large number of
Negroes in large metropolitan areas. They were marginal men
in that some of their attitudes, actions and human relationships
were conventional and respectable, whereas other attitudes,
behavior patterns and relationships reflected a position against
law-abiding society. They lived in two worlds, the criminal and
noncriminal.[18] Though not as a rule serious offenders, their
predisposition to violence, their heavy drinking, persistent
gambling and lack of respect for the police, when taken in combination, made them potentially dangerous.

These men appeared to be a strong, husky group in good health.
The medical records showed that only three were not organically
sound: one had stomach ulcers; one was an arrested case of

tuberculosis; and one had a punctured eardrum. They were friendly, cooperative, pleasant and very frank. All of them appeared to be charged with suppressed energy and gave the impression of being nervous, edgy and emotionally labile. Gay and humorous, they were verbally aggressive. They spoke warmly of family members as well as of several friends. They referred to most of their activities on the street in terms of group activity, e.g., parties, family reunions, poker games, dances, etc. All of them claimed respectable parents and made a point to mention this to the writer several times throughout the interviews.

The empirical data, both quantitative and qualitative, show clearly that the Negro drinker and assaulter differs in kind and degree from other criminal types in terms of theoretically relevant sociopsychological background factors. They came from a less criminogenic milieu than did those in the remainder of the sample, but because of certain aspects of their socialization process, they appear to have developed a certain criminal pattern of response.

These offenders, as adults, rarely committed their assaults until intoxicated. While we cannot know the psychodynamics of these cases, this fact suggests that parental efforts to build character and develop their conscience through discipline and religious training were to some degree successful. One can hypothesize that they may have needed alcohol to weaken learned inhibitions so that their aggression, resulting from continued frustration, could manifest itself. In this case, their responses of drinking, assault and gambling may be viewed in terms of their over-reaction to a rigid background. Their resentment of the authority of a father figure, to whom they reluctantly submitted during their formative years, may have been unleashed on other males. Sociopsychological, rather than strictly sociological, variables in the backgrounds of these offenders seem likely to have disposed them to this particular pattern of criminal behavior.

Horton, in a cross-cultural study, has shown that alcoholism is positively related to the amount of learned inhibition of sexual behavior and suggests that developing inner controls of any highly motivated behavior produces a disposition toward drinking as a means of circumventing the "conscience."[19] The same may be true in the relation between alcoholism and crime. Many crimes, especially *crimes of violence,* are committed under the influence of alcohol.[20] Perhaps this examination of the relatively "pure" cases of misconduct committed while under the influence of alcohol can provide clues as to why intoxication and crimes of violence seem to be related. These forty offenders had the usual frustrations of the Northern urban Negro, but because of a strict fundamentalist upbringing were unable to express hostilities—except when inhibitions were weakened by alcohol. Drinking and crimes of violence (as opposed to crimes against property) may be a result of the interactive effects of continued frustration and of parental and societal success in building up inhibitions to aggression.

INDICATORS FOR A MULTI-DISCIPLINARY APPROACH WITH DRINKERS AND ASSAULTERS

The constitutionalists would note the apparent restlessness and pent-up energy and the seemingly husky builds of these men—somatotyping might be indicated. The psychologists and psychiatrists might wish to further examine their relationships with, and their reactions to: dominant, rigid, puritanical fathers and permissive mothers; the relationship of intoxication to their offenses of violence; their incorporation of violence as part of a life style. The sociologist might wish to study these offenders in relationship to their atypical, patriarchal rather than matriarchal backgrounds, and also, the analysis of their pattern of violence and gambling in terms of typical patterns of the urban low-class Negro. In reference to this group, the legalist and correctional administrator would be dealing with occasional, nonprofessional offenders who were not committed to any pattern of property crime. Though not as a rule serious offenders, their predisposition to violence, their credo of the personal redress of wrongs and their drinking and gambling demonstrated them to be potentially serious offenders.

TABLE IV

COMPARISON OF DOUBLE PATTERN OF DRUNKENNESS AND ASSAULT WITH ALL OTHER OFFENDERS

Selected Social and Personal Attributes	Drinkers and Assaulters (N=40) N.W.C.*	All Others (N=360) N.W.C.	Sign of X²	Selected Social and Personal Attributes	Drinkers and Assaulters (N=40) N.W.C.*	All Others (N=360) N.W.C.	Sign of X²
Reared in more than one home	15	146	N.S.†	Weak parental family structure	13	201	.01
Mother figure southern migrant	30	144	.01	No parental family ties	22	260	.05
Mother figure domestic servant	38	262	.01	Reared in urban area	37	297	N.S.
Dependent family	28	268	N.S.	Reared in slum area	13	238	.01
Family broken by desertion	8	132	N.S.	Living in slum when arrested	31	270	N.S.
Demoralized family	5	191	.01	History of school truancy	12	191	.01
Criminality in family	7	164	.01	Disciplinary problem at school	28	160	.01
Mother figure dominant	8	211	.01	Street trades as juvenile	9	194	.01
Inadequate supervision—father	39‡	157	.01	No marital ties	13	275	.01
Inadequate supervision—mother	31	251	N.S.	Juvenile delinquent companions	8	228	.01
Conflict in family	33	201	.01	Member delinquent gang	3	139	.01
Overt hostility toward father	23	148	.01	Adjudicated juvenile delinquent	4	173	.01
Overt hostility toward mother	11	68	N.S.	Committed as juvenile	4	142	.01
Disciplinary problem at home	11	108	N.S.	Police contact prior to age 18	6	215	.01
History of running away	2	183	.01	Criminal companions as juvenile	5	158	.01
Inveterate gambler	28	142	.01	Drug addict	0	69	.01
Problem drinker	40	153	.01	Positive attitude toward work	30	123	.01

*Number with characteristic.

†Not significant.

‡Based on those with fathers.

Some men of their type should probably be incarcerated in forestry camps similar to those maintained in the State of California, or in similar situations where their physical energies may be utilized. Certainly, inactivity for them should be avoided at all costs in penal settings. Those sincerely interested in trades should be given the opportunity for training. On the other hand, those who demonstrate no such interest should be given the opportunity of hard manual labor. It is likely that a few of them could be placed on probation. In any event, in the investigator's opinion, they should be segregated from offenders who have a pattern of serious property crimes.

All of those who are therapy-oriented need specialized counseling in reference to their gambling, drinking and fighting, in which areas a new set of values would help. Perhaps they can be taught nonviolent methods of handling their personal problems. Case work and psychological counseling seem to be called for with them.[1]

REFERENCES

1. ROEBUCK, JULIAN B., and JOHNSON, RONALD: The Negro drinker and assaulter as a criminal type. *Crime and Delinquency*, 8:21-33, 1962.
2. CAVAN, RUTH SHONLE: *Criminology* (3rd ed.). New York, Thomas Y. Crowell Co., 1962, pp. 168-171.
3. TAPPAN, PAUL: *Crime, Justice and Correction*, p. 158.
4. *Uniform Crime Reports*, 1963, showed that out of 4,259,463 arrests, 1,078,427 were for drunkenness.
5. MACCORMICK, AUSTIN H.: Correctional views on alcohol, alcoholism, and crime. *Crime and Delinquency*, 9:20, January, 1963.
6. Special Study Commission on Correctional Facilities and Services, the County Jails of California: An Evaluation. Sacramento, California, March, 1957, p. 30.
7. PITTMAN, DAVID, and GORDON, C. W.: Criminal careers of the chronic police case inebriate. *The Quarterly Journal of Studies on Alcohol, 19*:255-268, June, 1958; BACON, SELDEN D.: Alcohol, alcoholism, and crime. *Crime and Delinquency*, 9:13-14, January, 1963.

8. SELIGER, ROBERT V.: Psychiatric orientation of the alcoholic criminal. *Journal of American Medical Association, 129*:421-424, October 6, 1945.

9. WOLFGANG, MARVIN E.: *Patterns in Criminal Homicide.* Philadelphia, University of Pennsylvania, 1958, pp. 136-137.

10. SHUPE, LLOYD M.: Alcohol and crime. *Journal of Criminal Law, Criminology, and Police Science, 44*:661-665, January-February, 1954.

11. BANAY, RALPH: Alcoholism and crime. *Quarterly Journal of Studies on Alcohol, 2*:688-690, March, 1942.

12. California Department of Health, Division of Alcoholic Rehabilitation: Criminal offenders and drinking involvement; a preliminary analysis. Publication No. III, Berkeley, 1960.

13. For a definition of these legal categories, see Appendix C, pp. 287-288.

14. *Uniform Crime Reports,* 1963, pp. 8-9.

15. McCLINTOCK, F. H.: *Crimes of Violence: An Inquiry by the Cambridge Institute of Criminology into Crimes of Violence Against the Person in London.* London, Macmillan and Co., Ltd., 1963, pp. 24-36.

16. McCLINTOCK, F. H.: *Crimes of Violence,* pp. 97-135.

17. See Table IV, p. 169.

18. CAVAN, RUTH SHONLE: *Criminology* (3rd ed.), pp. 186-201, in a hypothetical criminal typology classifies offenders as belonging to the criminal or to the noncriminal world.

19. HORTON, DONALD: The functions of alcohol in primitive societies. *Quarterly Journal of Studies on Alcohol.* September, 1943, pp. 292-303.

20. SHUPE, LLOYD M.: Alcohol and crime. *Journal of Criminal Law, Criminology and Police Science,* pp. 661-665.

21. Additional material on violent behavior is provided in Patterns of violence. *Annals of American Academy of Political and Social Science.* (The section on Criminal Violence is of particular relevance.) *364*:73-113, March, 1966.

Chapter X

THE MIXED PATTERN OFFENDER[1]
(Jack-of-All-Trades)

W HILE specialization is common, any prison population will contain a sizeable group of offenders (perhaps the largest group) who do not fall into any particular offender type. Several suggested hypotheses might be advanced to account for this "jack-of-all-trades" offender. Perhaps he is socially mobile and switches to more "advanced" types of criminal activity as he learns more complex criminal techniques during and after incarceration. Perhaps he specializes in a branch of crime that requires a kind of criminal apprenticeship so that he can "learn the ropes." Perhaps he has not been selected for such specialized training by his more "sophisticated" compeers because of low mental ability or lack of industry, finesse, self-discipline or opportunity.

This chapter compares criminals whose arrest records do *not* evidence a specialization in crime with those others whose offenses jell into a specific type. It attempts to discern the characteristics which presumably dispose the jack-of-all-trades offender to his varying pattern of crime.

THE JACK-OF-ALL-TRADES OFFENDER AS A CRIMINAL TYPE

These seventy-one offenders compared unfavorably with the remainder of the sample in twenty-two of the thirty-four attributes, while they compared favorably in only one—problem drinking.[2] Their environment appears to have been far more criminogenic than that of the rest of the sample.

The jack-of-all-trades offenders, when compared with the remainder of the sample, were significantly more often reared in more than one home, had mothers who were domestic servants, and came from economically dependent, demoralized, and criminal families. They had greater conflict within their family, less adequate supervision by the father (to whom they expressed more hostility) and had weaker parental ties. They were disciplinary problems at home, from which they more frequently ran away, and disciplinary problems in school, from which they were more often truant. As juveniles, these offenders worked in street trades, had delinquent companions, were members of delinquent gangs, and had police contacts prior to age eighteen. As to geographical environment, they were more often reared in slums and were more frequently residents of slum areas when arrested. They gambled significantly more often but were problem drinkers less often than the sample as a whole.

The men in this pattern group were literate (Stanford Achievement Test grade median—5.2), and young (median age—29.8) with a mean IQ of 85.8 (low, but approximately the same as the IQ for the entire sample). Logically, one would have assumed that Mixed Pattern offenders would vary in their level of intelligence and would consist, let us say, of one group so dull that more accomplished criminals would not teach them specialized criminal techniques and of another group whose ability was high enough to permit them to "advance" to other levels of crime, thus entering them into the "mixed-pattern" category. However, we found that the seventy-one members of the Mixed Pattern group did not vary significantly more in their IQ's than the members of other offender types.

Internal comparisons demonstrated these offenders to be more similar to the offenders in Single Pattern of Robbery and Double Pattern of Larceny and Burglary. Differentials in family background were of degree rather than kind.

The most significant qualitative difference between offenders of this type and other types (remainder of sample) was from the beginning to the end of their criminal careers, their extreme naïveté in the ways of crime. For example, here is a description of their typical burglaries. Usually, they did not specialize in any one type of building; they moved from private dwellings to apartment houses and from warehouses to stores. Nor did they specialize in the type of property they would steal. To use one offender's language, "We took everything that wasn't nailed down." "Everything" generally included money, jewels, furs, clothing, radios, television sets, checks, whiskey, cigarettes, etc. Vans for stolen goods or other means of transportation were rarely provided. Seldom did they make a "connection" with a "fence" prior to the offense or carefully time the execution of the crime. Once planned, the crime would generally be carried out regardless of unexpected obstacles—the appearance of an extra policeman, a cruising squad car in the vicinity of operation, a change in a policeman's timetable of rounds, a change or addition of a lock on a door, failure of a lookout to show up, etc. These offenders would blunder through these difficulties with false courage and a capricious hope for lucky breaks. The following remark by one of those interviewed illustrate the point:

> Once I got started, I had to go on with it . . . break on in and take the chance. You start thinking about the bread and you got to go. When I'm there set to go, the rollers (police) just got to get me, if they get me. The bust (arrest) just have to come.

Prior to the commission of the crime, these offenders did not make use of skillful "casing procedures." Tight organization was rare; they did not operate within a definite group of criminal acquaintances led by a fixed leader.

Most Mixed Pattern offenders, in discussing their juvenile delinquent activities, indicated that they had done some form of stealing before they were twelve. Although most of their delinquent activities appeared to have taken place in groups, they also mentioned stealing as "loners:"

> I stole clothing from stores with two or three fellows. Most of the time I stole with the other boys when we took a car or something. Sometimes when I saw a good chance I made my own score. I stole money from home, too, by myself.

From their discussions of juvenile gang activity, they were obviously followers rather than leaders. They neither planned nor schemed, and their stories did not highlight the physical courage and the flair for violence generally attributed to gang leaders. Moreover, they voiced no strong identification with a gang:

> There was five of us. We stole a lot of junk here and there in stores. Sometimes we stole a car. Tom divided the loot. He could beat up anybody in the block. Tom knew when a score was ripe. He could smell a cop a mile away I didn't get busted stealing with Tom. But then he was bossy. Sometimes I go along. Sometime I not go along. I just copped anything that wasn't nailed down.

As adults, their associations with other criminals were of a fluid variety—acquaintances but not strong brotherhoods in crime. Gang behavior was not evident:

> I ran with a few dudes I had done a bit with sometimes. We stumbled into each other at a bash (a get-together) or something, you know. They're O.K., but I'm not with them all the time. Sometimes we score together, then I don't see them in a long time, you know.

In discussing their criminal associates they disclosed some knowledge of and some contact with underworld activity—the illegal sale of whiskey and drugs, prostitution and gambling, though they didn't seem to belong to any organized underworld activity. Speaking in the criminal argot, offenders would make remarks like these:

> Sure, sure I know studs who sell whiskey and some who sell drugs. I know some pimps and a whole lot of whores. You get to know these people, but I ain't never been tied up with that stuff. No sort for me. Like other hustlers, I knew what was happening, but I really wasn't in the know. I wasn't inside no big operation.

The qualitative material gleaned from the interviews suggested that these men never developed professional roles in the higher echelons of the underworld because of their clumsiness, lack of self-discipline, frequent arrests and incarcerations, inability to settle down into one type of crime and their lack of opportunity for intimate association with more "sophisticated" criminals. An example:

> Well, you know, some time I thought about the big time. You got to work hard at one kind of game for that. I had to have quick bread though, all my life. I had to get what I could get. You know, any way I could get it. I grew up in the bottom with the small hustlers. The Cadillac boys didn't have nothing to do with us. One time I knew a

numbers man pretty good. I asked him for a job many times. He say, 'Man, what you talking about? You just don't have the class for the numbers.' I say, 'Well, I can learn.' He say, 'Hell, man, you been arrested for every petty crime in the book. You been locked up too much. All the cops know you too good. You got jail fever.' He say I should put the life down and get me a lunch pail. I guess he was right. Here I am in the joint again. I just couldn't settle down to no one type of hustle. Some small scores and many busts is the story of my life. I'm a jack-of-all-trades and no master of none.

For the most part, this group consisted of a mildly antisocial, nonprofessional bunch of grown-up juvenile delinquents. They were reared in lower-class, demoralized families, and they grew up in neighborhoods where older delinquent youths taught them to steal at an early age. They were products of the city slums and were loosely attached to the lower echelons of the underworld, resembling a group theoretically delineated by Walter C. Reckless as offenders with "ordinary criminal careers," in that ordinary criminal activities were a definite part of their life scheme.[3]

These institutionalized offenders (all of them had served time before, averaging 2.5 felonies per man) derived their meager economic support from their criminal activities (only nine had regular work histories). Unskilled, barely literate and intellectually inferior, they had been indoctrinated with the "fast buck" philosophy of life, though they were a far cry from being clever enough to live by it . Therefore, they kept coming back to jail. A number of their lengthy arrest histories (mean average arrests—18.3) revealed extensive criminal activity that progressed from the less serious (petty larceny, car theft, shoplifting) to the more serious (grand larceny and burglary) types of offenses, without, however, a specialization in any one type of offense. The District Attorney's Reports on all crimes for which they had served felony sentences showed various low levels of *modus operandi*.

Docile, easygoing followers, they were easily talked into taking appreciable risks for small "scores." They were not vicious, extremely courageous or colorful. They evinced no marked bitterness toward the police or the courts, as a rule accepted their sentences philosophically and made good prison adjustments. "Don't do the crime unless you can do the time" was a quite prevalent motto. They were that drab material which makes up most of a prison's population. Although not hardened criminals, many were vaguely aware that crime had not paid off for them, and most of them expressed hazy notions of "straightening up."

These offenders appeared to be in general good health and made few somatic complaints. The medical records showed sixty-five of this group to be organically sound: one was physically handicapped; one suffered from high blood pressure, hypertension; two were arrested cases of tuberculosis; two had stomach ulcers. They verbalized well without evidence of aggression and were friendly, cooperative and candid.

While the quantitative analysis does not indicate conclusively why these Mixed Pattern offenders did not develop criminal skills and specialization, the qualitative data do point to two probabilities. The first is that since such a thing as criminal progression (from unskilled to skilled varieties of crime) does exist, albeit to only a small degree in the careers of these offenders, it therefore should follow that criminal progression takes place most frequently within a certain specific criminal type. (That is, given a first offense—numbers, burglary, etc.—the offender may "progress" by acquiring new skills from more seasoned criminals. Once committed to a particular skill, the offender is not very likely to progress along other lines.) The second is that these offenders were "marginal men" who had, as adults, only superficial acquaintances with other criminals—a commonly found characteristic which might account for their classification as "Mixed Pattern—no progression."

They conceived of themselves as introverted. All of them expressed a dislike for large groups, crowds and noise, and desired to do their time in a cell. They were apprehensive about the D.C. Reformatory's open-dormitory housing facilities, and four of them asked for transfers. This fact suggests that these particular mixed-pattern offenders had limited contact with criminals because of their psychological makeup and hence were limited in what they could learn. This lack of learning made them "losers" with long records and little evidence of skill. In turn, being losers, they were avoided by fellow criminals who could teach them more skilled criminal techniques. This cycle of avoidance, naíveté, incarceration and more avoidance may well be the cause of the lack of pattern or progression in the careers of the seventy-one offenders.

INDICATORS FOR A MULTI-DISCIPLINARY APPROACH WITH MIXED-PATTERN OFFENDERS

Constitutional indicators were not apparent for this group. The psychologists and psychiatrists might wish to investigate further this mildly antisocial follower-type recidivist. What personality factors account for the persistence in crime of this type of offender who is cognizant of the fact that crime has not paid off for him? Could it be that this type of offender may find incarceration rewarding rather than punishing? The sociologists would recognize this type as those pursuing ordinary criminal careers. In further analyzing such criminal careers, the sociologist would want to know the illegitimate as well as legitimate avenues open to men of this type. They would also want to know why such offenders failed to close on any one type of crime and why *modi operandi* vary at different levels.

The legalist and correctional administrator should be aware of the treatment possibilities of these men, despite the fact that they are recidivists.

Perhaps for these reasons such offenders could be segregated into a special grouping within the confines of our present reformatory and prison systems. The present emphasis on vocational training, social education and counseling for this group of offenders in most modern reformatory and prison systems seems to be in keeping with their needs. Perhaps concentration on an indoctrination program that "crime has not paid" and will not pay for *them* would be of some value. Perhaps these men need to be *told* and *sold* on the idea that they are just not clever enough to make money in criminal pursuits. It is the writer's view that any form of moralization with them is useless. In his opinion *it is too late* to teach these men about the noble, unselfish way of life. They are intelligent enough to know that *crime does not pay some people.* They are also beyond Sunday-School age, and anyway, they never had, and they probably never will have "middle class" values. Counseling efforts, it seems, should be of a secular and of a practical variety. These men need to be inculcated with the *fixed idea* that they either get a lunch pail and go to work upon release or else come back to jail. The counseling service should furnish the inmate with definite steps which would appeal to his selfish interests in his endeavor to stay out of jail rather than with the flimsy material of the "good life."

The writer assumes, of course, that some of these men will seek help in an effort to stay out of prison, for minus a desire to remain in free society, there is no hope. The counselor should place his emphasis on the "staying out of jail" angle. The "departure from a criminal life" is only an important incidental. To illustrate this point, should the offender insist that all men have larceny in their hearts, that everyone has an angle, it may prove to no avail to attempt a complete change of this idea. Perhaps the counselor should appear to accept it in part, and then go on to show the inmate certain angles which will keep on the street— "angles" in legitimate activity. Should he insist on drinking in the future, the counselor could help him in the selection of bars where he is less likely to meet with "bums," "thugs" and police activity. The suggestion can be made that the safest place to drink is at home. Should he insist on gambling, it may be wise to encourage him to gamble not with strangers, but with friends who are amateurs. Should he persist in living a promiscuous sex life, it could be pointed out that females who have no children, no regular paramours or husbands, no criminal records and no addictions to alcohol or drugs are "safer bets" than women so encumbered.

The preceding illustrations are only tentative guide lines, which may be used in a type of directive therapy. It must be remembered that men of this type are imitators and followers. It is the writer's theory that they can be led in almost any direction.

TABLE V

COMPARISON OF MIXED PATTERN OFFENDERS WITH ALL OTHER OFFENDERS

Selected Social and Personal Attributes	No Pattern (N=71) N.W.C.*	All Others (N=329) N.W.C.	Sign of X^2	Selected Social and Personal Attributes	No Pattern (N=71) N.W.C.*	All Others (N=329) N.W.C.	Sign of X^2
Reared in more than one home	41	120	.01	Weak parental family structure	37	177	N.S.
Mother figure southern migrant	37	137	N.S.†	No parental family ties	58	224	.05
Mother figure domestic servant	61	239	.01	Reared in urban area	57	277	.05
Dependent family	61	235	.05	Reared in slum area	68	183	.01
Family broken by desertion	39	101	N.S.	Living in slum when arrested	65	236	.01
Demoralized family	60	136	.01	History of school truancy	46	157	.05
Criminality in family	38	133	.05	Disciplinary problem at school	41	147	.01
Mother figure dominant	44	175	N.S.	Street trades as juvenile	48	155	.01
Inadequate supervision—father‡	66	130	.01	No marital ties	49	239	N.S.
Inadequate supervision—mother	64	218	.01	Juvenile delinquent companions	63	173	.01
Conflict in family	54	180	.01	Member delinquent gang	33	109	.05
Overt hostility toward father	62	99	.01	Adjudicated juvenile delinquent	36	141	N.S.
Overt hostility toward mother	18	61	N.S.	Committed as juvenile	31	115	N.S.
Disciplinary problem at home	33	86	.01	Police contact prior to age 18	54	167	.01
History of running away	51	134	.01	Criminal companions as juvenile	30	133	N.S.
Inveterate gambler	45	125	.01	Drug addict	11	58	N.S.
Problem drinker	26	167	.05	Positive attitude toward work	17	136	N.S.

*Number with characteristic.

†Not significant.

‡Based on those with fathers.

REFERENCES

1. ROEBUCK, JULIAN B., and JOHNSON, RONALD: The Jack-of-all-trades offender. *Crime and Delinquency*, 8:172-181, April, 1962.
2. See Table V, p. 180.
3. RECKLESS, WALTER C.: *The Crime Problem*, pp. 153-179.

Chapter XI

THE CONFIDENCE MAN[1]

T
HE FBI classification, Fraud, covers the pattern of confidence game charges found in all ten records of the cases under study. This pattern group may be alluded to as short con men, since this appellation is used by the underworld and the police in labeling the kind of offenders and the kind of offenses they commit. FBI statistics for arrests show that Negroes are more likely to be arrested for every offense than whites, though the likelihood varies among offenses; e.g., the arrest ratio in reference to embezzlement and fraud favors Negroes 2.1 to 1, whereas in the case of aggravated assault the arrest ratio is 13.5 to 1.[2] In 1963, 50,680 persons were arrested for embezzlement and fraud, of which 7,333 were Negroes.[3]

Though they do not always agree on his etiology, sociologists and psychologists generally consider the confidence man to be a professional criminal who has high prestige in the underworld.[4] Confidence men are described in the literature as smooth, adroit, convincing talkers who live by their wits and their ability to manipulate people. Their criminal activity, a form of "grift," is nonviolent. Victims give their money or property to con men voluntarily because of the confidence they place in them and their own desire to get something for nothing. The con man, in short, plays upon the gullibility and the latent larceny of his victim, who is generally willing to engage in an illegal act for profit. In Sutherland's *The Professional Thief*, Chic Conwell, the title's namesake, comments on the successful confidence man as follows:

> Not all persons can be good con men. They generally must have a winning personality, shrewdness, agility, like the good things of life and be too lazy to work for them and have great egoism. They must,

first of all, be good actors. The whole con game is a matter of acting
. . . A confidence man must live by his wits.[5]

The elaborateness of the build-up, the period of time spent in
"setting up" the victim and "trimming" him, the number of
confidence operators involved in the swindle and the amount of
money taken from the victim determine whether a given confidence game or trick falls into the category of "big con" (sometimes called "long con") or "short con."[6] The "big-con" game
includes numerous accomplices and props. Through pre-arranged
stages, several operators (each one assuming a specific post)
work at conning the victim into getting all the money he possesses
or can command to put into a transaction they have devised. The
proper build up and subsequent "trimming" in the big-con game
require weeks of planning and at least four contact positions.
First in line is the "steerer" or "roper," an operator who selects
the victim, introduces him to the scheme and leads him to the
second contact, the "build-up man." The latter gradually sounds
out the victim regarding his resources, funds and gullibility. The
third contact stimulates his confidence. When the victim is ripe,
the fourth contact relieves him of his money and "shakes him off."
Together, the contacts form an apparently casual chain of oc-
currences, but each gives some signal for an operator to appear
and take his part in the conspiracy.[7] Often the victim of the big
con is "cooled off" rather than "shaken off" in order to prevent
him from making a complaint to the police. In the "shake off,"
the con man reminds the victim that if he reports the swindle he
may also go to jail because of his own participation in an illegal
act. He reminds him, in addition, that short of a jail sentence,
the victim risks exposure, ridicule and contempt from his friends
and the police if he reports his loss. In the "cooling off" process,
the con operator does not force the victim to realize he was just
another "easy mark;" rather, he consoles him and attempts to
redeem the ruse in a way that will make it easier for the victim to
accept the inevitable and retain his self-respect. Cooling off
represents a process of adjusting the victim to an impossible
situation.[8]

Short-con games require fewer actors and props, less preparation and less finesse and originality. They are geared toward smaller "scores" than the big-con games and the "take" is usually limited to the amount of money the mark has in his possession at the time. The method of operation is much quicker than in the big-con game; the operator must "hook the sucker and get rid of him fast." The short-con man usually works for brief periods in various cities, striking a location suddenly and then moving quickly in order to avoid contacts with his victim and the police.[9]

According to Maurer's researchers, most of the long-con operators have been recruited from the short-con men. They entered the confidence game when young and had the benefit of early training from skilled operators.[10] Confidence men may be placed along a continuum ranging from the unsuccessful, bungling, frequently arrested short-con man (flimflammer) whose *modus operandi* is dated and pitched at a low level to the highly successful, accomplished big-con man who is infrequently arrested and whose *modus operandi* is original and pitched at a high level.

While the highly successful long con, such as "Yellow Kid" Weil, has been dealt with in literature,[11] little is known about the short cons, the smaller operators who work in every big city and probably make up the largest group of confidence men found in correctional institutions.[12] Maurer claims that not many long-con men are caught, very few are brought to trial, fewer are convicted, and fewer still ever serve time in a prison.[13]

Previous comparisons of offender types involved statistical, quantitative measures. So long as the frequency of offenders in any cell of the expected distribution is at least five, the background of the sample of ten confidence men could be compared with that of the 390 other offenders by using such techniques as chi-square. It was impossible to fulfill this requirement. Therefore, the description of these con men in comparison with other offenders is necessarily qualitative rather than quantitative.

CHARACTERISTICS OF THE CON MAN

The ten con men shared a number of characteristics. They were of average ability (mean IQ—100) as compared with the general population and were considerably superior to the mean score of the remainder of the offender group (mean IQ—85). They had a median grade level of 6.4 on the Stanford Achievement Test, as compared with the 5.2 grade level of the remainder of the sample. They were older men, aged thirty and over (mean age—38), as compared with the remainder of the sample (mean age—30.4). At least eight of the ten were reared in slums in metropolitan areas (population 500,000 and over) and came from homes that were demoralized, criminalistic, in continuous conflict, dominated by the mother or on relief. Not one was reared in a rural area. Their criminal tutelage started early. All had delinquent companions before age ten, and eight belonged, in a loose sort of way, to delinquent gangs. All had police contacts, and eight had criminal companions before reaching eighteen years of age. The major difference between the delinquencies of this group and those of most of the offenders in the rest of the sample was the avoidance of violence. The con men had not been involved in fighting at home, at school or with neighborhood peer groups. They did not destroy property and did not participate in mugging or purse snatching. None carried weapons. Loitering on the street, gambling, running away from home, truancy and petty sneak thefts from school lockers, stores, playgrounds, and private homes constituted their delinquency pattern in the community.

Probably the most significant factor in the development of these men was their early reliance, from four to eight years of age, on deceit as a major tool of life. As we shall soon see, their early childhood experiences approved and rewarded deceit and made the practice of deception necessary.[14] The early necessity for and the practice, support and reward of deceit were found much less frequently in the case histories of the remainder of the sample. When the 390 cases were broken down for comparison into twelve criminal pattern groups the findings were the same; i.e., the con men had a higher incidence of childhood training in deceit than any single subgroup.

Coupled with this early practice of deceit was the dictum that violence doesn't pay. Conflicts between the parents, between parents and children and between brothers and sisters rarely resulted in physical violence as they did in the homes of most of the other cases (with the exception of 16 numbers men and 50 drug addicts) in the sample from which the con men were drawn.

Three of the men were reared in homes where, when their passive fathers were absent, the mothers would entertain paramours for money. In return for keeping these love affairs secret from the father, the sons would receive money or favors from the mothers, such as protection from truant officers or phony sick excuses to school administrators. To teachers visiting the home, the mothers gave glowing and erroneous reports about their sons' accomplishments.

In three cases, the mothers were small-time bootleggers who sold to clients in need of whiskey during hours when the liquor stores were closed. Their sons recruited buyers from the street and at times helped the mothers hide the liquor prior to a police raid. Occasionally, the police would interrogate them along with their mothers, and in the process they learned to lie and feign innocence early in life. In two of these three cases, the mothers also intermittently operated a poker game, and the sons would serve drinks to the customers and help their mothers "cut the pot." As one of the ten men commented:

> I learned early that it was not always the man who held the best cards who won the pot. It was the man who could cheat and bluff . . . or the one who was in with my mother and could catch her signs fast enough to stay put, raise or fold. Callers went to bed early in my house. Of course mother didn't play. She just ran the game. She moved around and knew what everybody had. I never seen a successful gambler who was honest. She didn't allow no rough stuff either. She always told me the easy way is the best. Use your head. Any fool could fight—any fool could get bread with a gun. And get busted too.

In one of the cases, the mother was a check passer and a shoplifter, and her son would accompany her in some of her illegal activities:

> I learned from my mother that a good front and how you carry yourself is the main thing with the marks. She'd buy ten dollars worth of groceries and while I held them walk up to the man and give him a rubber check for fifty dollars. She talked fast, smooth and bold. You

know—like she had a million. Of course she always dressed the part. She had such a way about her that the clerks in stores where she stole dresses were afraid to question her though they had a good idea she had their 'rags' under her coat. She always said, 'Son, if you get in the life (life in the underworld) get a soft hustle. No rough stuff.'

In two cases, a pattern of stealing, lying and disobedience at home and at school was evident at age eight. The dominant mothers in both cases were in conflict with their husbands and reacted to their sons' behavior in a hostile fashion, frequently threatening corporal punishment. The two fathers, on the other hand, made light of the boys' behavior and repeatedly made restitution for their sons. In their talks with their sons' wives teachers, school officials and probation officers, the fathers evinced an unrealistic, overprotective attitude. They were unable or unwilling to set limits for their sons' behavior.

In the remaining case the mother was known in the community as the "root woman." She removed warts and treated headaches, rheumatism and other somatic ills with magic words and the use of herbs. With the help of her son she also made sacred candles that were supposed to insure health and happiness in the homes in which they were lighted.

Not one of these ten men closed on pimping, bootlegging, gambling, check passing, shoplifting or fake healing as a criminal career. What they learned in childhood was not so much a set of criminal techniques but rather a principle—the principle of deceit and nonviolence.

COMPARISON WITH THE NUMBERS MAN

Though there were differences, the criminal offenses of the con men were most similar to the offenses of those involved in the numbers racket; both types of crime were nonviolent and required planning and organizational talent. Despite other ostensible similarities—their high mental ability as compared with most other offenders under study and their distaste for violence—the numbers men and the con men were remarkably different in background and personality type. While the con men were upwardly mobile persons from slum environments who identified themselves with the underworld, the numbers men, despite their illegal activities, were products of, and identified with, the Negro middle class. Since the numbers game is condoned by many members of all classes in the Negro community, and con games are not, the numbers man may hold some claim to and gain some rewards of middle class membership, while the con man is judged a criminal and lives a marginal existence. The numbers man was found to be a well-integrated personality, whereas the con man approximated the sociopath. Thus, despite a certain similarity in the offenses of the con men and numbers men, quite different factors entered into their development, and the consequences (in terms of influence on the life styles of the offenders) of these two varieties of offense were equally disparate.

The con men were most similar in social background to the least specialized and least competent of all groups, the "jack-of-all-trades offender," in that both were products of the slums and were reared in economically and emotionally deprived homes. The early practice of deceit, however, was not a factor in the developmental histories of the "jack-of-all-trades offender." As a result of their deceitfulness, verbal ability, intelligence, egocentricity, nonviolence and fastidiousness in dress as well as their "fast-buck," something-for-nothing approach to life, the con men managed to work their way up in the criminal hierarchy despite their poor backgrounds. Their philosophy of life, as summed up by one of the ten con men, is as follows:

> There's a mark born every minute and a con man every hour. The con man is born to take care of the marks. Of course, I am a con man. There really are only two classes of people—marks and con men. I decided early in life that the angle boy gets the worm. I didn't make the rules. I just try to live by them. I'd rather be a con man than a mark.

Throughout their lives they were talkers, not fighters, and neatness ranked high among their values:

> I was no fighter, man. Heroes are stupid people—they are really marks. A smart stud gets what he wants without fighting. All you got to do is know what to say out of your mouth. I didn't want to get myself messed up. I wanted to be neat all the time. In my line of work you

got to have front. You know, dress well. Of course, I always liked nice clothes anyway. I wore the best. You know, Bannister shoes at forty dollars a throw, twenty-dollar sport shirts, and silk suits if I could afford. You know, I wanted to go first class.

A well-dressed young man with a ready tongue, fair intelligence and an aversion to foolish fighting might be expected to find a niche in society. These con men began seeking their niches early in life. By the age of eight, each of them had begun a long career of running away. When they ran, they ran far, hitching rides up and down the Eastern seaboard, covering all of the Northeast coast while still in their teens. While on these expeditions, each of the offenders found his mentor, an experienced con man looking for an apprentice. A teamwork approach is required in most games rigged to con a mark. One man sets up the mark and the other "knocks him off." Thus, the experienced con man is benefited by having a bright young apprentice who is not in the position to demand an equal division of the loot. The apprentice is benefited by learning a trade that requires no hard work, can be profitable, is reasonably safe, and is never short of customers. The following typical remarks of one con man probably indicate the mechanism and criteria for recruitment into the racket:

Well, when I traveled around the country from one big city to another I was always on the make for on easy dollar. I always dressed nice even if I didn't have enough to eat. I hustled alone at first—you know, at pool. Sometimes I pretended to be a pimp and collected a few bucks from guys dumb enough to give me money for broads they never saw. But I was on the look for some better con. I knew I was young. I had to learn from hustlers at your own level. Well, if you act and talk right you get to meet pretty good con men who need a partner. You see con men go in pairs, two or more. They bust up now and then and get themselves new partners. That's the way I met Diamond Tooth Slim. His partner was busted and in the joint doing a bit. Slim needed himself a boy. I bumped into him at a quiet bar. We talked over a few toddies spread over a few days. He was sizing me up and I was sizing him up. We made a deal for the 'high dice' game. Of course I didn't get much of a cut at first, but I was willing to write that off to learn. All those who get the call to be a con man don't get picked. Slim told me later he nearly passed me by, because he thought I talked a little too much at first. You know, I

tried too hard to impress him. He thought I was a little bit of a
Willie (country boy) who didn't know what was happening. It's not
enough to have larceny in your heart. All people have that. You got
to have the smooth, cool touch. And you got to be able to smell a
mark.

And so each of the ten offenders entered an apprenticeship
with an older con man, and after they learned their tutor's
techniques, they moved out on their own:

Well, I was doing O.K. with Long John, but then I got the urge to
move on. I wanted to go a little faster and get some prestige for
myself. After all, he was taking most of the big end of the string,
and I wanted to make my own money. He wasn't going to pull my
coat any further than he would his own.

These men were not marked successes at their vocation. Even
so, their reference group consisted only of con men. They had
broken home ties early, were wanderers who had developed no
permanent relationship with women and had few if any close
friends. They were acquainted with many other con men since,
as noted above, many con games require cooperative efforts.
Their favorite term for anyone who acted impulsively or who
employed violence in the pursuit of money was "fool." All con
men respect one another as not being fools. To be "smart" is to
have a "rep" as an ingenious con man who has made much money
and suffered few busts (arrests). Much jockeying for position
occurred within the group as each told anecdotes of previous
victories aimed at "putting down" his rivals and showing himself
off as "smart." The true criterion of success was money, and all
else was forgiven the "money man."

During the interviews they rationalized that their brand of
criminal activity was acceptable behavior in this "dog-eat-dog"
society, but they were quick to criticize other types of criminal
behavior as reprehensible:

You know how it goes in this dog-eat-dog world. You got to take the
other guy before he takes you. You know, the real sharpie outwits the
marks. Of course, it all depends on how you get ahead. My way was
no different from, say, a lawyer or businessman. You know, a lawyer
has a license to steal. The cops should lay off con men. We don't hurt
nobody. You can't con an honest man. The mark has more larceny in

his heart than we do. The cops should do their job and clear the streets of the muggers, heist men, hopheads and the rest. Why, it's dangerous for a decent man like me to walk down the street at night.

THE CON GAMES

Here are some of the more common games used by these offenders in conning "marks:"

High Dice is a game based on the mark's desire to be recognized as an important person in his community, a man to whom others will look for advice and help. This bunko requires two operators.

A well-dressed and friendly stranger appears at a station prior to the arrival of an incoming train from the South. He selects as his victim a well-dressed Negro man or woman who appears to have resources. The operator enters into conversation with the victim by inquiring about hotels, names of persons and the location of the Negro community.

While talking, both observe a Negro man (Operator 2) leaving the train in apparent bewilderment. He seems lost, and his dress and general demeanor classify him as a yokel. Operator 1 explains to the victim that he will talk to the stranger and see whether he can be of some help. He has a lengthy conversation with the yokel. He then walks back to the waiting victim and explains that the simple fellow is a farm laborer who has saved all of his last year's wages and has come to the big town to spend it on a good time. He wishes to meet an honest person who will give him lodging and take care of his money. He will pay well for this kind attention. The con man elaborates upon the evident simplicity of this yokel and how a smart person could obtain most of his money without great effort. He then suggests that the victim board this yokel at his home. Why would he not secure the yokel's money for himself? The victim agrees to meet the yokel and have a talk with him. Operator 1 calls the yokel over to the victim, introduces them, explains that the victim has become interested in him and is willing to board him and show him the town. The yokel appears impressed by this kindness.

He explains that he has six hundred dollars, is frightened of the big city and is afraid that city slickers will rob him of his hard-earned money. He shows his money to the victim, expressing a desire that the victim take care of it for him and asks whether the victim knows how to handle big money. He desires some proof that the victim will be careful and not lose it. Has he (the victim) any money? If he has some money of his own, the yokel will gladly let him take care of his.

At this point, Operator 1 expresses amazement that anyone would carry so much money on his person. He turns to the victim and asks whether he would carry so much money on his person and also inquires where he keeps his money. Although the yokel has a fear of banks, he is willing to bank his money if the victim will withdraw his own and place it with his. Then the victim can place both lots in any safe place that he wishes. If the victim can take his money out of the bank, then the yokel is sure that his money will be safe.

Operator 1 pretends to be very much amused by the yokel's simplicity and fear of banks. He suggests that the victim make a withdrawal from his bank just to show this simple yokel that money can be withdrawn at any time. At this point the yokel suddenly becomes interested in some nearby vending machine and walks toward it—just far enough to be out of hearing.

Now Operator 1 suggests that the victim humor the yokel and not let all of that good money stray away from him. The yokel is too dumb to make a "kick" to the law and, after all, the victim will have continuous possession of his own money in addition to the yokel's roll. The victim weakens at this point and goes to the bank, accompanied by Operator 1, in order to prove to the yokel how easy it is to withdraw money. The yokel awaits their return. The victim, having been coached by Operator 1, shows his withdrawn money to the yokel. Although the yokel is surprised at the ease with which the victim can withdraw his money from the bank, he still is concerned about the way his money, and the victim's ought to be wrapped for safety. He tries to describe the method used by his "boss man" and holds up his hands as if measuring small distances. Suddenly Operator 1 understands and says, "It's one of those large brown envelopes!" He leaves to obtain one. During his absence the yokel holds his money in his hands, giving the victim a "big eyefull" (generally a dummy roll). Operator 1 returns with a large brown envelope which the yokel recognizes as the kind used by his boss man. Operator 1 takes the yokel's money and places both rolls in the large brown envelope. As the yokel (Operator 2) engages the victim in animated conversation, Operator 1 deftly makes a switch, placing the envelope with the two rolls of money in his breast pocket and handing the victim a similar envelope containing folded paper. The yokel now expresses himself as fully satisfied. He wishes to know where the victim lives, is given the name and address and promises to come to the victim's house within an hour or two. Each operator walks away in a different direction. The victim hurries away, his mind filled with the desire to open the package and look at his money.

The operators meet at a prearranged spot to divide the victim's money.

Pigeon Drop is an ancient game whose origin is unknown. Reportedly introduced into this country by Chinese immigrants early in the nineteenth century, it was later adopted by whites and still later by Negroes, predominantly. Endless varieties of this swindle prevail; but in all its modifications, certain basics must go into it, not the least of which is the "vic's" (victim's) own greed. Two players are active in this game (also known as "The Slip" and "The Drag"); sometimes—in a cruder form barely distinguishable from a polite robbery known simply as "stuff"—it is played by only one man.

The game consists of a story in three parts. The first part is enacted by the "catch man," who approaches the vic with a plausible but dramatic tale designed to win sympathy and show trust. The second part is executed by the "hit partner," who moves into the conversation on signal to report some "found money," usually described as a bookie's receipts. Through several ruses which may employ a "switch" (sleight-of-hand transference of the vic's money) or a direction to a fictional "boss," the money which the victim is asked to "show" as evidence of "good faith" or "financial responsibility" comes into the possession of the players. In the "blowoff," the third part of this bold drama, the vic is given some final instructions which allow the players to leave his presence before he discovers he has been mulcted.

Many variations of the *Spanish Prisoner Game* have evolved in the past thirty years. The props common to each consist of a worthless but impressive negotiable paper for a large sum of money, a purported smuggled letter from a dejected prisoner (customarily a Latin American) and a picture of the prisoner's "charming" daughter. For whatever arbitrary reason the operator may choose, the prisoner's letter promises the marked Galahad his daughter's hand and a sizeable portion of his estate (or some secret treasure, or whatever else the mark has been prepared to find enticing), if a certain sum of money is given to a certain courier to effect his daughter's escape from "this villainous country." One may easily imagine the infinite variety of themes that may be used in this stock drama to fit the times and the breed of persons being tricked. The "Spanish Prisoner" is now occasionally the "American Prisoner," a wealthy businessman in jail for income tax evasion. But all the features of the game—the beautiful young daughter and hidden funds that require some bribery or "grease" before they can be brought into use (with the victim providing the grease)—remain substantially the same.

Three Card Monte, which requires two operators (one to rope in the mark and one to manipulate the cards) is, theoretically, a game of chance, requiring the use of three ordinary playing cards, two of a black suit and one of a red suit. The "sucker" is inveigled into believing how easy it would be to capitalize on the fantastic odds (purely illusory) and witlessness (equally imaginary) of the operator, who promises to double the bet if the sucker can put his finger on the "red card," which the operator deftly proceeds to manipulate in various positions face down.

The Greasy Pig is worked in much the same fashion as Three Card Monte, except that three nut shells are used, and a pea-shaped object becomes the elusive goal in the game to claim the stakes. The pea is shifted from one cover to another by a few quick movements of the hands and resides as often as not under the operator's fingernails instead of under the shell. No matter how devilishly simple these proposals may seem to the guileless person, once he gives in to the temptation to lay hold of this easy money, the fever to beat the confounding game is unrelenting. Never does it seem to occur to the mark's own larcenous bent mind that a man's game rarely, if ever, gives away any odds other than to himself.

The ten con men also practiced, in addition to these games, the "Badger Game" (in which a prostitute lures a mark to her room and a con man, posing as a jealous husband, breaks in on them in the midst of their activities and is ultimately paid off by the mark) and the "Murphy Game" (in which the con man poses as a pimp, is paid by a mark to procure a prostitute and then runs off with the money). "A long con man" would not usually resort to these low-level techniques.

LACK OF INGENUITY

Occasionally, a con man would show ingenuity. One, for example, was proud of having sold two lions and an elephant to a remarkably gullible circus owner in Chicago via telephone, receiving a cashier's check for the not-yet-delivered, nonexistent animals. Most of the games, however, were old (the Spanish Prisoner Game can be traced back to the defeat of the Armada) and crude. Although the con man prides himself on being smart, these short cons were markedly lacking in creativity. They were not "money men;" their careers were full of short scores and many "busts." In manipulating their victims, they depended on sudden attack and speed and on quick exits from the city of their operations. They seldom used careful planning or long-con techniques such as "cooling off" the mark. Their failure as successful criminals may perhaps be explained by this obvious lack of finesse. Perhaps they broke away from their tutors in crime too soon. Perhaps a longer apprenticeship would have helped. Perhaps, too, they did not have what it takes—the self-discipline, study habits, perseverance or personality—to make a big-con man. In any event, they showed little insight into the cause of their failures, but rather naively attributed failure to fate or, as they often put it, "Kismet:"

> I could always set up a mark and I could always finish him off, but I just had a jinx for arrest. *Some* guys pull them off. I did, too, but somehow I took the falls—just one of those things.

They lived in cheap furnished rooms, waiting to make a score. When they did score, it was like this:

> You know, when I had a little bread, I lived it up. You know, a good hotel, good food, good drinks and a few slick chicks. But when the bread was sliced too thin the holiday was over. Then I had to blow.

The con man would again return to a cheap rooming house and lead an impoverished life until he found a mark and made another score.

The arrest histories of these men were lengthy (mean arrests per man—18, and at least four workhouse sentences and two felonies in every arrest history), and the charges ranged from petty theft up to grand larceny. In most cases, however, once a confidence game charge is noted, the other types of charges rarely appear afterward. This lends some credence to their own belief (shared by the police): "Once a con man always a con man."[15] Charges for violent crimes against the person were practically nonexistent.

The District Attorney's Reports showed that these men operated at a rather low criminal level. Usually the marks were "set up" for a loss of not more than 250 dollars. Whether operating alone or in pairs, these con men did not have tight organization, leadership, timing or careful planning. At times they were conned out of the take by their own confederates and various women companions. They, too, were marks. Yet, despite the fact that their stories and the institutional records showed this to be the case, they were reluctant to admit being conned by others. As one of them remarked:

> You know, I was conned by broads from time to time, but I didn't stay still long enough to be conned by no man. I guess we all are easy marks for women. What about you? You know how it goes.

The idea that "all you got to do is know what to say with

your mouth" did not disappear as a result of getting "busted." Once inside the penitentiary the cons shifted operations and became "jail house lawyers," attempting to gain release through appeals. Nine of the ten mentioned technicalities in the law which they believed should have precluded their arrest. Eight of the ten were writing writs for fellow inmates for which they were "paid off" in cigarettes, although none of the writs composed during previous periods of incarceration had proven effective. Their attempts at "conning" were even less effective inside than outside the penitentiary.

As a group these men seemed in the interviews to be older than their chronological age. They had many different kinds of physical complaints and did not appear to be strong.[16] All of them reacted to the interviewer in an apparently friendly and cooperative manner. They spoke softly in a breezy, chatty way, and their verbal expression seemed to be better than their educational levels indicated. They were prone to "projection," in that they attempted to express their opinions as if they were the opinions of the interviewer. They expressed few warm ties of affection with others and seemed to be shrewd, calculating, and interested in others only for what they could get out of them. As one con man said:

> You know what a friend is? He is someone who wants something you can give him—something you got. I am a taker, not a giver.

A qualitative assessment of the personality characteristics of these Negro con men indicates a sociopathic trend.[17] They divided humanity into two groups, con men and marks. They definitely committed themselves to the ranks of the con men, felt superior to the marks and rationalized their socially disapproved behavior by insisting that all people have larceny in their hearts and "you have to take others before they take you." Their interpersonal relationships were defective in that they expressed few if any emotional ties and evinced little interest in other people, except in terms of exploitation. When they did make a "score," they exhibited an inability to forego immediate pleasures for future gains and long-range goals. Hedonistic, they lived in the present without consideration of the past or future.

They demonstrated a lack of insight into the causes of their behavior, were unable to profit from their mistakes and attributed failure to fate.

While certainly not among the most expert of con men, they had developed a rather high degree of proficiency as compared with most of the offenders in the remainder of the sample (390 cases).[18] Their reference group was that of con men, and they judged themselves (and others) according to the degree to which behavior was consonant with the values of con men. Since status depended on success, and they were in jail and thus seemingly unsuccessful, they blamed fate for their incarceration and continued to operate as con men in prison—in this case, attempting to con their way out to freedom. With this set of values, the con men's likelihood of making any marked change in their behavior patterns is questionable, but because of the small size of the sample and the type of data utilized, the findings are tentative and replications with larger samples are necessary.

INDICATORS FOR A MULTI-DISCIPLINARY APPROACH WITH CONFIDENCE MEN

The constitutionalists could somatotype samples of confidence men checking on the author's impressions of the slight and frail physical build of the ten men under study. They may find replication with larger samples of confidence men which might indicate a connection between slight physiques and nonviolent temperaments. Additionally, the constitutionalists would note the frequent occurrence of criminality and deviant behavior found among the parents of the author's sample of confidence men and the early age at which the confidence men entered into delinquent and criminal activity. The psychologists and psychiatrists would probably close on the nature of the interpersonal relationships existing between the confidence men and their parents, which provided for the early necessity for and the practice, support and reward of deceit. The dearth of violence in the home situation and the reinforcement for nonviolent behavior might lead them to analyze the personalities of other confidence men in terms of similar childhood conditions.

The sociologists, in studying the career patterns of other samples of confidence men, might receive leads from the subjects under study regarding the recruitment practices of confidence men, the social types who select confidence games as a criminal style, differential opportunity within the confidence rackets and the similarities of the confidence man's *modus operandi* to techniques employed in some legitimate enterprises.

The legalist and the correctional administrator would note the higher recidivism of confidence men, their persistence in the same order of crime and their consistent *modi operandi*. Though nonviolent, they would recognize them as a serious group of offenders unlikely to succeed on probation and parole.

It is the writer's opinion that this type offender is quite rigid in his antisocial attitudes. Perhaps this offender type should be incarcerated in penitentiaries with longer prison sentences than those generally given for their type of offense. Certainly they are would-be professional criminals, and as such they should not be incarcerated with nonprofessional criminals. It has been the writer's prison experience that these offenders are quite vociferous in a penal setting. Many times they "con" themselves into "prestige jobs" as defined by other inmates. They are past masters at conniving; and of course they are eternally seeking an angle to "beat" anyone they can. This goes for other inmates as well as prison employees! The influence of these notorious recidivists on novices in crime is not salutary. Present methods of training and treatment seem to have failed with them. Though tractable and nonviolent, they express no interest in personality modification.

REFERENCES

1. ROEBUCK, JULIAN B., and RONALD C. JOHNSON: The "Short Con" Man. *Crime and Delinquency, 10*:235-248, July, 1964.
2. JOHNSON, ELMER H.: *Crime, Correction, and Society*, pp. 83-84.
3. *Uniform Crime Reports, 1963*, p. 111.
4. BLOCH, H. A., and GEIS, G.: *Man, Crime, and Society*. New York, Random House, 1962, pp. 199-202; MAURER, D. W.: *The Big Con: The Story of the Confidence Man and the Confidence Game*. Bobbs-Merrill, 1940, p. 201; SCHUR, E. M.: Sociological

analysis of confidence swindling. *Journal of Criminal Law, Criminology, and Police Science,* September-October, 1948, pp. 296-304; JENKINS, R. L.: *Breaking Patterns of Defeat—The Effective Readjustment of the Sick Personality.* Philadelphia, Lippincott, 1954, pp. 148-158; PODALSKY, E.: The swindler: A fascinating sociopath. *Pakistan Medical Journal,* October, 1957, pp. 1-4; BROMBERG, W., and KEISER, S.: The psychology of the swindler. *American Journal of Psychiatry,* May, 1938, pp. 1441-1458; RECKLESS, W. C.: *The Crime Problem* (3rd ed.). New York, Appleton-Century-Crofts, 1961, pp. 174-177.

5. SUTHERLAND, EDWIN H. (ed.): *The Professional Thief.* University of Chicago Press, 1937, p. 3.

6. MacDONALD, J. C. R.: *Crime Is a Business: Buncos, Rackets, Confidence Schemes.* Stanford, Calif., Stanford University Press, 1938, pp. 1-10. See also SODERMAN, H., and O'CONNELL, J. J.: *Modern Criminal Investigation.* New York, Funk and Wagnalls, 1951, pp. 380-388.

7. For an overview of the *modus operandi* used in various con games, see DIENSTEIN, W.: *Techniques for Crime Investigation.* Springfield, Ill., Charles C. Thomas, 1956, pp. 70-80; and O'HARA, C. E.: *Fundamentals of Criminal Investigation.* Springfield, Ill.; Charles C. Thomas, 1956, pp. 290-294.

8. GOFFMAN, ERVING: On cooling the mark out: Some aspects of adaptation to failure. *Psychiatry,* November, 1952, pp. 451-463. Also on cooling off the mark, see FITZGERALD, M. J.: *Handbook of Criminal Investigation.* New York; Greenberg Publishers, 1951, pp. 173-190.

9. MacDONALD, J. C. R.: *Crime Is a Business,* pp. 2-3.

10. MAURER, D. W.: *The Big Con,* pp. 175-178.

11. WEIL, J. R., and BRANNON, W. T.: *"Yellow Kid" Weil.* Chicago; Ziff-Davis, 1948.

12. BARBASH, J. T.: Compensation and the crime of pigeon dropping. *Journal of Clinical Psychology.* October, 1951, pp. 92-94, reports a study of twenty-five "short con" offenders in the Eastern State Penitentiary, Pennsylvania. He hypothesized an etiology based on compensation for feelings of inferiority.

13. MAURER, D. W.: *The Big Con,* p. 15.

14. JENKINS, RICHARD L.: *Breaking Patterns of Defeat,* pp. 148-158, cites grift as an example of motivation behavior of a highly adaptive sort. He theorized that early childhood experiences

which make deceit necessary and reward it, makes for a "budding grifter." Although he used illustrative cases of children whom he considered "budding grifters," he did not research the childhood experiences of known con men. The case histories of the ten men under study definitely support his thesis.

15. FITZGERALD, M. J.: *Handbook of Criminal Investigation,* p. 187, notes that the confidence man follows his trade despite the number of times he is arrested, and he rarely engages in other types of crimes. Maurer makes the same point in *The Big Con,* p. 173.

16. The medical records showed that two were organically sound, three were partially crippled in the legs, one had a stiff left arm, one suffered from myopia, one was a diabetic, and two had heart murmurs. All ten were small-boned and slight in physique.

17. The above personality assessment was in part validated by inspection of the MMPI scale 4 scores (Pd), which showed that all of these con men had T scores above 75. No other criminal category scored higher on this scale with the exception of the armed robbers.

18. The *modus operandi* of the sixteen numbers men, organized professional criminals, was pitched at a much higher level than that of these ten con men. The fifteen men in the single pattern of burglary were also more proficient.

Chapter XII

THE OTHERS

TO THIS POINT, six criminal patterns have been analyzed in a systematic and detailed fashion. In this chapter four of the remaining seven criminal patterns are analyzed in less detail: Triple Pattern of Drunkenness, Assault and Larceny; Double Pattern of Larceny and Burglary; Single Pattern of Burglary; and No Pattern.

Three criminal patterns were not included for analysis as separate entities. The category Single Pattern of Sex Offenses included fifteen men who were disparate in offense type and personality makeup. Nine were "true" homosexuals. In short, these men did not appear to constitute a homogeneous group. The Single Pattern of Auto Theft and the Single Pattern of Check Forgery and Counterfeiting categories had fewer than ten cases (eight and four respectively).

TRIPLE PATTERN OF DRUNKENNESS, ASSAULT AND LARCENY

This pattern constituted a middle-aged (median age—48.80), illiterate (S.A.T. grade median—3.2), intellectually inferior (I.Q. median—83.0) group of slum dwellers who as young adults migrated to the District of Columbia from the South. Twenty-seven of the forty-three men in this group were reared on farms in the South, where they remained with their parents, share-croppers and tenant farmers, past their eighteenth birthdays. Six of the sixteen men in this pattern who were reared in urban areas grew up in small southern towns (rural-area-service centers of less than 5,000 population where a strong rural flavor was present). All six had worked as farm laborers prior to their migration to the District. Four of these sixteen were reared in southern cities exceeding 25,000 population. Only six were reared in the District. In short, thirty-seven men in this group were southern migrants, all of whom had lived in the District for at least five years prior to the present incarceration. Fifteen out of the sixteen men in this group who were reared in urban areas were reared in slum neighborhoods. Forty-three were living in a slum area at the time of their last arrest.

The remarks of these men during the interview situations concerning their dwellings throughout their adult years indicated a slum existence of long duration.

> I allus lived in basement room or, you know, lived in a rooming house. Always cold. Didn't have no hot water most times. These city people sure live like rats.

The statistical results showed that these men were products of one closely-knit family group that was not marked by economic dependency, parental desertion, demoralization or criminality. The father figure was generally the dominant parental figure in a family situation where adequate supervision by both parents was in evidence. They were well integrated into their family group during the formative years, as was shown by their lack of expressed hostility toward the father figure, their lack of conflict with family group members during their formative years and their infrequent home runaways.

The statistical results further revealed that their early school and community adjustments were satisfactory. They were neither truancy nor disciplinary problems at school. Neither had they worked at street trades as juveniles, nor had they had frequent juvenile delinquent or criminal companions. None had belonged to a juvenile delinquent gang, and only two admitted to juvenile delinquent companions. Only three had criminal companions prior to their eighteenth birthday, and only three were "picked up" by the police prior to age eighteen. It may be that the simple rural and small-town environments that produced these men precluded any high incidence of delinquency. The following typical remarks made by one interviewee seem to indicate this:

> You know, I didn't have no time to get in trouble when I come up. I worked all time on farm wid the old man. I didn't have no time to run no streets. Anyway, won't no streets to run . . . plenty furrows in the field to run. I run um.

The difficulties of this group seem to be associated with a breakdown in their primary group controls following their migration as "loners" to the District of Columbia from the South and with their personal vice, alcoholism. Their adult lives appeared to be devoid of parental or conjugal group ties. In short they cut themselves loose from primary group controls. Mail and visiting contacts with their parents and siblings in the South were rare and casual. The ensuing remarks by one interviewee demonstrate this point:

> I got five broders and four sisters. They scattered all over. Most dem in de old country (South). I know de county but don't know box number. I ain't been home in ten years. Last time I been home mother died.

Only eight were living with wives at the time of their present incarceration. Nine had never been married; nineteen were separated; two were divorced; and five were widowed. The thirty-five who were "other than married" reported temporary liaisons with several paramours throughout the years. Conjugal ties for most of them were nonexistent. These statements by an interviewee when questioned about his marital state illustrate this point:

> You know I got no wife. Don't wont no regular woman. They is trouble man, trouble sho as you born. I tried living with many these wenches. I like to live with one for a while, then I put her out and go on to another. Sometime she put me out.

Probably the most significant thing about this group of offenders is their problem with alcoholism and its concomitants. Only eight were regularly employed immediately prior to their present incarceration; and most of them (N=30) were living at a bare subsistence level in various rooming-house situations. All had a history of the following experiences: (a) intoxication for at least four days straight with no sober intervals; (b) blackout periods—periods of lack of lucidity when awake; (c) the excessive use of alcohol; (d) lack of control over where, when or with whom drinking occurred; (e) dismissal from jobs because of drinking during working hours; (f) heavy solitary drinking; (g) physical altercations when under the influence of alcohol.

Heavy drinking was approved of in their cultural milieu. None began this habit in a solitary fashion. Their addiction usually occurred following a period of at least five years of excessive social drinking; and their dependence on alcohol seems to have been acquired and developed in a social way. Their stories during the interviews about excessive drinking (in disordered living quarters in slum, rooming houses and in street alleys) with "drinking friends," who had been incarcerated at one time or another at the D.C. Jail and at the D.C. Workhouse, bear this out. These "drinking friends" and criminal companions were also generally migrants from the South. The following comments by one of the interviewees were typical:

> You know dese city folks drink a lot. I like my drink. Got to have sompin outa life. I usually drinks wine with a few friends from the big foot country (South). You know I feel more to home with dem. We'll been to jail together.

Work to them appeared to be a "sometime thing," which they engaged in only sporadically for the purpose of securing alcohol and maintaining themselves at the bare subsistence level. Thirty-eight of the forty-three men expressed negative or indifferent attitudes toward work. All were unskilled laborers.

Most of them expressed a general uneasiness at being in a penitentiary situation where they felt out of place. They referred to the D.C. Reformatory as a place where "real criminals" were kept. Apparently, these offenders did not conceive of petty theft, assault and intoxication as constituting "real" criminal behavior. Thirty-eight mentioned a desire to be transferred to the D.C. Workhouse at Occoquan, where they said they would feel more at home. All of these men had served at least two previous sentences at the D.C. Workhouse; thirty-five had served three or more sentences there. There affinity for the Workhouse is illustrated by these remarks:

> I don belong here. These peoples are mean. They don't eben smile.

> Please, let me work for Mr. John over to the Workhouse. You know de
> brickyard. I ain't got no biznis her wid dese slickers.

The high incidence of intoxication charges, the low average
felony commitments (1.3 per man including the present charge),
the high average misdemeanor commitment (15.0 per man) and
the high average arrest rate (25.2 per man) revealed in their
criminal histories clearly demonstrated this group's similarity to
a workhouse population. Though the arrest records were lengthy,
they did not indicate criminal progression. The offenses of
intoxication, larceny and assault appeared throughout the arrest
histories, with no indication of any patterned sequence of
occurrence.

In discussing their criminal companions and their criminal
activities, none of these men claimed any knowledge of organized
underworld activity. They expressed no knowledge of drug
trafficking, organized prostitution, the numbers racket and afterhours clubs. Not one claimed an acquaintance with a professional
gambler. Very few of them claimed to have been friendly with
men who had been convicted of housebreaking, forgery or robbery. Their lack of criminal sophistication can be ascertained
from the following remarks:

> I don know nothin about no crime activity. Ain't no criminal. Don know
> no people who break in folks houses, rob, and carry on. Dope, don
> know what tis.

The District Attorney's Reports and the interview materials
indicated a very low level of *modus operandi* in these cases.
They did not reveal that any of these men belonged to any
organized underworld activity. Their intoxication charges were
generally connected with drinking activities in public alleys, in
parks, in pool rooms and on the street. Most of their larceny
charges were concerned with petty theft from their drinking
companions, employers and rooming-house patrons. Their
charges of assault generally resulted from drunken scuffles, altercations and fights with male drinking companions. Planned
violence was not the rule, and rarely were the victims of such
assaults critically hurt. Generally, the assaults occurred as incidents of the moment following disagreements over such things

as petty gambling debts, the division of food and whiskey, the division of stolen goods and women's sexual favors.

Fighting and the use of force were acceptable behavior to them as a method of redressing personal wrongs; however, their aggressive behavior seemed to be of an attenuated variety. Their prevailing view of violence may be paraphrased in the following manner:

> It is at times necessary to fight. Be sure not to get seriously injured, and, at the same time, do not inflict serious damage to your adversary. Mark him up with your fist or your knife, but refrain from maiming or killing him if you can possibly do so.

All of them claimed to carry knives on the street, though they insisted these weapons existed for defense purposes only. The point is they were prepared for violence, which was quite a reality in their scheme of life. Such a view is discerned from this typical quotation:

> You gots ta be ready. Dese city slickers will knock you brains out your head for a quarter . . . specially when you bout high. You gots ta hab sumpin for de rascal.

Definite taboos against calling the police (called the "man") to settle any disturbances, fights or personal difficulties existed. The policeman was "the man who locks you up," and he was not to be trusted as a peacemaker.

> You stump you toe on de street the police going to lock you up. They ain't *nothing!* Why dey don let a drinking man alone. Don dey lock up dem robbers? All dey do is make trouble for man habing little fun.

Usually the police appeared at the scene of an assault by accident in the course of their routine beats. They were called in as a general rule only in cases where the victim was critically wounded. Since most of the assaults of these men were "simple assaults," and since most of them occurred in the street, they were apprehended in what may be termed an accidental manner.

The men in this pattern were at the Reformatory either because they happened to steal some object (or money) exceeding in value $99.99; or because they happened to be involved in some street scuffle resulting in a charge of aggravated assault. Both constitute felony charges.

These offenders appeared to be physically weak and in poor health. Three were arrested cases of tuberculosis; two were active cases of tuberculosis at the time of their commitment; six suffered from a heart condition; five had ulcerated stomachs; four had arthritis; three were physically handicapped; ten of the forty-three had at one time or another been treated for delirium tremens at D.C. General Hospital (five of these ten had been under mental observation at St. Elizabeth's Hospital). Their many physical complaints during the interviews included weak eyesight, nervous stomachs, weak hearts, headaches, weak backs, weak legs, shortness of breath, hemorrhoids, ruptures, acnes, and other skin disorders.

They had little power of verbalization. There was a pronounced thickness of speech and a slurring of words. Their vocabularies were quite limited, and they searched for words in a halting fashion in order to express their thoughts. Their span of concentration was quite brief. This was shown by their repeated shifts from one topic to another without completing one train of thought. They appeared to be dependent personalities who evaded responsibility. At the same time they were verbally aggressive individuals who attempted to prove an independence they did not possess. They spoke often of friends, relatives and acquaintances in terms of what they had done for them and in terms of what they expected from them in the future. They expressed a strong desire to remain free of any responsibility to others, e.g., wives, paramours, girl friends, and children. On the other hand, they insisted that they could take care of themselves providing they got a few "good breaks." They expressed a wish to live by themselves in order that they could do as they pleased.

They were subject to marked mood swings, which indicated a possible cycloid bent. This was indicated by their expressions of gaiety during part of the interview, e.g., smiling, laughing, joking and vocalizations of general optimism about the future. On the other hand, they expressed grief and dejection during other parts of the interview, e.g., crying, wringing of the hands, apathetic and listless reactions to questions, remarks of pessimism about the future and "sob stories" concerned with self-pity. They seemed to be eternally seeking for warmth and companionship from their companions, with little success. They expressed strong object relations with friends, and they insisted that they liked people. Most of them feared being alone; they appeared, however, to drive potential close friends away from them because of their severe personal demands. They expected many personal favors, and they were greatly disappointed when they were not forthcoming. They appeared to be extremely disappointed when casual acquaintances failed to extend complete loyalty to them.

They expressed strong feelings of inadequacy and inferiority. Though vaguely aware that they were inadequate in some way, few of them appeared to have any real insight into their difficulties. This was shown by their verbal attacks on white collar workers and people who had money and education. They claimed to despise what they termed "city slickers," who by them were defined as parasites. They claimed that the "big man" always took advantage of them; that people in general, and the cops specifically, picked on them because they were honest and straightforward in their views and actions. Most of them spoke of the South in a sentimental, nostalgic manner.

In general demeanor they were awkward, uncouth and decidedly naive and unsophisticated. They kept their hats on during the interviews; they chewed gum in an open-mouthed, loud fashion; they interrupted the interviewer from time to time; they slouched down in their seats with a lack of any semblance of dignity; and they shuffled in and out in an abrupt manner.

In sum, the offenders in this pattern constituted a group of dull, unskilled, lower socioeconomic migrants from the rural South. They brought with them a set of mores which permitted petty theft and violence and a decided distrust of the police. Their code also called for the personal redress of wrongs. The excessive use of alcohol complicated their problems of adjustment to an urban environment.

This type of alcoholic offender, a habitual criminal type, could be placed in a farm, forestry, or work-camp institution with an indeterminate sentence. Those unable to work could best be handled in short-term institutions, again with indeterminate sentences. Many offenders of this type are now serving time in various reformatories and prisons where they are misplaced and where their peculiar problems are not dealt with.

The many inadequacies of this group preclude their adjustment to any but the simplest of environments—rural areas and villages with a rural flavor. Therefore, extensive vocational and academic training for them would prove to no avail. They are generally not interested in training, nor are they capable of mastering skilled jobs at a level which would enable them to compete with well-adjusted skilled men in the "free world." Work and training at simple manual tasks are in order for men of this type.

The four most common types of treatment for alcoholics should probably be attempted: aversion techniques; psychotherapy; group therapy, and an Alcoholics Anonymous program. Release on an experimental basis to villages and farm communities where "live-in" jobs are available and where informal group sanctions prevail is advocated. In cases of failure on release, the offender could be returned to the institution. Any released man could return voluntarily, and some would probably remain indefinitely. Such an institutional situation would undoubtedly cut down appreciably the number of chronic alcoholic offenders on the street; and it would also operate to diminish many costs associated with the repeated arrests, trials and incarcerations of this type offender.

DOUBLE PATTERN OF LARCENY AND BURGLARY

These sixty-four men comprised a group of young offenders (median age—28.4) who for the most part were reared in urban areas. Fifty-eight were products of the District; four came from other urban areas; only two were reared in rural areas. As a group they were of less than average intelligence (median IQ—82.0; their S.A.T. grade median was 4.2).

The statistical results revealed that these men compared quite unfavorably with the men in the total sample—in reference to the thirty-four characteristics as measured by chi-square. Regarding internal comparisons, they were found to be very similar to the men in the mixed pattern and the armed robber types.

These offenders were reared in slum areas where unfavorable home and neighborhood conditions prevailed. They were subjected to criminal contagion throughout their lives. Fifty-five were products of homes where criminality was in evidence. Many of their siblings and quite often their fathers had served felony sentences. Fifty-eight grew up in demoralized homes. Forty of these men had the experience during their formative years of breaking into houses with an older brother. Although forty-one mentioned their membership in a juvenile delinquent gang, only three claimed to be gang leaders. They were juvenile delinquents "grown up" who remained in slum dwellings. A pattern of maladjustment since early childhood was easily discerned in their backgrounds.

Their stories during the interviews concerning their juvenile delinquent activities indicated certain qualitative, life-history differences between them and the robbers and the men found in the mixed-pattern group. Though they entered delinquent careers (as was the case with the robbers) from age six to nine, when most of them were stealing from home, in the street and at school, they spoke less frequently of violence and street fighting than the men in the other two patterns. The following remarks made by one interviewee were common:

> Yeah, I stole things like money and coats and gloves. Sometimes I broke in a store or warehouse. I didn't want no rumble, so I didn't carry any heat (weapon, mostly firearms) with me. That tough stuff was no good. I could get the bread (money) without getting my brains knocked out. I don't like no cutting or punchin'.

Their disciplinary problems at school were almost invariably concerned with stealing. Rarely was their a problem of destruction of property or a fight. Their reaction to family conflict was seldom one of open rebellion but rather of flight. They were persistent home runaways. Though most of their early stealing was of the group variety, they spoke more frequently of stealing alone than did the robbers or the mixed type offender.

> You know, I copped (stole) with a bunch of studs (fellows) once in a while. But you know, I don't want no trouble. Somebody else was always getting too much when I copped that way. Some big sucker took it, you know. I soon found out that if I copped alone I got all

the bread then I don't haf to worry about no big sucker taking most of the bread.

The stories of these men in reference to their criminal companions and their criminal activities showed an association throughout their adult lives with other criminals on about their same operational level. Gang activity was virtually nonexistent after they passed their teens. A loose association with several criminal companions at different time intervals was the rule.

Well, I met studs here and there where I hung out at 12th and U and at 7th and T street. We gassed about things. We might knock a joint off together some place, you know. Maybe so, then maybe not. I didn't have no special studs to cop with. That way don't nobody know too much 'bout my business.

They spoke with some knowledge of the organized underworld, and they claimed acquaintances and working agreements with criminal fences, but such agreements apparently were not on a highly professional level:

Yeah, I had my man (fence) to drop my stuff (stolen goods) too. Those suckers were something. They didn't want to pay you nothing: Then sometimes they took your stuff and then you had to hunt all over town for them to get your money. Never knew *one* that went to jail. They are really some slick dudes.

Most of them stated that they had lived through the years on money made from criminal activities.

These men suffered from social isolation. They were products of families which did not have strong ties. Only five maintained close ties with their family group. Sixty-one were "other than married," though thirty-three had been married. When asked about their marital status, they generally referred to a paramour or a common-law wife.

Married? I don't want no woman and crum-snatchers (children) to worry my mind. I like my bitches one at a time, you know; I live with one a while, then when she blows me hot or messes with my bread I kick her out and get me another chick.

In short, these men lived marginal, personally disorganized lives. Over one half of them were inveterate gamblers (N=35). Thirty-seven were "problem drinkers," and three were drug addicts. Few expressed a positive attitude toward legitimate work or had ever worked regularly. Their attitudes toward work may be understood in terms of the following remarks:

> Work? Man, I can't get no job that pays me nothing. Those people don't want me for nothing but a flunky. I got to get something out of life. Yeah, I'll work alright . . . for myself!

Their arrest histories were long (mean average: 16.3). An overwhelming number of these arrests were for property charges. Less frequently than with the men in the other two patterns were non-property charges found. An occasional charge of drunk or disorderly conduct was uncovered. There was little evidence of criminal progression. Their adult arrests began with charges of larceny and housebreaking and ended with the same charges.

These men were much more frequently arrested alone than was the case with the men in the mixed pattern and armed robber pattern. This indicated that they more frequently operated as "lone wolves" in their criminal activity.

The District Attorney's Reports exhibited *modi operandi* at a low level of operation. There was evidence of some planning and skill in connection with a few of their housebreaking charges. But in the same case at a later date, the offender who previously demonstrated some criminal skill in connection with a few of his housebreaking charges, often displayed a lack of technique in the commission of another crime—usually petty theft. In short, these men were inconsistent in reference to *modus operandi*. Their lack of a consistent professional technique probably accounts in part for the fact that they were frequently thoroughly institutionalized. They averaged 3.1 felony convictions per man. They were part of the unsuccessful, lower-echelon underworld. This is attested to by the fact that though they were acquainted with criminal fences, they rarely made pre-arrangements with these fences prior to their criminal acts. In short, they carried to the fence a haphazard assortment of stolen goods for his assessment and selection.

These offenders did not express feelings of remorse, but rather the sentiments of a group of hardened offenders who were sorry only because they had been caught. As was the case with the robbers, many (N=50) of these men insisted they were not guilty of what they were charged. They frequently claimed false arrest. Forty stated that they planned to seek release on the basis of legal writs.

They appeared to be in fairly good health. The medical records disclosed that fifty-one were organically sound; three had stomach ulcers; three were epileptics; one had a heart condition; two were physically handicapped; three were arrested cases of tuberculosis; one was an active case of tuberculosis. Forty-five were underweight by ten to twenty pounds. They expressed many somatic complaints, e.g., backaches, weak eyes, toothaches, headaches, nervousness, etc.

Most of them were cooperative during the interviews, although they seemed to be emotionally flat, cold and detached. The majority talked freely in a matter-of-fact way about their past. They did not seem to be either excessively aggressive or passive. All seemed to be openly antisocial, and they expressed negative attitudes toward the police, courts and correctional agents. They thought of themselves as "hustlers" who were after the fast and illegal buck. They all seemed to be resigned to their life of crime—the only life they knew and the only life they were interested in knowing.

Twenty men were diagnosed as psychopathic personalities by psychiatrists at other institutions. Three men had a history of treatment for schizophrenia at St. Elizabeths Hospital. All three of these were drug addicts.

Seemingly, the "antisocial reaction type" (psychopathic personality) was the prevailing personality type in this group, as was the case with the robbers; however, these men were not as preoccupied with violence as were the robbers; nor did they appear to be as forcefully energetic and as physically strong. The observed degree of restlessness and edginess was less than that found among the robbers.

In summary, these men constituted a group of institutionalized, confirmed, antisocial recidivists, who were juvenile delinquents "grown up." They were reared in demoralized, criminalistic family groups where conflict was the rule. Their reaction to the unhappy home situation was flight—running away from home. In mid-adolescence, most of them made the permanent break. At an early age, they learned to steal with associates, and they had been stealing ever since. Generally small in stature and probably lacking in physical courage, they consistently engaged in offenses of a nonviolent nature. Though members of juvenile delinquent gangs, they were rarely gang leaders, and quite frequently they were "loners" in the commission of their crimes. Theft and burglary were the rule. They had many criminal acquaintances and loosely defined working agreements with criminal fences. At times, some of their burglaries demonstrated a slight degree of criminal professionalization; at other times, their offenses showed little criminal finesse.

Three factors probably had precluded their developing into highly skilled professional thieves. First, they were of less than average intelligence. Second, a large proportion were personally disorganized. (Thirty-five were inveterate gamblers; thirty-seven were problem drinkers; and three others were drug addicts.) And third, a high proportion had deep-seated personality difficulties. Three were at one time psychotic; twenty had been diagnosed as psychopathic personalities; the remaining forty-one appeared to have many traits ascribed to "antisocial reaction type."

The writer has no new suggestions for the treatment of this type of offender. In his opinion, they should not serve their time in open dormitory situations alongside offenders less criminally processed. These would-be professional criminals have not made the grade, although they insist on trying again and again. It is unlikely that they understand the reasons for their failure. Most of them keep hoping for the "big score." If past is prologue, they will keep trying. They are certainly not interested in working unless they can spell out the conditions of employment. Prognosis in the way of rehabilitation is dim. Perhaps detention in penitentiaries with longer sentences is called for here. Experimentation with them in reference to therapy techniques is always a possibility of course. The present methods of training and treatment are (in this writer's opinion) certainly not applicable to men of this type. In fact, current methods appear to be a waste of time and money.

SINGLE PATTERN OF BURGLARY

This type (N=15) was older (median age—43), more intelligent (median IQ—103) and better educated (S.A.T. grade median—6.4) than the men in the total sample.

They resembled the men found in Double Pattern of Larceny and Burglary in reference to most of the thirty-four personal and social characteristics; there were certain significant differences between them. Only one was reared in a rural area, and in only two cases did they have mother figures who were from the South. This indicates that they were more indigenous to the city than were the men in Double Pattern of Larceny and Burglary.

Criminal processing started early. All had delinquent companions during their formative years; and all had been members of a juvenile delinquent gang. Twelve were adjudicated juvenile delinquents. All had police contacts prior to age eighteen; and eleven had criminal companions prior to age eighteen.

In discussing their juvenile delinquent activities during the interviews, they indicated an early pattern of group stealing in well-organized delinquent gangs.

> I started stealing early—around nine or ten. A group of us used to shoplift. Two of us would pretend to be buying something to get the clerks' attention. One boy was the lookout and sign-man. When he gave the sign, one of us snatched the loot. One of us blocked for him. Jimbo, an older boy, taught me the tricks. I started out as the block man. Jimbo was the big man. He told us what to do.

Thirteen men claimed that they were at one time or another the leaders of a group of juveniles who shoplifted and broke into houses and warehouses. These groups, however, appeared to be small—three or four at the most. The ensuing quotation was typical:

> I soon found out the leader got the most money. As soon as I learned the ropes I found me two or three younger guys who would take the risks. Then I planned the job and acted as lookout and let *them* break in. Course, I had to tell them what to do. I also had to find a place to sell the loot. I took my chances, too.

The juvenile activity of these men indicated an early aptitude for well-organized, nonviolent crime. They spoke of infrequent fights. Apparently they had other ways of manipulating their peers.

In reference to later community adjustment, thirteen were residing in slum areas at the time of their last arrest; here they were to a great extent cut loose from noncriminal primary-group ties. Only one offender maintained strong ties with his family group. Only seven had marital ties at the time of their arrest. Though three were drug addicts, two were problem drinkers, and eight were inveterate gamblers, they did not speak of these indices of personal disorganization as being motivating factors in their criminality. These factors appeared to be incidental concomitants of their organized life in crime. The three addicts had well-established criminal records prior to their use of drugs. The following quotation pointed this up:

> Sure I use heroin, but I'm not a dog-type junkie. I'm clean on the street, and I watch my shots. I don't get too bad a habit. When I feel myself slipping, I just cut down the dosages. I was thirty before I used drugs.

Twelve men were highly mobile. They traveled throughout the northeastern part of the United States from one big city to another, returning to Washington as a sort of home base. They admitted traveling as professional thieves; however, they refused to discuss their criminal activities in detail.

> Sure I moved around quite a bit. You know I got business deals here and there. In 'the life' you got to make tracks to make that bread (money). You know what I mean.

Their remarks in reference to their criminal companions indicated a long association with fellow burglars, many of whom had been their juvenile delinquent companions. All were acquainted with fences, with whom they claimed a close business association throughout their adult lives. They spoke in the criminal argot, and they were acquainted with the organized underworld. The following typical quotation made by an interviewee illustrated these points:

> I did business with people you could trust. You know, sneak thieves that I done a bit (time) with, who knew the ropes. We knew every-

body that there was to know in 'the life.' We always would do business with a buyer (fence). You just had to know him right, and, you know, lay it on the line to him right. No man with a bag on his back could do business with the guys I did business with.

These men also had a consciousness of kind. They alluded to their criminal companions in the interviews as "fellow sneak-thieves," "second-storey men," "real housebreakers," etc. All made a point of the fact that they seldom resorted to force.

The arrest histories were long. Not one had fewer than fifteen arrests. Twelve had served at least one prior felony sentence. Criminal progression from petty theft and grand larceny to burglary was noted. There were very few non-property charges in evidence; and violent crimes against the person were rare.

The District Attorney's Reports revealed that these men operated at a rather high criminal level. A majority of the following procedures were noted in most of their *modi operandi*. There was a specialization in type of building burglarized. There was specialization shown in the type of property stolen, e.g., furs or men's suits, women's dresses or money, radios or TV sets, expensive jewelry, etc. Other less valuable property was left behind. There was a "connection" made with a fence *prior* to the offense. In short, a market was ascertained prior to burglary. Vans and trucks for the transportation of the stolen goods were provided for. Casing procedures well in advance of the commission of the crime were in evidence. The type of locks on doors was carefully noted. Entrances and exits were checked, and the wiring for burglary alarms was observed. Police activity in the neighborhood of the target of operations was noted. Careful timing in the execution of the offense was in evidence. Practice "dry runs" were made on occasion. Tight organization was present. There was usually a definite leader, "the brains," who planned the job. Usually a mob of three or four operated together. There was a prearranged plan for the storing and division of the "loot."

The reports of these men indicated no feelings of remorse for the commission of the present offense. As a group, they appeared to be in good general health. The medical records showed that thirteen were organically sound. One suffered from diabetes. One had a heart condition. They made very few somatic complaints. They reacted in a fairly cooperative, courteous manner during the interviews, though they were extremely evasive when discussing their criminal activities. They tended to be matter-of-fact in their reactions rather than friendly; however, none of them responded in a belligerent manner. In no case was excessive passivity or aggressivity noted. They all expressed antisocial attitudes in that they subscribed to the "fast-buck philosophy" and to the idea that everyone has a streak of larceny. However, they were only mildly negative in their attitudes toward the police, courts and correctional agents.

There seemed to be a sort of emotional coolness about these men. Externally they seemed to be unperturbed and at ease. The restlessness and edginess found among the "robbers" were not present. They accepted their sentences philosophically as occupational hazards and burdens. No remarks were made about self-reform. They conceived of themselves as professional criminals.

In sum, these men comprised a group of professional and semi-professional criminals. They were juvenile delinquents "grown up," who evinced an early aptitude for organized, property crimes. They were leaders as juvenile members of well-organized groups of thieves. Their personalities seemed to be well integrated. Violence was not their style. Their adult criminal style followed the same pattern. These professional burglars were precocious and intelligent. Crime, in a sense, *had* paid for them. Their lives were organized around criminal activities; and they seemed to be well satisfied with themselves as they were.

Professional burglars should be housed in penitentiaries rather than in reformatories with nonprofessional offenders where they might act as successful criminal role models. The reform of any type of professional criminal is obviously difficult. Improvement in law enforcement methods of detection and apprehension and court procedures might repress this as well as other types of professional crime. Moreover, changes in some laws relating to arrests, interrogation, search and seizure, wire tapping, entrapment, admission of evidence, etc., need to be made. At present, the law and the courts have partially handcuffed law enforcement agents in their endeavor to apprehend and bring to justice professional criminals. Longer sentences also should be meted out to those convicted.

Beyond measures of apprehension and control, certain treatment methods could be tried with this type of offender. Since deep-seated personality problems are not found among this well-integrated group, compulsory group therapy and group counseling might work. Perhaps along with some other types (e.g., the robbers) various experimental methods of individual and group therapies could be attempted.

NO PATTERN

The No Pattern type (N=32) comprised a group of young offenders (age median—24.4) who, for the most part, were reared in urban areas under favorable home and neighborhood conditions. Twenty-nine were products of the District, and only three were reared in rural areas. They were a literate group (S.A.T. grade median—8.5) with average intelligence (IQ median—103). Both the total sample and the internal comparisons demonstrated this pattern's general "superiority."

The statistical findings, coupled with the interview impressions, indicated the resemblance of this pattern to a class of offenders referred to by Ruth Cavan as "criminals who live in the non-criminal world."[1] Neither personal disorganization nor criminal contagion through childhood contacts in slum areas explained their etiological development. These occasional, situational offenders appeared to find their associates and satisfactions in conventional society among noncriminals. As one offender stated:

> Criminal companions? I had no criminal companions that I knew about. At least the people I run around with didn't get arrested and go to jail. I just didn't hang around with thugs, you know. I worked every day. My wife and children come first, and I have no time to run the streets. The 'life' these men talk about here I know nothing about . . . care less.

Only one had a criminal companion prior to age eighteen. None spoke with any intimate knowledge of the organized underworld. They did not speak in the criminal argot; they made a point of expressing their shame at being in prison; and they also made a point of disclaiming any connection with the underworld. Twenty-three had regular work habits prior to the present incarceration. This extracted quotation was characteristic:

> I sure let my wife and family down by coming to jail. It worries me. My wife has bills I should be taking care of. I'm no real crook. I never robbed or broke in a house. I wouldn't spit on these hoodlums I got to live with here on the street. They are nothing.

When questioned in the interviews about their juvenile delinquent activities, they disclaimed any sustained illegal activity. Seven stated that they associated quite frequently with one or more companions who had been to the National Training School for Boys; however, they denied participating in illegal behavior with these companions. The only two offenders who were adjudicated juvenile delinquents were apprehended in a stolen car while "joyriding." None of these men mentioned a juvenile delinquent act as serious as robbery, housebreaking or assault. All of them denied having criminal companions as adults.

A study of their arrest records and the District Attorney's Reports, showed that their criminal acts generally grew out of an immediate, unexpected, unplanned situation. *Modi operandi* were at a low level. In giving their version of the instant offense, twenty claimed to be under the influence of alcohol at the time of the commission of their crimes.

Ten of these men were arrested for and were serving time for having intercourse with a girl under sixteen years of age. In no case was the victim a relative of the offender, and in no case was she less than fourteen years of age. In all ten cases the victim agreed to the sex act and there was no evidence of violence present. All ten were under the influence of alcohol at the time of the offense. Three were "problem drinkers." None had been arrested on a sex charge previously.

In five cases the victims were the children of the inmate's nextdoor neighbors. In five cases they were the relatives of the inmate's landlady, and they lived in the same house with the offender. In all ten cases the sexual act seemed to have occurred as a result of an accidental, unplanned situation—the physical presence of a well-developed, willing sex partner, in the absence of other family group members presented the opportunity. The offenders' state of inebriation could have dulled their critical judgments and rendered them more susceptible in these situations.

Five of the men in this pattern were convicted of aggravated assault. All five claimed to be under the influence of alcohol at the time of their criminal acts. This is substantiated by the District Attorney's Reports. Three of them were "problem drinkers." Four unexpectedly discovered their wives (N=2) or girl friends (N=2) in what they interpreted as compromising situations with other men. Immediate physical attacks resulted: two upon the two wives and two upon the two assumed boyfriends. Knives were used in two cases; chairs were used in three others. In all five cases, a sudden violent attack was precipitated by an unexpected, emotionally charged situation. None of them had been arrested on an assault charge previously.

Twelve were convicted of grand larceny. In ten cases property was stolen from employers. In five cases property was stolen from landlords. All twelve claimed they took property, e.g., radios, furniture, clothes, etc., on the spur of the moment when the opportunity offered. They stated, moreover, that they were not in the habit of stealing. Eight were "problem drinkers" and four of these eight were under the influence of alcohol at the time of the crime; however, each claimed that alcohol had nothing to do with his motivation. None of these men had been arrested for grand larceny previously.

Five were convicted of embezzlement. One was a "problem drinker" and the only one under the influence of alcohol at the time of his crime. All five said that they appropriated money which did not belong to them on the spur of the moment. They stated that they were motivated by the unexpected need of their families for money, which they could not procure in a legitimate way, e.g., crises of childbirth, sickness, pressing debts and unemployment. All insisted that they had planned to replace the stolen money. The opportunity to take money with a good chance of replacing it at a later date without being detected proved too great a temptation for these men who claimed no previous embezzlements and who had no previous arrests for same.

They appeared to be physically strong and in general good health. The medical records showed that only four were not organically sound: one was an arrested case of tuberculosis; one was physically handicapped—minus left arm; one had stomach ulcers; one had a heart murmur. They expressed very few somatic complaints.

The majority of these offenders verbalized well without apparent aggressivity or passivity. They expressed positive attitudes toward all basic social institutions, and they were not antagonistic to the police, court machinery and correctional agents. One offender reacted in a verbally aggressive manner. He appeared to be somewhat rebellious; and he evinced some indications of "antisocial reaction." One offender was quite reticent and evasive and appeared to be somewhat withdrawn, passive and dependent in personality type. With the exception of these two cases, they appeared to be courteous, friendly, cooperative and candid in demeanor and speech. Most of them (N=30) appeared to have normal, well-integrated personalities. All made a point of the fact that they did not consider themselves to be criminals. Most of them expressed some apprehension at finding themselves in a penal setting. All were products of middle-class homes.

In sum, the lives of these men were not organized around criminal activities. Their offenses seemed to be incidental to a conventional life organization and unimportant to their total scheme of things. They in no sense considered themselves criminals, but rather the victims of a set of peculiar circumstances which they did not think would occur again. It is true that fifteen were "problem drinkers;" however, 48 per cent of the men in the total sample fell also into this category. Certainly with the exception of these fifteen, they appeared to constitute a normal, well-integrated group of men. They did not appear to be menaces to the general community, and there seemed to be no reason why similar cases could not be placed on probation rather than incarcerated in penitentiary situations. Imprisonment seems to offer no advantages to this group. They did not seem too much in need of case work services, counseling, psychiatric and psychological examination and treatment or vocational and academic education; their past histories established their ability to adjust.

The expense in time, money and energy in reference to their incarceration appears to be a great waste. In fact, imprisonment places these "noncriminals" in a situation where they are exposed to antisocial attitudes, and where they may learn criminal techniques. It has been the writer's experience, however, that cases of this kind usually hold themselves aloof in a sense from the general inmate population. They neither identify themselves with the inmate body nor with the prison administration. They tend to consider themselves strangers and visitors in the prison situation—enforced tourists, if you will, who are to an extent on the outside looking in. Their contacts with the machinery of law enforcement, the courts and correctional agents appear to be neutral in effect.

Perhaps a psychiatric examination, the findings of which could be made as part of the pre-sentence report to the judge, would prove useful. Those found to be suffering from any deep-seated personality difficulties could be weeded out for commitment—or for group and individual therapy as a condition of probation on an "outpatient" basis. The possibility that the offense for which they were convicted represented the first manifestation of a permanent personality disorganization attendant upon a psychosis probably could be ascertained. However, as has been previously stated, the writer thinks that the great majority of cases found in this kind of criminal category would prove to be well-organized individuals who could easily make adequate adjustments in the free world.

No Pattern, a residual category comprising thirty-two men with less than three arrests was found to be a distinctive group of offenders. It has been the writer's observation that men of this type stand out like sore thumbs in penal settings. They are aware of their "squareness," and they appear to be proud of it. There are other research findings which show this kind of occasional offender to be a distinctive type.[2]

REFERENCES

1. CAVAN RUTH: *Criminology*, (3rd ed.), pp. 186-201.
2. GIBBONS, DON C.: *Changing the Lawbreaker*, pp. 106-110.

Chapter XIII

RECENT RESEARCH TRENDS

FOR OBVIOUS reasons this chapter must be limited in scope. The author has selected only a few illustrative materials which lend support to or challenge some of the foregoing typological attempts. No effort is made at a comprehensive overview of the literature in this area.

H. J. Eysenck, in his recent book, *Crime and Personality*, suggests a biological-psychological-physiological theory of criminal behavior which he relates to *scientific laboratory procedures.*[1] Eysenck's basic thesis is firmly rooted in heredity. His approach is far more sophisticated and experimental than that employed by previous and current biological criminologists. He poses a personality typology linked to criminal behavior. Eysenck is a British, stimulus-response behaviorist psychologist, and is a sharp critic of psychoanalytic psychology. He holds that some neurotic disorders can now be treated successfully by behavior therapy, employing the procedures of psychology as a laboratory science. Moreover, he calls for further refinement of behavior therapy theory and laboratory experimental therapy techniques which might be applied in the treatment of some forms of delinquent and criminal behavior.

Eysenck postulates that all behavior is either instrumentally conditioned (learned behavior involving the skeletal nervous system) or Pavlovian conditioned (involving the autonomic nervous system). Learned behavior occurs because a stimulus and response are paired. Conditioned behavior involves contiguity without reinforcement. Moral behavior is conditioned rather than learned.

Eysenck's psychological-physiological system is based on the autonomic nervous system as underlying the behavioral traits of emotionality or neuroticism.[2] This autonomic system consists of two antagonistic parts, the sympathetic and the parasympathetic systems. The sympathetic system is devoted to fight or flight reactions. When in action, it increases the heartbeat, the rate of respiration, the flow of blood and adrenalin, and it retards digestion. The parasympathetic system, when in action, inhibits the action of the sympathetic system by slowing down the heart, slowing down the rate of breathing, and aiding digestion. Eysenck equates emotionality and the autonomic system. He maintains that persons who are subject to strong emotions, even under conditions which would not call forth such strong emotions in normal persons, have been endowed by heredity with an autonomic system, the sympathetic branch of which is particularly strongly reactive to external stimuli. He points to the ascending reticular formation of the brain which is situated at the top of the spinal cord at the bottom of the brain as the most likely part of the nervous system serving as the locus of inhibition and excitation.[3]

Drawing on several studies which utilize rating devices, self-ratings, objective personality tests, and typological constructs (a syndrome of correlated traits), Eysenck reports the existence of two polar personality types: extraverts and introverts.[4] He found that several objective personality tests correlate highly with experimental evidence of a person's habitual behavior tendencies (as measured, for example, by motor suggestibility tests, sensory suggestibility tests, social suggestibility tests and body-sway tests). The extreme extravert model is sociable, craves excitement, takes chances and acts on the spur of the moment. He is impulsive, aggressive, temperamental, emotional and unreliable. The extreme introvert model is quiet, retiring, introspective, serious, self-controlled and reliable. Unlike prior conceptualizations, Eysenck's view is that the extravert is low on excitation and high on inhibition; the introvert is high on excitation and low on inhibition. The introvert conditions readily; the extravert conditions poorly.

Eysenck generally recognizes the absence of pure discreet categories and would assign persons to particular positions on the continuum of extraversion-introversion. People suffering from mood disorders, psychasthenics or dysthymics, are generally found at the introverted extreme of the continuum; whereas the hysterics and psychopaths are found at the extraverted extreme.

By employing neuroticism and extraversion-introversion scores resulting from questionnaires of various "neurotic" and "criminal" groups (anxiety state patients, obsessional patients, psychosomatic patients, female prisoners, hysteric patients, male prisoners, psychopathic patients, and unmarried mothers), Eysenck found a high degree of introversion for the neurotic groups and a high degree of extraversion for the criminal and psychopathic groups.[5] The psychopaths comprised the most extremely extraverted group, followed by the hysterics. Those suffering from anxiety states, the obsessive-compulsive groups, the phobics and the reactive depressants were extremely introverted.[6]

Eysenck links inhibition and excitation to personality with the following postulates: Individuals differ in the rate of buildup of inhibition, the strength of inhibition toleration and the speed with which inhibition dissipates; extraverts build up inhibition quickly, demonstrate high degrees of inhibition and dissipate inhibition slowly; introverted people build up inhibition more slowly and to a lesser degree and dissipate it more quickly; introverts develop excitation more quickly and strongly, extraverts more slowly and weakly. In support of these propositions, high correlations are demonstrated between traits of introversion and extraversion (as determined from objective personality tests) and specific behavioral responses obtained in the laboratory (as tested by vigilance tests, tapping metal stylus tests, eye blink tests, puff of air tests, galvanic skin response tests, etc.).[7]

Eysenck further attempts to establish a strong hereditary predisposition leading to extraverted or introverted behavior and to strong or weak emotionality with four separate strands of evidence:

1. Studies in which identical and fraternal twins have been subjected to laboratory experimental tests of extraversion and neuroticism which reveal that the influence of heredity was as strong in relation to emotionality as many scholars have shown it to be in relation to intelligence.

2. Questionnaires given to identical and fraternal twins assessing extraversion and emotionality which show that identical twins are more alike than are fraternal twins.

3. Studies of parents, their children, cousins, and relatives which show them to be similar on tests for emotionality, neuroticism, and extraversion-introversion in relation to their degree of consanguinity.

4. Studies of twins by J. Shields of Maudsley Hospital in London (in which 44 pairs of identical twins were reared together, 44 identical twins were reared separately, and 28 pairs of fraternal twins were reared together) were examined in reference to intelligence, extraversion and neuroticism. The startling findings revealed that though all of the identical twins were similar, those identical twins reared apart were much more similar than those identical twins reared together. Eysenck claims that these results destroy the argument that identical twins behave more similarly than fraternal twins because the "environment treats them" more alike than it does fraternal twins. He explains the relative dissimilarity of identical twins reared together when compared with those reared apart in terms of the efforts of the twins reared together to work out separate personalities and identities for themselves.[8] This explanation is an unsupported conjecture; however, it does not negate the findings which it attempts to explain.

Eysenck differentiates between the processes of conditioning and learning, unlike many psychologists who view conditioning as one kind of learning. Rational learning is related to problem solving and to hedonism of the moment. Conditioning operates by contiguity rather than by reinforcement. The central nervous system is involved in learning. The autonomic nervous system, concerned with the glands and the smooth or involuntary muscles, is involved in conditioning. Moral behavior, in the main, is conditioned—not learned. Conditioning produces a conscience through and by conditioned fear responses and autonomic "unpleasures" associated with antisocial activities. Stimulus generalization, the association of all those activities potentially dangerous, punishment producing, and fear and anxiety producing, contributes to the process. In short, antisocial, criminal or tabooed behavior engaged in by an individual represents a conditional stimulus; the unconditional stimulus is the immediate punishment of whatever kind that follows the prohibited, discovered behavior; and the response is the pain and fear produced in the individual. The normal individual, in the process of growing up, acquires a repertoire of conditioned fear responses to various behaviors disapproved by various authority figures and peers. When childhood temptations are great, tabooed behavior may be given in to, but the resulting, autonomic fear-anxiety reactions are generally sufficient to deter further repetition of the disapproved act.[9]

Eysenck's view is that many criminals and delinquents are psychopaths who do not condition readily. Law-abiding people are usually introverts who do condition readily. Dysthymic neurotics are over-conditioned. Eysenck does not claim that all psychopaths are criminals or that all criminals are psychopaths; however, he does maintain that psychopaths contribute more than their share to the delinquent and criminal population. Unfortunately, he fails to define what he means by this "delinquent and criminal population."

Eysenck reports experimental conditioning studies which indicate that psychopaths and extraverts generally exhibit less conditioning in experimental situations than do normal people.[10] He also examines the results of a number of studies which utilize objective personality tests (some with control groups) demonstrating that people who commit crimes and other antisocial acts are more extraverted than people who are free of such transgressions. These studies include traffic violators, accident-prone victims, unmarried mothers, criminals, criminal psychopaths and delinquents. He also quotes several somatotype studies from England and the United States which indicate the correlation between body build and temperament, and which he reports are in support of his thesis that criminals show a temperamental tendency toward extraversion (including studies of T. C. N. Gibbens, P. Epps and R. W. Parnell, William Sheldon, and Sheldon and Eleanor Glueck).[11]

Eysenck is cognizant of the fact that people are not subjected to an identical system of conditioning. Differentials in conditioning procedures may vary from family to family in reference to their social class position, religious and ethnic affiliations, degree of respectability, and degree of criminality. He admits that conditioning is relatively specific, and though specificity of responses is not universal, it does limit the generality of his theories. Introverts condition well whether conditioned in the "right" or "wrong" directions. The major thesis stands; Extraverts condition poorly whether conditioned in the "right" or "wrong" direction.

Eysenck affirms that the efficacy of punishment for criminal or antisocial behavior depends upon the kind of motivation involved. Behavior motivated by reward can be deterred by punishment, e.g., some kinds of theft, fraud, kidnapping, tax evasion. Behavior motivated by frustration cannot be deterred by punishment, e.g., sex crimes and murder. Punishment in the latter case may even strengthen the frustration-instigated behavior and may render it a stereotyped pattern. Punishment when used should be employed simultaneously with the act or as soon as possible after the act which precipitated it. Inasmuch as the time lag between the criminal act and punishment is appreciable, and because the immediate reward of the criminal act is usually relatively certain, neither legal punishment nor the threat of legal punishment effectively deters the criminal.[12] Moreover, there is no certainty of punishment because the criminal act may go undetected.

Conditioning therapy (on an experimental basis) founded on the treatment techniques of J. B. Watson, J. Wolpe, and O. H. Mowrer are recommended by Eysenck for the treatment of delinquents and criminals. The treatment goals are to decondition the criminal's very powerful impulses, to perform certain acts and to create new conditional responses of a culturally desirable nature. Laboratory techniques utilizing conditioning and reconditioning treatment methods with neurotics (anxiety states, reactive depression, hysterical and obsessive compulsive symptoms), transvestites, homosexuals, and enuretics are noted in support of conditioning therapy. Electric shock and apomorphine were used as treatment aids.[13]

Eysenck suggests that treatment and control procedures with

offenders should be based on their personality type; e.g., extraverts require firmness, but introverts (who generally engage in crime as a result of conditioning in a poor environment) require a more permissive approach. The "real" potential criminals (highly extraverted and emotional children and psychopaths) must be submitted to a rigorous and efficient system of conditioning during childhood by parents with the help of experimental psychologists. In his opinion, all children should be tested for their conditionability in a laboratory situation connected with the school. These tests would be part of the standard operating procedure of the school, along with the current standard procedure of administering intelligence tests. Potential pre-delinquents and pre-criminals, selected by these conditioning tests, would be subjected to the appropriate conditioning procedure required to combat natural tendencies toward criminal and antisocial behavior.[14]

Eysenck also recommends drug therapy (for criminals and delinquents) which acts on the nervous system directly to alter the position of individuals in relation to the extraversion/introversion continuum. Stimulant drugs for extraverts and depressant drugs for introverts would be used as treatment agents to directly modify behavior, and they might also be utilized in conditioning therapy. Several successful drug-therapy experiments on juvenile delinquents and children with behavior disorders are recorded.[15] Eysenck admits that his two proposed treatment techniques: (a) conditioning and (b) drug therapy, are still in the experimental stage; and he does not claim that these methods offer a panacea for crime and delinquency.[16] He does contend that these methods are more in line with a scientific approach to behavior than are the psychoanalytical and related treatment methods.

Apart from the development of his psychological-physiological system and his typology of extraverts and introverts, Eysenck quotes results from a series of studies of twins authored by different investigators in different countries, with a subject group of 225 pairs of twins (one of each pair a known criminal). Fraternal twins and identical twins utilized were in equal proportion. The over-all finding was that twice as many identical as fraternal twins were concordant (both criminal). A series of additional studies of twins, including juvenile delinquents, children with behavior disorders, homosexuals, and alcoholics showed high concordance for identical twins as compared with fraternal twins.[17] Eysenck explains that several factors militated for an underestimate rather than an overestimate of concordance among identical twins: brain damage supposedly affecting one twin, making him a criminal, but not affecting his co-twin; several diseases affecting two fraternal twins; the underreporting of crimes committed by identical twins. These explanations are obviously weak and unsupported.

Eysenck concludes that his quoted twin data prove that heredity plays an important role in predisposing a given individual to crime. In the opinion of this writer, the twin data examined by Eysenck indicate that, in any environment, persons with similar genotypes are likely to be on the average more similar in their behavior than persons with different hereditary endowments.[18]

Finally, in this section, Eysenck lists four plausible reasons why the studies of twins (and, for that matter, other biological approaches to crime) have been discredited by many scholars.

1. There is a strong prevailing belief in the United States and Russia that with the proper manipulation techniques people can be made over in the required image. Heredity obviously sets limits to the manipulator and is therefore unacceptable.

2. The belief in some countries that man is born free and equal has led some to the erroneous conclusion that man has the same innate ability and personality potential—and that there are no limits to human perfectability.

3. The belief in the freedom of will is supported by strong religious overtones.

4. There is a strong belief that the acceptance of heredity as an important factor in determining or limiting behavior leads to "therapeutic nihilism."*[19]

C. R. Jeffery, a recognized sociological criminologist, offers three major criticisms of Eysenck's work.

---

*Dr. Philip Himelstein, Professor of Psychology at University of Texas at El Paso, reviewed my assessment of Eysenck's work.

1. He refutes the thesis that criminality has a biological base, drawing on the negative evidence in this area found by American criminologists.

2. He denies Eysenck's personality typology and insists that human behavior is learned behavior.

3. He argues that criminal behavior is learned behavior and not conditioned behavior. Conditioning explains very little social behavior since it deals with physiological responses. In short, criminal behavior is operant behavior that is maintained by its consequences, both material and social.

Jeffery approves of Eysenck's work at several points.

1. "Behavior is always determined, especially by the law, as an agent of social control."

2. A scientific approach to behavior and its treatment must replace some current unreasoning ways of dealing with offenders.

3. Jeffery concedes that the future of criminology may rest on laboratory procedures rather than on psychoanalytic procedures. "If in the future modern learning theory is applied to the alleviation of behavioral disorders, the volume by Eysenck may well rank as one of the most significant contributions to the field in the decade."[20]

In this writer's view, Eysenck has marshalled significant data from many experimental studies in support of his extraversion-introversion personality continuum. He has probably come to closer grips with the nature of the relationship existing between "whatever it is that is constitutional" and persistent criminal behavior (the perennial problem of biological criminologists) than has any other behavioral scientist. He points to the autonomic nervous system of the extreme extravert (psychopathic personality) as the inherited, organic key to the problem. He has demonstrated a relationship between extraversion and inhibition and between introversion and excitation. Moreover, he suggests the ascending reticular formation as the physiological locus for this particular trait.

Unfortunately, Eysenck does not always distinguish between psychopathy and crime and between psychopaths and criminals. Despite this failure, he is quite aware of the fact that not all delinquents and criminals are psychopaths. He is probably justified in his claim that psychopaths contribute more than their share to the delinquent and criminal population—certainly to that population which is incarcerated. Eysenck's position reinforces the view that, barring other factors, the psychopath is more likely to become criminal than the non-psychopath. Certainly, Eysenck has established beyond a doubt that the functioning of the psychopath's nervous system varies from that of the introvert's. This is his major contribution.

Eysenck's suggestion that we provide conditioning tests for schoolchildren is reasonable in the light of his laboratory findings. One does not have to accept all of his behavioral learning theory to accept this procedure. The writer agrees with Jeffery that most criminal behavior is learned. On the other hand, he agrees with Eysenck's position that psychopaths are more likely to become delinquents and criminals than non-psychopaths.

Eysenck's work establishes the experimental efficacy of conditioning and deconditioning treatment techniques with certain types of neurotics, delinquents, and criminals. His data on drug therapy also supports such "experimentation" with some kinds of delinquents and criminals. Certainly, behavior therapy based on laboratory procedure should be included in correctional treatment repertoire.[21]

The theories and writings of the delinquent subculture theorists have led to many investigations, some of which support and some of which do not support the findings of Cohen, Cloward and Ohlin, and Miller. Robin's Philadelphia study of more than seven hundred male Negro members of twenty-seven delinquent gangs purports to support the claims of Cloward and Ohlin in reference to the existence of a "conflict" subculture of delinquency. It is of note, however, that these gangs engaged in many kinds of delinquent and criminal activity other than physical violence.[22] The findings of Spergel in two separate studies (delinquents in New York City and young adult criminals in Chicago) support the thesis of Cloward and Ohlin; e.g., he discovered "criminalistic" and "conflict" subcultures. Additionally, he found an expected discrepancy between these offenders' aspirations and their expectations when compared with non-offenders.[23]

In this writer's view Short and Strodtbeck have examined the theories and findings of the delinquent subculture theorists with more precision than have any other investigators. Short and Strodtbeck's work, *Group Process and Gang Delinquency*, is probably based on more scientific empirical findings than any past or current work on delinquent gangs.[24]

Short and Strodtbeck delineated behavior patterns of gang boys observed in the Program for Detached Workers of the YMCA of Metropolitan Chicago. Data were gathered on a series of Negro and white gangs over a period of three years (1959-1962). Part of their inquiry was designed to bring data to bear on the delinquent subcultural theories of Cohen, Cloward and Ohlin, and Miller. Early in their research endeavor they found that these theories were geared to one level of explanation, the environment of lower-class youngsters. In short, these theories sought explanation for the behavioral delinquent boys in terms of the culture and social structure of the larger society (Merton, Cohen, Cloward and Ohlin) or the lower-class culture (Miller). Other levels of explanation (e.g., personality variables, etc.) were either ignored, assumed, or considered as environmentally determined. Gang norms, according to these delinquent subcultural theories, are explained by the operation of culture or in terms of reactions to cultural and social structure. The modification (of gang norms) and the process by which they become transferred into behavior through the internal development of the group are not dealt with by the delinquent subculture theories.[25]

According to Short and Strodtbeck, none of the preceding theories explores systematically or abstractly the etiological importance of gang interaction. This weakness led them to work on other levels of explanation in addition to the external system, e.g., the nature and the role of the following types of influences on gang boys and non-gang boys: (a) the environment; (b) characteristics of individuals including self-concept; (c) norms of the group; (d) group process—process by which variables at the preceding levels of explanation (a, b, c) become translated into behavior.[26] Discussion of their work will be limited to their findings as they relate to the delinquent subcultural theories.

Short and Strodtbeck reason that the three theories of delinquent subculture of Cohen, Ohlin and Cloward, and Miller lead to the expectation that gang boys will place higher value on deviant or illegitimate images than will middle-class boys, i.e., Cohen because of reaction formation, Miller because these images match the focal concerns of lower-class culture, and Cloward and Ohlin because these images reveal adaptations to the relative unavailability of legitimate opportunities for members of the lower class. Cohen's theory also suggests that gang boys will particularly value deviant images even higher than middle-class images.[27] All three theories, according to Short and Strodtbeck, indicate that middle-class values, as represented in the middle-class images, are not supported as highly by gang boys as by middle-class boys.[28]

A sample of six populations were selected to test the *image expectations* mentioned above: (a) Negro gang boys; (b) white gang boys; (c) lower-class Negro boys residing in the same neighborhood as Negro gang boys; (d) white lower-class boys residing in the same neighborhood as white gang boys; (e) white, non-gang, middle-class boys; (f) Negro, non-gang, middle-class boys. The data were gathered by means of a semantic-differential image scale which was rated by all members of the six population groups. The images to be rated were chosen to represent conspicuous examples of dominant goal activity, leisure time activity and ethical orientation for each of five theoretical subcultures: middle class; lower class; conflict; criminal; and retreatest. A "smart sucker" scale was also employed. The results consisted of mean scores for both evaluation (image ratings on sematic—differential image scale) and the smart sucker scale accorded to each of seventeen images by each of the six populations. Analysis of variance and other statistical techniques were utilized to test for the over-all significance of these data. *All six populations evaluated images representing conspicuous features of a middle-class style of life equally highly.*[29] Moreover, no image representing the other four subcultures was evaluated significantly higher than the middle-class images by any one of the six populations. Middle-class images were evaluated significantly higher by all of the populations than nearly all other subcultural images. Short and Strodtbeck demonstrate that the explanation for the disparity between the three delinquent subcultural theories and their data (Short and Strodtbeck's) are not to be found in the distinction between moral validity and legitimacy.[30]

The statistical findings, however, did indicate that gang boys evaluate illegitimate images higher than do non-gang boys (in support of Cohen and Ohlin and Cloward), and that gang and lower-class boys evaluate illegitimate images higher than do middle-class boys (in support of Miller). It was also found that gang, lower-class and middle-class boys differ most in their attitudes and behaviors proscribed (rather than prescribed) by the middle class, and that they tend to be ordered as listed with respect to their tolerance toward these behaviors.[31]

Other findings of Short and Strodtbeck (Chicago data) challenge, if not negate, many propositions of the delinquent subcultural theorists. Parent delinquent subcultures and highly specialized delinquent subcultures were not found. Delinquent subcultures were found, but they were far from the pure types posed by Cohen, Ohlin and Cloward, and Miller. The retreatest subculture and the criminal subculture as envisioned by Ohlin and Cloward were not in evidence in Chicago. Conflict gangs were found among Negro boys but not among whites. Moreover, a variety of types of behavior were found to be common to all gangs under study. Some cliques within gangs specialized in specific patterns of criminal and delinquent behavior (organized thieving activities).[32]

Short and Strodtbeck discovered that gangs become coalesced in ways much more complex than current delinquent subcultural theories (theories of Cohen, Cloward, Ohlin, and Miller) have specified.[33] Furthermore, they determined that the delinquent boy's locus of status concern was not related to the social class system of the larger society; rather, it was related to his face-to-face relationships within the gang.[34] What is probably more important, however, is the fact that Short and Strodtbeck perceived considerable variation in "position discontent" among gang members.[35] Their studies revealed that, in many instances, middle- and lower-class boys agreed on positive goals. Lower-class boys did not personally reject the goals denied them. In short, the hypotheses of reaction formation of Cohen was not supported. Middle-class norms were legitimated by gang boys. Gang boys were less alienated from conventional institutions, generally, than the delinquent subculture theorists suggest.[36]

In a recent book, *Delinquency and Drift,* Matza refutes the notion of Cohen, Cloward and Ohlin, and Miller that the delinquent subculture stands in opposition to the conventions of middle-class morality. Matza sees the delinquent subculture as a compromise subculture manned by juveniles who are encircled by the conventional order. In short, the subculture of delinquency is dependent on and integrated with the conventional order. Members of delinquent subcultures are of two minds, and they are not fully committed to a delinquent and criminal life. Members of delinquent subcultures engage in both law-abiding and non-law-abiding behavior. Many of them attend school, have girl friends and hold down part-time jobs. They express shame and guilt relating to their illegal acts, and they accept the legitimacy of the legal norms which they from time to time violate. According to Matza, gang members drift into and out of a delinquent way of life. Most delinquents (60 to 80 per cent) do not become adult offenders. They mature, secure jobs, get married, join the service, and cease "juveniling" around. This "reform" occurs, regardless of the intervention of correctional agencies.[37]

Gibbons' typologies of juvenile and adult offenders, based on a role-oriented approach to offender types in which deviant patterns are described in terms of offense activity and social-psychological characteristics, are in part supported by the research literature. Some of these types are spelled out in more detail than the others. Additional types not mentioned by Gibbons are in evidence, as recognized by Gibbons. Further research will, in all probability, fill in these gaps.[38] Gibbons, along with this author, has not avoided the dimension of personality in his typological attempts. Hopefully, an increasing number of sociological criminologists will further explore and integrate the personality dimension in their typological attempts.

REFERENCES

1. EYSENCK, H. J.: *Crime and Personality.* Boston, Houghton-Mifflin Company, 1964.
2. *Ibid.,* pp. 64-70.
3. *Ibid.,* pp. 92-94.
4. *Ibid.,* pp. 22-42.
5. *Ibid.,* p. 42.
6. *Ibid.,* p. 41.
7. *Ibid.,* pp. 120-128, 143-157.
8. *Ibid.,* pp. 89-92.
9. *Ibid.,* pp. 106-111.
10. *Ibid.,* pp. 40-43.
11. *Ibid.,* pp. 123-124.
12. *Ibid.,* pp. 142-153.
13. *Ibid.,* pp. 155-158.
14. *Ibid.,* pp. 162-163.
15. *Ibid.,* pp. 163-165.
16. *Ibid.,* pp. 165-168.
17. *Ibid.,* pp. 53-57.
18. DOBZHANSKY, THEODOSIUS: *Heredity and the Nature of Man.* New York, The New American Library, 1964, pp. 72-74.
19. EYSENCK, H. J.: *op. cit.,* pp. 57-60.
20. JEFFERY, C. R.: Review of *Crime and Personality* by H. J. Eysenck. *Journal of Criminal Law, Criminology, and Police Science,* 56:231-233, June, 1965; see also JEFFERY, C. R.: Criminal behavior and learning theory. *Journal of Criminal Law, Criminology, and Police Science,* 56:294-300, September, 1965.
21. For another modern learning theory approach to delinquency (operant procedures in place of conditioning procedures), see SCHWITZGEBEL, RALPH: *Street Corner Research: An Experimental Approach to the Juvenile Delinquent.* Cambridge, Harvard University Press, 1964.
22. ROBIN, GERALD D.: Gang member delinquency: Its extent, sequence and typology. *Journal of Criminal Law, Criminology, and Police Science,* 55:59-69, March, 1964.

23. SPERGEL, IRVING: Male young adult criminality, deviant values, and differential opportunities in two lower class Negro neighborhoods. *Social Problems, 10*:237-250, Winter, 1963; SPERGEL, IRVING: An exploratory research in delinquent subcultures. *Social Service Review, 35*:33-47, March, 1961; SPERGEL, IRVING: *Racketville, Slumtown, Haulburg.* Chicago, University of Chicago Press, 1964.

24. SHORT, JAMES F., JR., and STRODTBECK, FRED L.: *Group Process and Gang Delinquency.* Chicago, The University of Chicago Press, 1965.

25. *Ibid.,* pp. 18-19.

26. *Ibid.,* pp. 19-20.

27. *Ibid.,* pp. 53-59.

28. *Ibid.,* p. 59.

29. *Ibid.,* pp. 48-52.

30. *Ibid.,* pp. 72-76.

31. *Ibid.,* p. 76.

32. *Ibid.,* pp. 91-101.

33. *Ibid.,* p. 101.

34. *Ibid.,* p. 212, 249.

35. *Ibid.,* p. 269.

36. Spiller's findings involving two gangs in Roxbury, Massachusetts, negate the thesis of Cohen, Cloward and Ohlin, and Bloch and Neiderhoffer: Lower-class boys do not internalize middle-class success goals. Spiller also quotes other studies which challenge the delinquent subculture approach. See SPILLER, BERTRAM: Delinquency and middle class goals. *Journal of Criminal Law, Criminology and Police Science, 56*:463-478, December, 1965; for further information and criticism of the delinquent subcultural approach, see HARTUNG, FRANK E.: *Crime, Law, and Society.* Detroit, Wayne State University Press, 1965, pp. 54-88.

37. MATZA, DAVID: *Delinquency and Drift.* New York, John Wiley and Sons, Inc., 1964, pp. 33-50, 59-64.

38. GIBBONS, DON C.: *Changing the Lawbreaker,* pp. 283-292.

Appendix A

ARREST HISTORY SOURCES AND
LEGAL LABELING PROCEDURES

I. *Sources*

A chronological arrest history on each of the four-hundred cases
was derived from the official records. This history served as the
basis for the assignment of individuals' "arrest-pattern cate-
gorioo." No reoordings or analysis of arrest histories were made
until all data concerned with the social and personal characteristics and with the writer's clinical impressions had been
collected and entered in the four-hundred social case history
schedules.

A. *The District of Columbia Arrest Record* used in this
study was a photostatic copy of the files kept in the Central
Information Bureau of the Metropolitan Police Department
of the District of Columbia on each offender arrested within
the District. This photostatic copy is kept in the institutional
folder of each inmate confined in the Reformatory. The
D.C. Arrest Record is the most complete arrest record of
its kind in the United States. In the States, the Federal
authorities are not required to report their arrests to any
particular metropolitan police department. Local, county
and state police in the various states do not, as a rule, report
their arrests to any one central agency. In the District,
however, every law-enforcement agency within its geographical limits, including the Federal authorities, is required by law to make a daily report to the District of
Columbia Central Information Bureau. The reporting
agencies include fourteen precincts of the Metropolitan
Police Department, the Women's Bureau, Washington
Terminal Police, White House Police, Capitol Police, United

States Park Police, United States Building Guards, United States Marshals, United States Secret Service Agents, United States Internal Revenue Agents, United States Narcotic Agents, Federal Bureau of Investigation Agents, United States Post Office Inspectors, District of Columbia Health Inspectors and other publicly and privately operated police agencies armed with arrest powers. Immediate reports of all police actions engaged in by these agencies within the confines of the District of Columbia, including arrests and charges together with identification material, must be sent to the District of Columbia Information Bureau as required by law. This photostatic copy of the records maintained in the District of Columbia Central Information Bureau appears in chronological order of date of arrest and charge. It was used as the basic framework for the development of the arrest histories.

B. *The Federal Bureau of Investigation Abstract of Criminal Record* was the second source. All persons within the United States, its territories and possessions who have been photographed, fingerprinted and otherwise officially identified, and whose records have been reported to the Federal Bureau of Investigation, have a dossier concerning them on file in the Archives of the Bureau. Information pertaining wholly to criminal activity such as dates, places of arrests and imprisonments is extracted from the other information and compiled into that which is known as the F.B.I. Abstract of Criminal Record. This abstract contains records of arrests which do not appear on any one given local arrest record. Local police authorities report their "fingerprinted" arrests to the F.B.I. on a volunteer basis. Though not an all-inclusive index, this abstract is a valuable index in the assaying of the D.C. offenders "fingerprinted" arrests outside the jurisdiction of the District. The D.C. Police Records do not include such arrests. A copy of the F.B.I. Abstract of Criminal Record is included in the institutional folder of each inmate.

II. *Arrest Entries Eliminated*

From a careful, exploratory study of the two arrest-history sources, it was evident that all of the arrest entries contained therein were not usable for the purposes of determining arrest-history patterns. The following types of entries were ignored.

A. All entries concerned with minor traffic violations and certain regulatory laws concerned with building code violations, health regulations, licenses, etc.

B. Entries denoting arrests for "investigation" and "suspicious person," unless they were followed by subsequent criminal charges. Offenders with police records, especially Negro offenders, are frequently picked up by the police for purposes of investigation only to be released within a few hours or days with no official charge being placed against them in the "police blotter." Many arrests for "investigation" and "suspicious person" are of the indiscriminate type following a dragnet when the police are searching for an offender whose identity is unknown to them. Some Negroes are arrested for being present at some unlikely *place* or *hour* where and when *Negroes* are not ordinarily *expected* or *desired*. Such an unexplained presence at times results in an arrest for "investigation" or for "suspicious person." These arrests many times do not indicate criminal activity.

C. All juvenile delinquent entries, except those entries indicating charges which had been treated as adult offenses were not counted. Many juvenile complaints filed in the Juvenile Court do not eventuate into arrests, nor are they all handled in a strictly official manner. Such stumbling blocks as "the secrecy of proceedings," "transfer of the case," "prevention of stigma," "hope of the prodigal's parental redemption," etc., act to obstruct the listing of juvenile delinquent acts in terms of arrests by charge.

The social intake case worker attached to the Juvenile Court is permitted much latitude in determining the juvenile complaint papers to accept, the juvenile cases to appear before the Juvenile Court, the juvenile cases to be handled unofficially, etc. Such discretionary measures preclude the accurate tabulation of juvenile offenses by official definitive charges. Moreover, the entries denoting juvenile charges found in the source materials were many times indefinite as to the nature of the criminal or noncriminal incident which precipitated the contact with the Juvenile Court Authorities. Such entries as "Juvenile Letter," with no further explanation, were frequent. Finally, there appeared in the records many incidents of delinquency which seemed peculiar only to juveniles, e.g., truancy, running away from home, incorrigibility, vandalism being beyond parental control, etc. Such charges were deemed irrelevant and superfluous in determining arrest-history patterns. These general terms could be inclusive of anything from disobedience to a serious violation.

In summary, the lack of completeness of the juvenile record, its lack of uniformity and its vague and indefinite nomenclature precluded its intelligent translation into usable data for the purposes of determining arrest-history patterns. D. Arrests emanating from parole, conditional release and probation violations, which were not occasioned by new criminal charges, were ignored because they did not indicate additional criminal behavior.

III. *Recording Procedures*

First, a chronological list of arrests by criminal charges was made for each of the four-hundred cases from the D. C. Arrest Record. Duplications of entries were eliminated. In instances where one arrest was accompanied by several different charges, each charge was listed as a separate arrest. Different charges indicated different kinds of criminal behavior, and it was reasoned that this should be accounted for. These charges were recorded one after another as they appeared on the Police Record. The D. C. Police Department has no set standard (officially or in practice) for the order of recording a multiplicity of charges accompanying one arrest. They are entered in the record (at random) as they were reported by the arresting officer. In instances where one arrest was linked to several charges for the same kind of violation, only one charge was recorded.*

The next step in developing the arrest histories was the insertion of the arrests by charges appearing on the Federal Bureau of Investigation Abstract of Criminal Record (not cited on the D. C. Arrest Record) into the chronological list of arrests and charges developed from the D. C. Arrest Record, in their proper chronological order. All of these arrests occurred outside the jurisdiction of the District. The same method of listing arrests by charge was used as that employed above. The combined chronological listings of the arrests and charges from the D. C. Arrest Record and the F. B. I. Abstract of Criminal Record were then entered on a work sheet in the schedule for each inmate.

From a cursory study of these chronological lists of arrests and charges, it was obvious that three different legal nomenclatures were included: Federal charges; charges as defined by the D. C. Code; and various State charges. In order to avoid the complications involved in the three different nomenclatures found in the arrest histories, the charges for arrests were translated into the nomenclature utilized in defining offense categories found in the 1963 *Uniform Crime Reports for the United States* (with minor variations which are explained). For definitions of these offense categories utilized in the *Uniform Crime Reports* as well as the researcher's variations, see Appendix C.

The translation of the legal nomenclature from the three codes of law found in the arrest histories into that found in the *Uniform Crime Reports* was quite simple since most of the criminal charges noted (and all of the subsequent arrest pattern categories) were in terms of traditional criminal categories, e.g., assault, auto theft, forgery, robbery, etc. The refined charges by arrests were entered in the schedules on each of the four hundred cases. The chronological arrest histories were then ready for analysis.

---

*It was reasoned that the acts which led to charges of the same nature were essentially one unit of behavior, in view of their similarity and proximity in time. This procedure also had the virtue of producing a conservative estimate of the number of charges for the same kind of violation, and therefore led to a more reliable way of arriving at a given pattern classification.

Appendix B

THE SOCIAL CASE HISTORY SCHEDULE

THE SCHEDULE represented a tool devised for two purposes: (a) data collection from the official dossiers and (b)
data collection from the inmates in interview situations. The dual
nature of this schedule permitted the checking of one source
against the other. The four following parts constituted the
schedule:
1. Social and personal characteristics;
2. Qualitative clinical impressions;
3. Criminal pattern; and
4. Qualitative aspects of the official criminal record.

Parts 1 and 3 constituted the basic framework. Data from these
parts were used to determine the relationship between social
and personal characteristics and criminal patterns. The qualitative data provided for in Part 2 were utilized to record clinical
impressions of the offenders in the interview situations. Data
recorded in Part 4 pertained to length and nature of arrest
history, analysis of District Attorney's Reports and levels of *modi
operandi*. It was reasoned that this qualitative material would
shed light on the general personality traits of the offenders,
and that it would indicate the kind of criminal careers (if any)
these offenders possessed. The qualitative data were expected to
supplement the statistical findings.

PART 1: SOCIAL AND PERSONAL CHARACTERISTICS

This part of the schedule was structured to obtain data on
forty-two social and personal characteristics selected as significant
in their relationship to criminal behavior. Statistical comparisons
were made on thirty-four of these forty-two social and personal
characteristics which were considered to be more relevant and

upon which accurate and verifiable information was available for all of the four hundred cases. Among the discontinuous characteristics there were twenty-four on which information was collected in a dichotomous manner; i.e., the presence or absence of the given attribute was recorded. The data on the remaining discontinuous characteristics were registered into more than two classes. Tabulation of the data indicated that this classification was often too refined for the size of the sample. To avoid comparisons on a series of small frequency cells, these data were combined into two classes. In short, it was possible to dichotomize these remaining attributes without doing violence to the meaning of the combined data.

The areas of inquiry from which these attributes were chosen have been explored quite fully by many criminologists and represent fields of investigation in which researchers have claimed to find differentials between offenders and nonoffenders. By such a selective process, social and personal characteristics which were known to have a relationship to criminal behavior were made available for analysis. The areas from which these characteristics were taken roughly represent life-history periods. An examination of these areas in their relationship to criminality and the two independent factors of age and intelligence (also chosen for study) follows:

A. *The Eight Areas and the Two Attributes, Age and Intelligence*

1. FAMILY BACKGROUND

The family is the first social group in which the individual normally has membership. It is, therefore, the most important in early training and in the defining of social situations. It is the first channel through which the offender becomes familiar with his culture and competent or incompetent to live in it. It is here for the most part that his social values are molded. It is in the family background that one determines the success or failure of parental supervision during the formative years. Additionally, the family is the first group to which the offender attaches himself emotionally, and from which he receives or does not receive emotional satisfaction. The offender's present and past ties with his family group and the relations that he has had with this group offer a key to his behavior patterns.

Virtually all studies comparing the family background of delinquents and criminals with the family backgrounds of non-delinquents demonstrate marked differentials in terms of the high incidence of disorganization, demoralization, dependency and criminality found in the families of the delinquent and criminal group.

In considering this area of inquiry, the problem of securing information on several different family backgrounds in any one case arises. (It was assumed that a number of inmates had been reared in more than one home.) Such a task appeared to be arduous and in fact, unnecessary, because interest is in the family group that had exerted the most dominant and sustaining influence on the offender. The family group in which the offender had resided for the longest period of time from birth to age eighteen was selected as the one from which the family background factors would be taken. Interest was also focused on the kinds of social relations existing among family-group members, as well as family dependency, family disorganization, family demoralization and family criminality in this area.

2. NEIGHBORHOOD AND AREA BACKGROUND

Criminologists have been interested in area variation (in kind and volume) of crime and delinquency for many years, and several criminological studies have resulted from this interest. Generally speaking, crime is more prevalent in cities than in rural areas. Not only is crime concentrated in cities; but usually, the larger the city, the greater the per capita crime rate.

Shaw and McKay, in their chief study, *Juvenile Delinquency in Urban Areas,* have clearly demonstrated the high incidence of delinquency and crime in slum areas in several American cities. Next to the family, the neighborhood exerts the greatest influence in the process of socialization. The influence of the neighborhood is the influence of the type of people, the type families, social institutions, play groups, and other groups situated there. The attitudes and values of the inhabitants determine the atmosphere of the neighborhood. It is in the neighborhood that the offender is usually introduced to delinquency and crime—to the techniques of crime as well as to the attitudes which provide a rationale for criminal behavior. City slums contain areas of juvenile delinquency, and it is in these delinquency areas that criminal behavior is learned via play groups, delinquent companions and juvenile delinquent gangs.

The District of Columbia is not an industrial city; however, it was observed that many of its routine institutional cases were reared in the slum areas of the District—and that an appreciable number had resided, prior to their last arrest, in No. 2. Police Precinct, a notorious slum area with a high crime rate.

It was assumed that the Negro offenders represented by the D.C. Reformatory population had for the most part grown up in the District of Columbia slum areas and that they had lived in these areas throughout their lives. Specific interest was in the presence or absence of slum conditions (as a social characteristic) during the inmate's formative years and also at the time of his arrest. The presence of an urban or rural area background was of interest—as was the size of the urban area.

3. School Background and School Adjustment

The school is generally the first formal social institution to which the offender is compelled to adjust. It is the first testing ground set up by society outside the home situation. The school offers itself as the first proof of the offender's adaptability and capacity for socialization in a theatre of action in which there may be strict rules punitively enforced by non-parental authority. Rigid standards of behavior are set up from which there is little parental protection.

It is, moreover, in the school situation that many offenders first develop independent social relations with others, with schoolmates on an informal basis and with teachers on a formal basis. The school is interested in developing "good" boys and "good" girls who make average or better grades and who also conform to authority. A high premium is placed on success in school in the American culture. Those who for one reason or another fail to make a success in the school situation are subject to general social stigma, loss of status and, to some degree, social isolation from middle-class, respectable, law-abiding society.

Many studies in the past have shown the high incidence of truancy and academic failure on the part of delinquents when compared with non-delinquents. Differences between delinquents and non-delinquents in respect to school conduct have also been found. The author assumed the likelihood of a high incidence of academic failures, of school truancy and of school disciplinary problems among offenders in general. The view was, however, that marked differentials might exist in regard to those factors when different criminal types were considered. Focus was on school grade achievement, intelligence quotient, truancy and disciplinary problems at school in this area.

4. Work Background and Attitude Toward Work

"They just don't want to work for a living," is a common and trite expression used by many institutional employees in referring to their wards. Though not implemented by a clear-cut frame of reference and research findings, this view may constitute an implicit theory of crime causation.

An assumption was that certain types of offenders might vary in their work backgrounds and in their attitudes toward work, that the nature of certain jobs might predispose to delinquency and crime, (e.g., "street trades jobs"), that certain types of offenders had no desire or plans ever to work regularly. Work background and attitude toward work loomed as very important factors in determining social types. In this area, there was specific interest in "street trades jobs," occupational types, work habits and attitudes toward work at release.

5. Indices of Personal Disorganization

The relationship of crime to alcohol, drugs and gambling has been discussed pro and con by many writers.

a. Alcohol. In regard to alcohol, intoxication in certain situations is defined as a crime and drunkenness accounts for the largest single category of offenders for which arrests are made in the United States. Many "problem drinkers" and alcoholics find themselves in jails and workhouses for successive short periods of time. Many of these offenders appear to be habitual criminals by virtue of their personal vice, alcohol. Some of them serve time at one time or another in reformatories and penitentiaries.

On the other hand, it was expected that heavy drinking would be associated with other types of criminal behavior (not including intoxication *per se*), e.g., crimes of violence—assault and sex crimes.

b. Drug Addiction. The relation of the use of drugs to crime involves two aspects: (1) behavior connected with obtaining and using drugs and defined by law as criminal; and (2) behavior ascribed to be associated with the use of drugs and violating laws other than narcotics drug laws. The relative high incidence of drug use by criminals has been documented. Which comes first, drug addiction or criminality? Is drug use a motivating factor toward a criminal career or incidental to a criminal career? Drug-addict offenders were expected to vary in social and personality type from other types of offenders.

c. Gambling. The precise relationship between gambling and crime is not known. Many types of gambling are criminal in most jurisdictions, but not all gambling is criminal behavior. High arrest rates for gambling among Negroes is a known fact. Moreover, gambling has been assumed to be the chief means of recreation for members of the underworld.

d. Mobility. It was expected that a nomadic way of life lends itself more readily to criminal activity than a stable residential pattern. The homeless man who wanders from place to place has no primary group affiliations to exert the normal social pressures of conformity. He is more or less a law unto himself. It was further assumed that certain types of criminal behavior, e.g., confidence games, might be associated with high mobility.

In this area, interest was in the problem drinker, the drug addict, the inveterate gambler and the nomad.

6. MILITARY ADJUSTMENT

An offender's service record in the Armed Services offered itself as one criterion for the offender's social adjustment. Were some types of offenders apparently more successful in the Armed Services than others? Did failure to adjust in the Armed Services follow other behavior patterns of non-adjustment—criminal patterns?

In this area the researcher was specifically interested in the type of military discharge and the presence or absence of a confinement record in the service. Unfortunately, since three fourths of the research subjects had no history of military service, this attribute could not be used for comparative purposes.

7. MARITAL STATUS

The marriage situation offers another source from which social adjustment might be inferred. Social relations in the conjugal group also offer a source for behavior patterning. Studies show a higher proportion of criminals than of the general population to be unmarried or to have failed in marriage.

Criminologists have frequently called attention to the fact that offenders with extensive criminal histories have a tendency to sever ties with conventional social groups—the parental family group, church groups, law-abiding community groups and the conjugal group.

It was hypothesized that certain types of offenders would vary in this differential proportion and that such variation might help to determine a social type which would correspond to certain criminal patterns.

8. INDICES OF JUVENILE DELINQUENCY

It is generally assumed that juvenile delinquency is closely related to crime—that they merge into each other.

Much has been written about the adult offender's former association with delinquent companions and juvenile gangs and his commitment to juvenile correctional institutions. There seems to be no doubt that adults who are sentenced to reformatories and prisons demonstrate a high proportion of pre-adult delinquency involvement. On the other hand, some adult offenders' records reveal no juvenile delinquency. Certainly, some adult offenders have never been officially adjudicated juvenile delinquents. Additionally, it might be reasonable to assume that some juvenile delinquents never mature into adult criminals. Some might drop out of criminal activity.

Evidence of juvenile delinquency might constitute a necessary adjunct to the understanding of an adult criminal pattern. Some writers interpret juvenile delinquency involvement as a form of antisocial behavior which foretells the likelihood of violent crimes in the future. Others perceive juvenile delinquency as conformist behavior in reference to membership in certain groups. This researcher expected to find that certain types of adult offenders would vary in regard to their incidence of prior delinquency involvement. He hypothesized that higher rates of juvenile delinquency involvement would be found among serious property offenders than among other offenders.

Specific interest was narrowed to juvenile delinquent companions, adjudications, police contacts and criminal companions in this area.

9. AGE AND INTELLIGENCE

a. Age. Many criminologists have noted the factor of age in crime, and it is usually included in criminological research. Delinquency is usually known to come to official attention in later childhood. It increases in volume of reporting to the juvenile court up to ages sixteen to seventeen. Young adults, age group twenty to thirty, are arrested more frequently than any other age group. Some types of offenses, moreover, are more frequently committed by one age group than by other age groups. In short, some offenses have an older, and some have a younger age distribution; e.g., burglary is primarily an offense of persons under twenty-five years of age. Crimes of violence and aggression occur more frequently among the younger offenders than among the older offenders. Biological and sociological factors have been mentioned as causes of these differentials. Whatever the reasons behind them, age differentials for certain offenses have been found, and for this reason the age factor was included in this study.

b. Intelligence. The factor of intelligence is generally considered in most criminological studies which include an analysis of the social background and the personality factors of offenders. It was expected that differentials in intelligence among offenders with different criminal patterns might be marked. Certain types of offenses may call for more intelligence than others, e.g., check forgery as a way of life obviously calls for a higher degree of intelligence than petty theft; operating a lottery business at times calls for acute decisions which seem to require at least average intelligence.

B. *The Forty-two Social and Personal Characteristics*

1. AGE

a. Definition. Chronological age at time of last arrest.
b. Sources. Bureau of Vital Statistics, D.C. Reformatory letter written to parents or relatives of the inmate requesting certain developmental history.

2. INTELLIGENCE QUOTIENT

a. Definition. IQ as determined from the Lindner Gurvitz Revised Beta IQ Test. The following scale is self-explanatory.
   (1) 70 and below—defective.
   (2) 71-79—inferior.
   (3) 80-89—below average.
   (4) 90-109—average.
   (5) 110-119—above average.
   (6) 120-128—superior.
   (7) 129-Upward—very superior.
b. Sources. From test results taken at the D.C. Re-

formatory by a researcher who had a Ph.D. in psychology. Results were recorded in the offender's institutional folder.

3. REARED IN ONE HOME, TWO HOMES, THREE OR MORE HOMES

a. Definition. Each residence in a children's home or orphanage counts as one home residence.

(1) One home means that at no time did inmate live in more than one family group for a continuous period of one year or longer from birth to age eighteen.

(2) Two homes means inmate lived in two different family groups for a period of one year or longer from birth to age eighteen.

(3) Three or more homes means subject lived in three or more different family groups for continuous periods of one year or longer from birth to age eighteen.

b. Reasons for selection. It is generally agreed among the students of human behavior that residence in one parental family, everything else being equal, is more conducive to adjustment than is residence in two or more family groups. Many researchers in the field of criminology have called attention to the less stable family environments of delinquents and criminals as compared with control groups of non-delinquents and noncriminals.

c. Sources. Family letter, institutional case worker's Social History, and researcher's interview.

4. MOTHER FIGURE SOUTHERN MIGRANT

a. Definition. The mother figure migrated from the South to the District of Columbia or to points farther north, following her eighteenth birthday.

b. Reasons for selection. The writer assumed that many Negro inmates at the D.C. Reformatory constituted a first generation group in the District of Columbia; that is, they were born into the homes of migrant mothers

from the South. This was conceived of as a negative social background factor.

As a rule, Negro migrants who come to the city live in the most undesirable areas because of economic pressure and housing segregation policies. Southern migrants are known to have difficulty in adjusting to metropolitan life. Many of them are bewildered by the new and impersonal competition found in the city. Stealing may seem to be the way out. Others may react to the release from white restraints found in the South, *viz.*, rowdiness, vandalism, etc.

Washington, the first major city north of the Potomac receives many Negro migrants directly from the South. It was assumed, everything else being equal, that indigenous District of Columbia mothers would have less difficulty in rearing children than mothers who were southern migrants. The mother figure, rather than the father figure, was employed because children usually accompany the mother figure.

c. Sources. Family letter, institutional case worker's Social History and researcher's interview.

5. MOTHER FIGURE DOMESTIC SERVANT

a. Definition. The mother or mother figure worked as a domestic servant for a period of four years or longer during the inmate's stay in the home situation.

b. Reasons for selection. Domestic service is considered to be a low-status occupation by Negroes as well as by whites. It is generally associated with family economic pressure. Moreover, it entails long hours by the mother figure outside the home situation. It is the consensus among many students of juvenile delinquency that working mothers are a contributing factor to delinquency.

c. Sources. Family letter, institutional case worker's Social History and researcher's interview.

6. DEPENDENCY STATUS OF THE FAMILY GROUP

a. Definition.

(1) Independent. Family has never received financial aid from public or private social agency while the inmate was in residence from birth to age eighteen.

(2) Occasionally dependent. Family received financial aid from a public or private social agency not exceeding one third of the time (continually or intermittently) during the inmate's residence from birth to age eighteen.

(3) Dependent. Family received financial aid from a public or private social agency for more than one third of the time (continuously or intermittently) during the inmate's residence from birth to age eighteen. (The intervals mentioned are approximations.)

b. Reasons for selection. The high rates of family dependency among families of offenders have been noted by many criminologists.

c. Sources. Family letter, institutional case worker's Social History and researcher's interview.

7. The Family Group Broken by Desertion

a. Definition. The family group of inmate was broken by the desertion of either parental figure one or more times while he resided in the home situation from birth to age eighteen.

b. Reasons for selection. Much has been written about the broken home factor in relationship to delinquency and crime; however, the significance of this factor remains controversial. The writer reasoned that the *kind* of family break was the crucial issue. A broken home by desertion is the most frequent break referred to in recent studies of offenders. It is this kind of break that the writer considered most significant. Desertion, sometimes called the poor man's divorce, is usually a crime in itself. It may involve feelings of injustice and hatred, as well as serious economic handicaps for the deserted family. The high incidence

of desertion rates among urban Negroes has been noted by several criminologists who are interested in the relationship of this factor to crime.

c. Sources. Family letter, institutional case worker's Social History and researcher's interview.

8. DEMORALIZED FAMILY GROUP

a. Definition. Any one of the following factors was present in the inmate's home situation during any time of his residence from birth to age eighteen.

(1) The excessive use of alcohol by a family group member.

(2) The use of opiate drugs by a family group member.

(3) Prostitution by a family group member.

(4) The practice of adultery by the mother figure.

(5) Incestuous sex practices within the family group.

(6) Brutality practices by a family group member.

b. Reasons for selection. Many researchers have referred to the high incidence of demoralization (drunkenness, sexual license, illegitimacy, etc.) in the families of offenders when compared with the families of non-offenders.

c. Sources. Family letter, institutional case worker's Social History and researcher's interview.

9. CRIMINALITY IN THE FAMILY GROUP

a. Definition. While the inmate was in residence from birth to age eighteen, a criminal conviction resulted in any one of the following.

(1) More than one misdemeanor commitment of any member of the family.

(2) Juvenile delinquent commitment of any member of the family.

(3) Probation of any member of the family.

(4) Felony commitment of any member of the family.

(5) Repetitious criminal fines of any member of the family.

b. Reasons for selection. Many criminologists through the years have noted that criminal patterns may be acquired within the family circle itself, that parents may deliberately teach children to commit crimes and that offenders may acquire delinquent patterns through imitation of similar behavior by parents or other members of the family.

c. Sources. Family letter, institutional case worker's Social History and researcher's interview.

10. DOMINANT PARENTAL FIGURE IN THE FAMILY GROUP

    a. Definition.

        (1) Father figure. Father figure played the dominant role in the following.

           (a) Interpersonal relations with his spouse.

           (b) Decision-making in family crisis situations.

           (c) Disciplining the children.

        (2) Mother figure. Mother figure played the dominant role in the following.

           (a) Interpersonal relations with her spouse.

           (b) Decision-making in family crisis situations.

           (c) Disciplining the children.

        (3) Neither dominant. Neither parental figure dominated all three areas mentioned above. In situations where only one parental figure was present in the home situation, that figure was defined as the dominant parental figure.

b. Reasons for selection. The writer hypothesized that the presence of a dominant mother figure was related to the high crime rates of urban Negroes. The mother figure, rather than the father figure, is quite often the dominant parent in Negro families of the lower socio-economic class. E. Franklin Frazier, a serious student of the Negro family in the United States, found the matriarchal type of Negro family in the city to be characterized by a high incidence of juvenile delinquency.*

The presence of the matriarchal Negro family in urban areas is probably explained by several factors, some of which appear to be negative: (1) survivals of the Negro plantation family, which was predominantly matriarchal; (2) the low economic status and the economic insecurity of the Negro male in the city; (3) the relative assurance of employment in domestic service by the Negro female (such assurance in many cases places her in the role of the breadwinner and the family's mainstay); *†(4) high desertion rates among Negroes, which many times means the absence of a father figure in many Negro families.

In addition to the negative social significance of certain aspects of the Negro matriarchal families, there appear to be negative psychological aspects as well. The lack of the physical presence of a father figure in a home situation was considered to be a negative factor, as well as the presence of a father figure in a home situation dominated by a mother figure. Two views of the writer prompted this assumption. (1) Traditionally, in Western culture, the father figure is the true authority figure. The lack of paternal control in the cases of adolescent males may lead to excessive freedom. The lack of a forceful male who elicits respect and emulation may result in a lack of consideration for authority by many youths. (2) A dominant maternal influence might to some degree emasculate a son's true feelings of maleness.

c. Sources. Family letter, institutional case worker's Social History and researcher's interview.

---

*FRAZIER, FRANKLIN: *The Negro in the U.S.* New York, MacMillan,

†ROEBUCK, JULIAN B.: Domestic Service: With Particular Attention to the Negro Female Servant in the South. Master's Thesis, Duke University, Durham, North Carolina, 1944, pp. 80-85.

11. SUPERVISION BY THE FATHER FIGURE IN THE FAMILY GROUP

a. Definition. The father figure met one of the conditions listed below in his role as a father.

(1) Lax. Exerted the role of a passive or indifferent parent in regard to the inmate's activities.

(2) Regimented. Exerted the role of a stern disciplinarian in his stringent control of the inmate's activities.

(3) Erratic. Exerted the role of a vacillating parent in his inconsistent methods of regulating the inmate's activities.

(4) Adequate. Exerted the role of a firm, considerate and kind parent in his consistent control of the inmate's activities.

b. Reasons for selection. Parental supervision of children is a process of socialization. It is through parental supervision that the child gets a conception of differences between right and wrong and learns the varying consequences of different kinds of behavior. Previous researchers have called attention to the high incidence of inadequate parental supervision found in the backgrounds of offenders—indifference and laxity, severity, inconsistency.

c. Sources. Family letter, institutional case worker's Social History and researcher's interview.

12. SUPERVISION BY THE MOTHER FIGURE IN THE FAMILY GROUP

(See 11 above—same process utilized for mother figure.)

13. CONFLICT WITH FAMILY GROUP

a. Definition. Inmate's conscious conflict with any sibling or parental figure or other member of the family group involving tension or discord concerned with questions of status, family role, dominance, differences in values, rights and acceptance, from birth to age eighteen.

(1) Marked. Conflict was intense and enduring for at least one year. Inmate was keenly aware of a conflict situation which he found to be disturbing and a source of marked unhappiness.

(2) Traces. Conflict for at least one year appeared to have been greater than that found in normal family life, but conflict which did not cause marked unhappiness.

(3) Non-apparent. Self-explanatory.

b. Reasons for selection. Psychiatrists and clinical psychologists who have done research in criminology have stressed the early development of character and personality structure in the offender, which they claim evolves from his interpersonal relationships with family members—primarily the parents. According to them, the personality structure gets deeply imbedded in the unconscious emotional life of the individual, and it becomes the basis for unconscious motivation of behavior. Many of them refer to the high incidence of emotional tension, discord and conflict found in the families of offenders, which involves the offenders themselves, as well as their siblings and parents. Faulty interpersonal relations between parents and children is said to cause these difficulties. Healy and Bronner, the Gluecks, Friedlander and many others illustrate this point in their studies.*

Primary interest here was in ferreting out objective, overt conflicts which were produced by events in the external environment. Family conflict involving the inmate under study indicated an emotionally unhealthy home environment. An unhappy, emotionally unhealthy home situation could lead to an offender's escaping the home situation in order to find affection, security and recognition elsewhere. Elsewhere could be "street

---

*FRIEDLANDER, KATE: *Psychoanalytical Approach to Juvenile Delinquency.* New York, International University Press, 1947.

corner society" in a slum area where delinquents and criminals were present.

c. Sources. Family letter, institutional case worker's Social History and researcher's interview.

14. HOSTILITY EXPRESSED TOWARD FATHER FIGURE IN THE FAMILY GROUP

a. Definition. The inmate expressed a degree of enmity, antagonism, resentment or dislike toward the father figure, stemming from his basic lack of admiration or respect or both for said parental figure. The parental figure was not fully accepted. Inmate's feelings varied from ambivalence to hatred.

(1) Marked. Extreme dislike and (apparent) complete rejection of the father figure.

(2) Traces. Ambivalent feelings with partial acceptance.

(3) Non-apparent.

b. Reasons for selection. Many writers psychoanalytically orientated have associated antisocial behavior in general, and delinquency and crime specifically, with parental hostility. The reaction of an individual to parental rejection or parental deprivation of life and affection, or both, is said to be essentially one of hostility. The hostility felt for the parent or parents is claimed to be carried over to others in a symbolic manner.* The Gluecks, in their study *Unraveling Juvenile Delinquency,* found mutual hostility or indifference between parents and children characterized their delinquents in a startling proportion of cases. Sixty per cent of the fathers of the delinquents, but only 19 per cent of the fathers of the non-delinquents, were indifferent or hostile.*

---

*FRIEDLANDER, KATE: Latent delinquency and ego development. In Eissler, Kurt R. (ed.): *Searchlights on Delinquency.* New York, International University Press, 1949, pp. 205-215.

*GLUECKS: *Unraveling Juvenile Delinquency,* pp. 115-133.

c. Sources. Family letter, institutional case worker's Social History and researcher's interview.

15. HOSTILITY EXPRESSED TOWARD MOTHER FIGURE IN THE FAMILY GROUP

(See 14 above—same process utilized for mother figure.)

16. DISCIPLINARY PROBLEM IN THE FAMILY GROUP

a. Definition. The inmate was a disciplinary problem in the home situation if any one of the following conditions prevailed.

(1) Marked disobedience.

(2) Persistent lying.

(3) Marked insubordination.

(4) Persistent thievery.

b. Reasons for selection. These questions have often arisen: Do offenders represent individuals who have been maladjusted throughout life? Were they at one time "problem children"—disciplinary problems at home or at school? Does a pattern of maladjustment follow in all of their group memberships? Writers have taken sides in this great debate. The clinical psychologists and the psychiatrists are prone to stress the offender's faulty adjustment in the home situation. The sociologists are prone to argue that faulty adjustment in the home situation or, for that matter, faulty adjustment in any other group situation is not a prerequisite to delinquency. Some students of the problem have devised a dichotomy of offenders to answer the question—conformists and nonconformists. The conformist delinquent is depicted as an essentially well-organized personality who becomes involved in delinquent behavior as a consequence of the mores of the various groups to which he belongs; the mores in these groups define delinquent behavior as acceptable. The nonconformist delinquent is portrayed as a rebel against conventional norms and authority. He has emotional difficulties, and his motivation for delinquent behavior is interpreted in psychological rather than sociological terms. This type fails to adjust in any group situation.

It was assumed that different types of offenders might vary in regard to this factor; e.g., offenders with criminal patterns of violence would reveal this trait more frequently in their backgrounds than offenders with nonviolent criminal patterns.

c. Sources. Family letter, institutional case worker's Social History and researcher's interview.

17. HISTORY OF RUNNING AWAY FROM HOME

a. Definition. The offender during the formative years (to age eighteen) frequently departed from the home situation without the permission of the parental figures. A "runaway" is defined as one who made a premeditated departure (overnight or longer) from the home without the permission or knowledge of the parental figures. Frequency as used here referred to a pattern of behavior occurring for at least one year during which a minimum of three runaways were noted.

b. Reasons for selection. This factor has been referred to by many researchers in the field of delinquency and crime. Running away from home is generally interpreted as a step in the progression of a delinquent and criminal career. Home ties may many times be cut to be replaced by ties with delinquent and criminal companions—gangs.

Some writers have stressed the lack of emotional security in the home, which they claim drives the child from the home in search of other agencies to satisfy his basic needs. The sociologist is likely to stress the unsavory companions who are met in "street corner society" following home runaways, and the transfer of delinquent patterns as social patterns in this society. The psychologist views criminal activities participated in by youths who are runaways as methods of acting out frustrations and as vehicles of action which meet certain basic needs.

c. Sources. Family letter, institutional case worker's Social History and researcher's interview.

18. PRESENT FAMILY TIES OF THE FAMILY GROUP

a. Definition. The cohesiveness within the family of orientation (excluding the inmate) as shown by visiting contacts, correspondence, family reunions and mutual aid.

(1) Minimum requirements for labeling ties as "strong."

(a) In situations where either one or both parental figures were alive, one parental figure and the majority of that parental figure's children constituted a closely-knit group—a group whose members accepted each other and shared intimate contacts.

(b) In situations where both parental figures were dead, the majority of their children constituted a closely-knit group.

(c) In situations where the inmate represented an only child, both parental figures were alive and living together.

(2) Requirements for labeling ties as "weak." Some contacts existed between parental family group members, but they failed to meet the minimum requirements noted above.

(3) Family ties absent. Self-explanatory.

b. Reasons for selection. The sociologists and the psychologists have stressed the dearth of family cohesion among the parental families of offenders—lack of strong ties in the family group was interpreted as a negative social characteristic.

The researcher was aware of the fact that "present family ties" did not necessarily reflect the social past; however, he settled for this, because the family ties throughout the past were extremely difficult to determine.

c. Sources. Family letter, institutional case worker's Social History and researcher's interview.

19. INMATE'S PRESENT TIES WITH HIS FAMILY GROUP

a. Definition. The inmate's ties with the family group as shown by mail and visiting contacts met one of the following conditions.

(1) Minimum requirements for labeling ties as "strong."

(a) In situations where either one or both parental figures were alive, the inmate received regular visits or regular mail from one parental figure and from the majority of his siblings, who constituted a closely knit group.

(b) In situations where both parental figures were dead, the inmate received regular visits or regular mail from the majority of his siblings, who constituted a closely-knit group.

(c) In situations where the inmate represented an only child of two living parents, he received regular mail or regular visits from both. The parents live together.

(d) In situations where the inmate represented an only child of one living parental figure, he received regular mail or regular visits from this figure.

(2) Requirements for labeling ties as "weak." Inmate received some mail or visits or both from one or more members of the family group, but they in no way met the minimum requirements above.

(3) Family ties absent. Inmate received no mail and no visits from any member of the family group.

b. Reason for selection. There appears to be a consensus among many sociologists that the confirmed criminal has made a break with the noncriminal world.

Parental and conjugal group ties are believed to be weak or nonexistent for many criminals. Offenders in general are referred to by many prison staff members as individuals who lack strong family ties. It is not at all clear many times whether the lack of strong parental group ties is suggested as a cause or effect of criminal activity. Be this as it may, the lack of strong parental group ties does appear to characterize incarcerated offenders.

Mail and visiting contacts offered the most concrete basis for ascertaining the strength of present family ties.

c. Sources. Institutional mail and Visiting Record and researcher's interview.

20. AREA REARED IN

a. Definition. The inmate lived for the longest period of time between ages six and eighteen in one of the following:

(1) Rural area (area of less than 2,500 population).

(2) District of Columbia.

(3) Other urban area (population between 2,500 and 25,000).

(4) Other urban area (population over 25,000).

b. Sources. Family letter, institutional case worker's Social History and researcher's interview.

21. REARED IN SLUM NEIGHBORHOOD (applies only to those inmates who were reared in urban areas—2,500 or more population).

a. Definition. The inmate lived for the longest period of time between ages six and eighteen in one of the following.

(1) In the District of Columbia in a dwelling or dwellings situated in one or more of the eleven "urban renewal areas" as designated by James W. Rause and Nathaniel S. Keith in their study, *No Slums in Ten Years* (see item 22 for explana-

tion). The domiciles were surrounded (within a radius of one square block) by a majority of the following conditions: physically deteriorated, overcrowded domiciles; tenement houses; roominghouses; outside toilets; high rates of dependency; high rates of home renters; commercial or industrial surroundings; juvenile delinquent street gangs; presence of adult criminals.

(2) In *other* urban areas in a dwelling or dwellings situated in a neighborhood or neighborhoods (an area within the square block of inmate's residence), which was or were characterized by the majority of the slum conditions required in the above item 1. The "square-block" area rather than the area within a radius of one block of inmate's residence was used in defining the neighborhoods for this group of inmates because the researcher was not so well acquainted with the various urban areas from which they came as he was with the District of Columbia. Maps designating square-block areas were not available for this group.

b. Sources. Researcher's interview and the "Urban Renewal Areas" as taken from the Rause-Keith map.* (see item 22). The researcher designated the neighborhoods of the inmates reared in the District of Columbia with the use of a compass and the "Urban Renewal Area Map." The inmate was then quizzed on the criteria mentioned above, which revealed the presence or absence of slum conditions. Thus the designation "Reared in Slum Neighborhood" was determined by the researcher's qualified judgment of the inmate's reports during the interview.

---

*RAUSE, JAMES W., and KEITH, NATHANIEL S.: *No Slums in Ten Years.* Washington, Government Printing Office, 1955, pp. 26-32.

22. Living in Slum Area when Arrested
   a. Definition.
      (1) Inmates with District of Columbia addresses
      at the time of arrest. The inmate's D.C. address at
      the time of his arrest on the current charge was
      found by the researcher to exist within one of the
      eleven "urban renewal areas," slum areas,
      delineated by Rause and Keith in their study, *No
      Slums in Ten Years*. (The researcher was not con-
      cerned here with any legal residence requirements.
      Visitors and transients with only temporary D.C.
      addresses were included along with bona fide
      D.C. residents.)

      Rause and Keith's study, initiated on October
      1, 1954, was financed by the District of Columbia
      Government. The District Commissioners con-
      templated the development of a workable program
      for slum prevention and elimination in the District
      of Columbia as authorized under Section 20 (j)
      of the District of Columbia Redevelopment Act of
      1945. Mr. Keith (at present a private redevelop-
      ment and housing consultant, formerly [1949-
      1953] Director of the National Slum Clearance
      and Urban Redevelopment Division for the
      Housing and Home Finance Agency) and James
      W. Rause (past Chairman of President Eisen-
      hower's Sub-Committee on Urban Redevelopment
      during the year 1953) were under contract to the
      District of Columbia Government to delineate
      and identify the slum areas in the District of
      Columbia, and to make recommendations for their
      improvement or removal. Eleven "urban renewal
      areas," "slum areas," were delineated on a num-
      bered, square-block map of the District of Co-
      lumbia. These areas were mapped on the basis
      of an analysis of the 1950 Housing Census data for
      the District of Columbia, an analysis of previous

slum studies of the District of Columbia by the National Capital Planning Commission and personal field investigation by Rause and Keith. Technical aid was received from engineers and cartographers employed by the Redevelopment and Land Agency, a District of Columbia agency, which at the time of the study was engaged in the slum clearance of Southwest Washington.

The following criteria were utilized by Rause and Keith in the determination of eleven "urban renewal areas."

(a) Substandard housing.

(b) Ratio of home owners to home renters.

(c) Population congestion.

(d) Conflicting land uses.

(e) Facilities for the recreation and play of children.

(f) Street cleanliness and street lighting.

i. Southwest Washington. This urban renewal area constitutes that area between the Capitol and the Mall and the Potomac River. It is bounded on the north by Independence Avenue, on the east by South Capitol Street and Canal Street, on the south by P Street and by Maine Avenue on the west and southwest.

ii. Northwest Renewal Area. This is an area within the boundaries roughly corresponding with the Second Police Precinct. It is bounded on the west by 14th Street, on the north by U Street and Florida Avenue, on the east by the Washington Terminal Company Tracks and on the south by Massachusetts Avenue and K Street, N.W.

iii. Northeast Renewal Area. This is an

area bounded on the south by East Capitol Street, on the west by Second Street and the Washington Terminal Company Tracks, on the north by Florida Avenue and on the east by 16th Street, N.E.

iv. Southeast Section. This area is bounded by 19th Street on the east, the Anacostia River on the south, South Capitol Street to C Street on the west and by East Capitol Street on the north.

v. Foggy Bottom. This area lies between New Hampshire Avenue on the east, Virginia Avenue on the south, Rock Creek Parkway on the west and K Street on the north.

vi. Washington Circle Area. This area lies to the north of Washington Circle, bounded on the east by New Hampshire Avenue, on the south by Pennsylvania Avenue, on the west by Rock Creek Parkway and on the north by P Street.

vii. The Area North of Massachusetts Avenue. This area is east of 18th Street, N.W., south of Florida Avenue, west of 14th Street, N.W. and north of Massachusetts Avenue. It adjoins the Northwest boundary of the Northwest Urban Renewal Area.

viii. The Area North of U Street. This area is north of U Street, N.W., east of 14th Street, N.W., south of Park Road and Harvard Street, N.W. and west of Georgia Avenue and 11th Street, N.W.

ix. The Area South of Massachusetts Avenue. This area is south of Massachusetts Avenue, N.W., west of North

Capitol Street, north of D Street, N.W. and east of 4th Street, N.W. It is separated from the Northwest Urban Renewal Area by the boundary of Massachusetts Avenue, N.W.

x. Marshal Heights. This is a triangular-shaped area that lies in the easterly corner of the District. It is bounded on the north by Ayers Place, on the east by Hillside Place, on the south by Southern Avenue and Fifth Street and on the west by St. Louis and 49th Streets, S.E.

xi. Barry Farms. This area is bounded on the west and south by Suitland Parkway, S.E., on the northeast by Howard Road and on the east by Elvans Road, the continuation of First Place and Sheridan.

(2) Inmates with addresses in other urban areas at the time of their arrest. (There were no inmates in the study with rural addresses.) Transients, visitors and other nonresidents of the District of Columbia (without District of Columbia addresses) whose last address existed at a dwelling unit situated within a slum area as reported and defined by the inmate in the interview situation.

b. Reasons for selection. Criminologists have made much of the fact that their research findings reveal that many offenders live in slum areas. A high incidence of this factor was expected; however, it was also expected that differentials in addresses in slum areas existed among different types of offenders. Expected also was a very high incidence of slum addresses among institutionalized recidivists, alcoholic offenders and drug-addict offenders. It was reasoned that the confirmed recidivist remains in slum areas because of his break with respectable, law-abiding society. It is in the slum area that he is likely to find his companions in crime and the anonymity necessary to his antisocial scheme of life. It was assumed that the drug addict and the alcoholic would be likely to reside in slum areas because of their derelict status and because of the ready availability of their personal vices. Contrariwise, it was assumed that certain offenders with criminal patterns indicating professional crime might avoid slum area addresses.

c. Sources. The inmate's verified address as reported by the District of Columbia Police Department, which is entered on the offender's District Jail Commitment Card (which is found in the institutional folder) at the time of his commitment to the D.C. Jail. This address was spotted on a numbered, square-block map of the District of Columbia, upon which the writer superimposed the eleven "Urban Renewal Areas" delineations of Rause and Keith. If the address was found to exist in one of the eleven urban-renewal areas, the subject was considered to have lived in a slum area at the time of his arrest; if not, he was considered to have lived in a non-slum area at the time of his arrest.

23. STANFORD ACHIEVEMENT TEST GRADE MEDIAN

    a. Definition. Median grade level as determined from the Stanford Achievement Test, Intermediate Battery Partial, Form L.

        (1) 0-1.9.
        (2) 2-3.9.
        (3) 4-5.9.
        (4) 6-7.9.
        (5) 8-9.9
        (6) 10-10.4.

b. Reasons for selection. The writer reasoned that differentials in educational level as well as in intelligence were significant among offenders. Certain types of crimes appeared to call for higher levels of education than others; e.g., the operator of a lottery game needs some knowledge of bookkeeping and accounting. On the other hand, simple theft and crimes of violence do not require high educational achievement.

c. Sources. From test results taken at the D.C. Reformatory, which are recorded in the offender's institutional folder.

24. HISTORY OF SCHOOL TRUANCY

a. Definition. Inmate was called to the attention of a truant officer or a school official for persistent truancy.

b. Sources. Family letter, institutional case worker's Social History and researcher's interview.

25. DISCIPLINARY PROBLEM AT SCHOOL

a. Definition. Inmate was suspended or expelled from school at some time for disciplinary reasons.

b. Sources. Family letter, institutional case worker's Social History and researcher's interview.

26. WORKED AT STREET TRADES AS A JUVENILE

a. Definition. Inmate worked six months or longer prior to age eighteen at any of the following jobs: newspaper street jobs; huckster trade; bell-hop; delivery boy; porter; shoeshine boy; golf-course caddy; bowling alley pinsetter; employee at a race track.

b. Reasons for selection. This factor has been discussed by many criminologists as a negative social factor, and its high incidence among juvenile delinquents is often commented on. The vernacular of "street corner society" is often picked up in these jobs—also the philosophy of the "fast buck." Contacts with juvenile delinquents, criminals, alcoholics, prostitutes, drug addicts and gamblers are often mentioned as a consequence of "street trade" jobs.

c. Sources. Family letter, institutional case worker's Social History and researcher's interview.

27. OCCUPATIONAL TYPE

a. Definition. Inmate was one of the following types.

(1) Skilled laborer. Inmate worked for at least

six months as a skilled laborer, which is defined as a worker who used tools and processes which are usable only by one who has been trained for a period of time (over six months) in trade school or as an apprentice. He was familiar with the technical aspects of his skilled job, e.g., blueprint reading.

(2) Semiskilled laborer. The semiskilled worker used tools and processes requiring some training and he worked for at least six months as a semiskilled laborer. He had had a period of experience under guidance or study at the trade. The processes, however, were not greatly complicated, and the period of training was short (three months).

(3) Unskilled laborer. The inmate worked at any kind of rough task for which he had no training. Mere strength of hand or keenness of eye—untutored through any course of apprenticeship training—was the only requirement.

(4) Clerical worker. Self-explanatory.

(5) Other.

b. Sources. (Definitions for skilled laborer, semiskilled laborer and unskilled laborer were adoptions of those used by Sheldon and Eleanor Glueck in their *Five Hundred Criminal Careers**) D. C. Reformatory letters to former employers requesting employment verification, institutional case worker's Social History and researcher's interview.

28. WORK HABITS

a. Definition. The inmate's employment pattern met one of the following conditions.

(1) Regular worker. Employed in the five-year period prior to last incarceration, for one year or longer by the same employer, or continually em-

---

*GLUECK: *Five Hundred Criminal Careers,* p. 114.

ployed (with less than three week's break in employment) in any number of jobs for a period of one year or longer.

(2) Irregular. Sketchy work history which does not meet the above requirements for regular employment.

b. Sources. Institutional case worker's Social History and researcher's interview, D.C. Reformatory letters to former employers requesting employment verification.

29. ATTITUDE TOWARD WORK ON RELEASE

a. Definition. Inmate expressed one of the following attitudes in regard to work on release.

(1) Positive attitude. Subject expressed a keen interest in seeking permanent employment upon release. He thought that steady employment was necessary to his social adjustment.

(2) Indifferent attitude. Subject expressed no definite plan to seek permanent employment upon release or parole termination date. He indicated that he would work if necessary; however, he was not convinced that regular employment was essential to his social adjustment.

(3) Negative attitude. Subject did not plan to seek permanent employment upon his release. He denied that work was necessary to his social adjustment (beyond conditional release or parole termination date).

b. Reasons for selection. On the basis of the following assumptions, it was reasoned that this attribute might vary with different offender types.

(1) The writer surmised that offenders with brief arrest histories without criminal patterns and offenders free of alcohol or drug addiction would have a more regular work history and a more positive attitude toward work than those offenders who did have criminal patterns and those of-

fenders who were addicted to alcohol or narcotic drugs.

(2) It was assumed that offenders with criminal patterns indicating property crimes were primarily concerned with criminal activity as a means of livelihood. Such offenders were expected to have negative attitudes toward work.

(3) Offenders suffering from drug addiction or alcoholism were expected to be personally disorganized to the extent that regular work habits prior to incarceration were precluded. It was further hypothesized that these offenders would not express positive attitudes toward work.

c. Sources. Researcher's interview.

30. MOBILE

a. Definition. Subject led a nomadic life since his departure from the family group, not because of seasonal employment or other employment conditions which necessitated "job mobility."

b. Sources. Institutional case worker's Social History and researcher's interview.

31. INVETERATE GAMBLER

a. Definition. One who spent most of his leisure time gambling at cards, dice, race tracks, lottery games, etc. A considerable amount of this gambler's earnings had to be spent in this activity.

b. Sources. Institutional case worker's Social History and researcher's interview.

32. PROBLEM DRINKER

a. Definition. A history including any two of the following factors.

(1) Intoxication for three days or more with no sober intervals.

(2) Frequent blackouts (periods of lack of lucidity when awake).

(3) Lack of control over where, when and with whom drinking occurred.

(4) Drinking on the job.

(5) Loss of employment because of drinking.

(6) Excessive solitary drinking.

(7) Several physical altercations or fights while drinking.

b. Sources. Institutional case worker's Social History and researcher's interview.

33. OPIATE ADDICT

a. Definition. Inmate was addicted to opiate drugs or to opiate derivatives.

b. Sources. D.C. Jail Physician's Certification of Drug Addiction, which is a part of the D.C. Jail classification material.

34. TYPE OF SERVICE DISCHARGE

a. Definition. Inmate received one of the following.

(1) Honorable.

(2) Other than honorable.

b. Sources. Records: Administration Center, Department of the Army, St. Louis, Missouri; Officer in Charge, Discharged Naval Personnel, Record Branch, Bureau of Naval Personnel, Garden City, Long Island, New York; Commandant, U.S. Marine Corps Headquarters, Washington 25, D.C.; Commandant, U.S. Coast Guard Headquarters, Washington 25, D.C.

35. CONFINEMENT IN THE ARMED SERVICES FOLLOWING CONVICTION BY COURTS-MARTIAL

a. Definition. Inmate was confined beyond company restrictions in a stockade, disciplinary barracks or prison.

b. Sources. See b under 34 above.

36. MARITAL STATUS

a. Definition. Inmate's marital status at the time of his current arrest was one of the following.

(1) Married. Offender was living with a legal wife at time of arrest.

(2) Single. Never married.

(3) Separated. Legally married, but not living with wife at time of arrest.

(4) Divorced. Divorced prior to last arrest.

(5) Widowed. Widowed prior to last arrest.

b. Reasons for selection. Expected was a higher proportion of married men among the offenders with short arrest histories (not demonstrating a criminal pattern) than among the offenders with criminal patterns and long arrest histories. Assumed was that extended criminal activity shown by criminal pattern or long arrest history was associated with unsuccessful marital relationships or lack of marital ties.

c. Sources. D.C. Reformatory letter to clerk of the court concerned requesting verification of marriages and divorces, institutional case worker's Social History and researcher's interview.

37. JUVENILE DELINQUENT COMPANIONS

a. Definition. Subject associated with one or more delinquents (adjudicated by a court as a juvenile delinquent) on a friendly basis during his formative years (to age eighteen).

b. Reasons for selection. This factor indicated the subject's contacts in the formative years with companions from whom he might have assimilated delinquent and criminal behavior. Criminological research has demonstrated the high incidence of this factor among offenders. A higher incidence of this factor was expected among property offenders than offenders with pattern of crimes against the person.

c. Sources. Family letter, institutional case worker's Social History and researcher's interview.

38. MEMBER OF A JUVENILE DELINQUENT GANG

a. Definition. Juvenile delinquent gang was defined as an unsupervised closely knit group of three or more members who participated (in unison) in illegal activities. Illegal activities were not necessarily the major purpose of gang membership; however, transgressions of the law had to be in evidence occasionally. There were recognized leaders, stated meeting places and some planned illegal activities. At least one group member had been adjudicated a juvenile delinquent.

b. Reasons for selection. Many sociologists have commented on gang membership as a first step toward a life of crime. Thrasher summarizes the influences of undirected juvenile gangs as follows: "The undirected gang or gang-club demoralizes its members. It aids in making chronic truants and juvenile delinquents and in developing them into finished criminals. It augments racial friction in some areas . . . it promotes the corrupt alliance between crime and politics."*

The Gluecks, in *Unraveling Juvenile Delinquency,* found that more than half of the delinquents studied were members of gangs. Membership in a juvenile delinquent gang reveals early, organized, planned, delinquent behavior. Antisocial roles along with criminal values and criminal techniques are often developed in such groups. A high incidence of this factor was expected among the offenders with clearly established property offense patterns.

c. Sources. Family letter, institutional case worker's Social History and researcher's interview.

39. ADJUDICATED JUVENILE DELINQUENT

a. Definition. Subject was adjudicated a juvenile delinquent by a juvenile court or was convicted of a criminal act as a juvenile in any court. (This applies only to cases where juvenile authority was not waived.)

b. Reasons for selection. Adjudication by a court brings the formal force of law machinery to bear upon the offender. He is likely to become aware of his redefined status as a delinquent in the eyes of the court and in the eyes of his family, schoolmates, playmates, etc.

---

*THRASHER, FREDERICK H.: *The Gang* (2nd ed.). Chicago, University of Chicago Press, 1936, p. 367.

Such adjudication at times further solidifies the offender's conception of himself as playing a criminal role. It indicates, generally speaking, serious delinquency involvement.

c. Sources. Family letter, institutional case worker's Social History, Federal Bureau of Investigation Abstract of Criminal Record, District of Columbia Police Record of arrests and researcher's interview.

40. COMMITTED AS A JUVENILE DELINQUENT

a. Definition. Subject was committed to any institution as a juvenile delinquent by a board of public welfare, juvenile court, children's court or other court.

b. Reasons for selection. Commitment to a juvenile correctional institution usually indicates serious delinquency. It definitely incurs social stigma against the offender. There is, moreover, the element of forceful *restriction* many times interpreted as punishment. Juvenile delinquents who are committed to correctional and penal institutions are usually recidivists. Within the institutional framework, many delinquents learn to think of themselves as junior criminals. There is ample opportunity for the untutored to learn from the wiser, experienced offender. Criminal processing is likely to continue. Many criminologists point out that "graduates" of juvenile institutions make up a large percentage of reformatory and prison populations.

Most of these offenders with juvenile commitments were expected to have criminal patterns of one kind or another. The circularity involved in items 37, 38, 39 and 40 was perceived; however, all of these were included in order to perceive a clearer view of juvenile delinquency involvement.

c. Sources. Family letter, institutional case worker's Social History, researcher's interview, Federal Bureau of Investigation Abstract of Criminal Record, District of Columbia Police Record of Arrests.

41. AGE OF FIRST POLICE CONTACT

   a. Definition. Age subject was picked up by the police for any reason. The "pick-up" did not necessarily result in an official arrest accompanied by a charge.

   b. Reasons for selection. Age might indicate the approximate date of initial criminal processing of the offender by law-enforcing machinery. It could indicate the offender's involvement in criminal or delinquent behavior.

   c. Sources. Family letter, institutional case worker's Social History, researcher's interview, Federal Bureau of Investigation Abstract of Criminal Record, District of Columbia Police Record of Arrests.

42. CRIMINAL COMPANIONS

   a. Definition. Subject (between ages 6 and 18) associated with one or more criminal companions on a friendly basis. A criminal is defined as an adult offender (18 years of age or over), who was known to have been engaged in criminal activity (excludes members of the family group).

   b. Reasons for selection. The companionship factor in crime has established significance. Criminal companions indicate the likelihood of the transference of learned criminal patterns. There is a common assumption that the young offender learns from the older, more experienced offender. Sociologists have pointed out that the serious property offender has, in many cases, had tutelage in crime.

   c. Sources. Family letter, institutional case worker's Social History and researcher's interview.

PART 2: QUALITATIVE CLINICAL IMPRESSIONS

A. *Interview Reactions of Offender*

   Physical and mental reactions: e.g., alertness or listlessness; posture, bearing, poise; frankness or evasiveness; cooperation or negativeness; emotional or matter of fact; aggressive or passive; hostile or friendly.

B. *Personal Characteristics*

    1. Diagnostic signs of neurosis, psychosis, borderline psychosis or neurosis, psychopathic personality.

    2. Attitudes.

        a. prosocial or conventional attitudes.

        b. antisocial attitudes.

        c. deviant attitudes in specific areas, e.g., sex.

        d. specific attitudes toward law-enforcement agents, the court and correctional agents.

    3. Self-concept.

        a. noncriminal (includes self-appraisal and role definition).

        b. criminal—professional, would-be professional, semiprofessional, criminal only by legal definition.

        c. Social deviant—alcoholic, drug addict, gambler, a misfit of whatever type.

C. *Physical Health*

    1. Interview impressions of offender's over-all physical appearance and health, e.g., looks, size, apparent vigor and strength.

    2. Offender's conception of his health status including somatic complaints.

    3. Presence of organic or functional disease, physical handicaps, severe injuries, deleterious effects of past illnesses or injuries.

D. Social-psychological types—an assessment of the offender from A, B and C above.

Sources. Researcher's interview, institutional case worker's Social History, family letter, previous institutional records, psychological and medical records in official dossier.

PART 3: CRIMINAL PATTERN

A. Raw arrest history data as found in the original official sources—a listing of all arrests.

B. Refined arrest history—chronological recordings of arrests (minus duplications, juvenile arrests, regulatory regulations arrests, traffic arrests, etc.) by charge, date, place and disposition.

C. Designated criminal pattern following analysis, e.g., "robbery."

Sources. The District of Columbia Arrest Record and the Federal Bureau of Investigation Abstract of Criminal Record.

PART 4: QUALITATIVE ASPECTS OF THE OFFICIAL CRIMINAL RECORD

A. Arrests. Age of first arrest, length of arrest history, time intervals between arrests, lone arrests, arrests with others, reaction to arrest.

B. Results of content analysis of District Attorney's reports on all felony charges.

C. Levels of *modi operandi* indicating: (1) adventitious crime; (2) amateur crime; (3) semiprofessional crime; (4) professional crime; (5) violent crime.

Sources. Researcher's interview, institutional case worker's Social History, previous institutional records, the District of Columbia Arrest Record, the Federal Bureau of Investigation Abstract of Criminal Record, the District Attorney's reports.

Appendix C

THE LEGAL DEFINITIONS OF OFFENSE-GROUP CATEGORIES UTILIZED IN THE UNIFORM CRIME REPORTS*

1. Criminal homicide. (a) Murder and non-negligent man-slaughter—all willful felonious homicides as distinguished from deaths caused by negligence (do not include attempts to kill, assaults to kill, suicides, accidental death or justifiable homicides). Justifiable homicides are limited to: (1) the killing of a person by a peace officer in the line of duty; (2) the killing of a person in the act of committing a felony by a private citizen. (b) Manslaughter by negligence—any death which the police investigation establishes was primarily attributable to gross negligence of some individuals other than the victim.

2. Forcible rape. Rape by force, assault to rape, and attempted rape. Excludes statutory offenses (no force used—victim under age of consent).

3. Robbery. Stealing or taking anything of value from the person by force or violence or by putting in fear, such as strong-arm robbery, stickups, armed robbery, assault to rob, and attempt to rob.

4. Aggravated assault. Assault with intent to kill, or for the purpose of inflicting severe bodily injury by shooting, cutting, stabbing, maiming, poisoning, scalding or by the use of acids, explosives or other means. Excludes simple assault, assault and battery, fighting, etc.

5. Burglary—breaking or entering. Burglary, housebreaking, safecracking or any unlawful entry to commit a felony or a

---

*Uniform Crime Reports for the United States. Washington, Government Printing Office, 1963, pp. 43-45.

theft, even though no force was used to gain entrance and attempts. Burglary followed by larceny is not counted again as larceny.

6. Larceny—theft (except auto theft). (a) Fifty dollars and over in value; (b) under fifty dollars in value—thefts of bicycles, automobile accessories, shoplifting, pocket-picking or any stealing of property or article of value which is not taken by force and violence or by fraud. Excludes embezzlement, "con" games, forgery, worthless checks, etc.*

7. Auto Theft. Stealing or driving away and abandoning a motor vehicle. Excludes taking for temporary use when actually returned by the taker or unauthorized use by those having lawful access to the vehicle.

8. Other Assaults. Assaults and attempted assaults which are not of an aggravated nature.

9. Arson. Willful or malicious burning with or without intent to defraud. Includes attempts.

10. Forgery and counterfeiting. Making, altering, uttering or possessing, with intent to defraud anything false which is made to appear true. Includes attempts.

11. Fraud. Fraudulent conversion and obtaining money or property by false pretenses. Includes bad checks, except forgeries and counterfeiting.

12. Embezzlement. Misappropriation or misapplication of money or property entrusted to one's care, custody, or control.

13. Stolen property (buying, receiving, possession). Buying, receiving and possessing stolen property and attempts.

14. Vandalism. Willful or malicious destruction, injury, disfigurement or defacement of property without consent of the owner or person having custody or control.

15. Weapons (carrying, possessing, etc.). All violations of regulations or statutes controlling the carrying, using, possessing, furnishing and manufacturing of deadly weapons or silencers. Includes attempts.

---

*The norm "larceny" used in the researcher's categorization includes petty, grand, and all sub-classifications. The writer reasoned that the shades of meaning between the different types of larceny included in this classification were not great enough to warrant more than one criminal category for larceny.

16. Prostitution and commercialized vice. Sex offenses of a commercialized nature and attempts, such as prostitution, keeping bawdy house, procuring, transporting or detaining women for immoral purposes.

17. Sex offenses (except forcible rape, prostitution and commercialized vice). Statutory rape, offenses against chastity, common decency, morals and the like. Includes attempts.

18. Narcotic drug laws. Offenses relating to narcotic drugs, such as unlawful possession, sale or use. Excludes Federal offenses.*

19. Gambling. Promoting, permitting or engaging in gambling.

20. Offenses against the family and children. Non-support, neglect, desertion or abuse of family and children.

21. Driving under the influence. Driving or operating any motor vehicle while drunk or under the influence of liquor or narcotics.

22. Liquor laws. State or local liquor law violations except "drunkenness" (Class 23) and driving under the influence (Class 21). Excludes Federal violations.

23. Drunkenness or intoxication.

24. Disorderly conduct. Breach of the peace.

25. Vagrancy. Vagabondage, begging, loitering, etc.

26. All other offenses. All violations of state or local laws except Classes 1-25.

---

*Researcher's categorization includes all types of narcotic drug law charges.

INDEX

291

begining of delinquency, 71
contacts with law enforcement persons, 71
definition, 70
personality, 70
proposed treatment, 70
self-concept, 70-71

B

Bacon, Selden D., 170
Badger con game, 195
Balistrieri, James, 95
Banay, Ralph, 157, 171
Barbash, James T., 47, 56, 200
Baughman, E. Earl, 14, 28
Beck, Bertram M., 48, 57
Behavior pattern typology of Huffman, 77-80
  accidental, 78
  basis, 77-78
  deprivational, 78
  formula used, 77
  personality demoralization, 78-79
    basis, 78
    definition, 78
    highly advanced, 78
    marked, 78
    occasional, 78-79
  personality disorganization, 79
    definition, 79
    personality pattern disturbances, 79
    personality trait disturbances, 79
  provocational, 78
  sociopathic behavior reaction, 79-80
    definition, 79
Bell, Daniel, 106, 116
Bemmelen, J. M., 36
Bergler, Edmund, 152
Berman, Louis, 38, 41
Bier, William C., 135
"Big con" game, See Confidence man
Biological constitution and criminality
  application of theory, 31
  classification of criminals, 31-33
    by body build, 33
    by Ferri, 32-33
    by Garofalo, 33

by Kretschmer, 33
by Lombroso, 31-32
psychopathic criminal, See Psychopathic criminal
tendencies leading to, 34
theory, 31
Bloch, Herbert A., 22, 23, 29, 30, 41, 47, 56, 76, 94, 95, 199, 241
Bordua, David J., 93
Boring, Edwin G., 12, 28
Born criminal
  defined, 32
  theory, 31
Bovet, Lucien, 29
Brancale, Ralph, 42, 47, 55
Branham, Vernon C., 55
Brannon, W. T., 200
Brill, Leon, 135
Bromberg, Walter, 42, 47, 55, 56, 200
Bronner, Augusta F., 263
Brown, J. F., 42, 55
Burglary, 216-220
  acceptance sentences, 219
  acquantance with organized underworld, 217
  antisocial attitudes, 219
  arrest histories, 218
  as adjudicated juvenile delinquents, 216
  as leaders of juvenile offenders, 216
  attitude toward law enforcement personnel, 219
  casing procedures, 218
  community adjustment, 217
  consciousness of kind present, 218
  criminal companions, 217-218
  criminal progression, 218
  definition, 287-288
  delinquent companions during formative years, 216
  drug addicts, 217
  early aptitude for nonviolent crime, 217
  early criminal companions, 216
  early criminal processing, 216
  early pattern of group stealing, 216
  emotional coolness, 219
  geographical origins, 216

H

L

Lange, **Johannes, 38**

Larceny

burglary and, 210-216, *See also* Double pattern

classifications included in use of term, 288

definition, 288

drunkenness, assault and, 202-210, *See also* **Triple pattern**

robbery, differs from, 106

types crimes, 288

Legal norms, **3-4, 7-8**

Legal offense categories, 19-20

behavior categories within confines of, 19

burglars, 19

classification crimes and criminals using, 20

criminologists using, 19-20

drug law offenders, 19

gamblers, **19**

prostitution and commercialized vice, 19

study *modus operandi*, 20

use of, 19

Legalist approach to armed robbers

poor probation and parole risks, 114

serious recidivists, 114

Legalistic approach to criminal typology

criminal defined in terms of, 3

definition, **3**

description of, 3

legal norms, 3-4

position of, 3

rejection of by behavioral scientists, 6-7

reply by legalists, 7

rejection social deviancy from criminological research, 8-9

Legras, A. M., 38

Lejins, Peter P., 37, **41, 48, 57**

Lemert, Edwin M., 5, 19, 27, 29, 95

Lenz, Adolph, 33, 35, **40**

Lindner Gurvitz Revised Beta I.Q. Test

results study numbers men using, 137

use of to study offenders, 255-256, *See also* **Intelligence**

Lindesmith, Alfred H., 76, 94, 95, 134

Lindner, Robert M., 42, 55

Lombroso, Cesare, 13, 31, 32, 34, 39

"Long con" game, *See* Confidence man

Lottery law violators, *See* Numbers man

Lottier, Stuart, 19, 29, 95

M

MacCormick, Austin H., 170

MacDonald, J. C. R., 200

Maladjusted youth, types of, 49

Marijuana, use by jazz musicians, 123, 126

Martin, John M., 11, 27, 30

Matza, David, 239, 241

Maurer, David W., 95, 184, 199, 200, 201

Mayman, Martin, 12, 27

McCall, George J., 152

McClintock, F. H., 158, 160, 171

McCord, Joan, 35, 36, 40

McCord, William, 35, 36, 40

McCorkle, Lloyd W., 28

McKay, Henry D., 59, 249

Meerloo, Joost A. M., 135

Menninger, Karl, 12, 13, 14, 15, 27, 28

Mentally defective offender, 45, 46

crimes of, 45

factors causing defective reasoning, 45, 46

treatment, 46

Merton, Robert, 22, 60, 236

Methodology, dimensions of, 23

Miller, Walter B., 58, 62, 63, 93, 235, 236, 237, 238, 239

Mixed pattern offender, 172-180

approach correctional administrator, 178

approach legalist, 178

approach psychologists and psychiatrists, 178

approach sociologists, 178

as criminal type, 172-178

as disciplinary problems, 172

as gamblers, 173

as inadequate underworld material 175

ERRATA

The butterfly on Plate 16 is an Eresimus butterfly, *Danaus eresimus*, not a
Monarch butterfly.

A FIELD GUIDE TO
WILDLIFE
IN TEXAS AND THE SOUTHWEST

Other books by George Miller

Texas Photo Safaris
Texas Parks and Campgrounds: North, East, and
    Coastal Texas
Texas Parks and Campgrounds: Central, South, and
    West Texas

A FIELD GUIDE TO
WILDLIFE
IN TEXAS AND THE SOUTHWEST

BY GEORGE OXFORD MILLER

★
TexasMonthly.Press

Texas Monthly Press, Inc.
P.O. Box 1569
Austin, Texas 78767

A   B   C   D   E   F   G   H

Library of Congress Cataloging-in-Publication Data

Miller, George Oxford. 1943-
    A field guide to Texas wildlife / by George Oxford Miller.
        p. cm. —(Texas Monthly field guides)
    Bibliography: p.
    Includes index.
    ISBN 0-87719-126-3 : $21.95.
    ISBN 0-87719-072-0 (pbk.) : $14.95
    1. Zoology—Texas. I. Title. II. Series.
QL207.M55 1988
591.9764—dc19   88-20054
                                                                CIP
Printed in Singapore by Tien Wah Press (PTE.) LTD

In Memory of
My Loving Mother and Father

If a man inflict a thousand ills upon a beast, it can neither ward him off with speech nor hale him into court. Therefore it is essential that ye show forth the utmost consideration to the animal, and that ye be even kinder to it than to your fellow man.

Train your children from their earliest days to be infinitely tender and loving to animals. If an animal be sick, let the children try to heal it, if it be hungry, let them feed it, if thirsty, let them quench its thirst, if weary, let them see that it rests.

—'Abdu'l-Bahá

The passage from Bahá'í scriptures is reprinted from *Selections from the Writings of 'Abdu'l-Bahá* (©1978 by the Universal House of Justice) with permission of the publisher, Bahá'í World Center Publications, Haifa, Israel.

ACKNOWLEDGMENTS

One of my major goals in writing this book was to present the latest scientifically accurate information available about the many animals I chose to include. A number of individuals who have done considerable research and devoted much of their lives to studying the various animals reviewed portions of the manuscript. I thank Alan Tennant, the author of *The Snakes of Texas*, for reading the snake sections; Dr. Merlin Tuttle, the president of Bat Conservation International, for reviewing the section on bats, and Frank Johnson and Tom Stehn of the Aransas National Wildlife Refuge for their updated information on the whooping crane. Special thanks go to Dr. C. J. Durden of the Texas Memorial Museum for his information on butterflies, Bruce Thompson of the Texas Parks and Wildlife Department for information on nongame mammals in Texas, and Ann Sorensen, formerly with the Texas Department of Agriculture Fire Ant Project, for information on imported fire ants. Many others answered questions about particular animals. Bill Lamar and Jim Stout of the Tyler Zoo helped with some of the snake photos, as did George Regmunel of Armand Bayou Nature Center and Alan Tennant; Edgar Black of Black's Barbecue in Lockhart, Texas, graciously allowed me to photograph his jackalopes; and Margaret Campbell assisted in finding photogenic ticks. I am especially grateful to my wife, Delena Tull, for the time she spent reading the manuscript and for her valuable editorial suggestions.

CONTENTS

REPTILES 167

INVERTEBRATES 217

TEXAS' VANISHING WILDLIFE: ENDANGERED AND THREATENED ANIMALS

BOOKS FOR FURTHER READING

I've Got a Question

(Everything You Wanted
To Know About Animals
But Were Afraid to Ask)

Once, while working at the Austin Nature Center, I received a frantic phone call. "There's a bat under the eaves of my house! Could it be one of the flesh-eating kind like I saw in the movies?" Another alarmed caller, who must have seen Alfred Hitchcock's film *The Birds,* wanted to know if the flocks of grackles in the trees would attack humans. One lady threatened to move back to Michigan if another worm-like snake invaded her bathroom. These few examples show that many people suffer from needless fear based on misinformation and ignorance.

Unfortunately animals usually suffer the most from humans' lack of knowledge. Every spring, people brought to the Nature Center jars containing snakes chopped to pieces. "Was it poisonous?" they asked. Invariably the shredded snake was a beneficial species. Harmless rat snakes, racers, and hog-nosed snakes were the most frequent victims. Once a rancher brought in three red fox cubs. "We shot the mother and didn't want the babies around," he explained. "We were afraid they would kill our cattle." The skeptical rancher would not believe that foxes eat mice, not cows. The Nature Center has a compound of cages filled with animals injured and orphaned, some accidentally, but most by people with the "chicken hawk" mentality— any bird with claws is evil, so kill it. A corollary states that any animal that has a mouth can bite, so kill it.

Not all questions we received were based on fear or prejudice. The majority came from genuinely concerned citizens trying to act responsibly toward the wild animals

1

around them. As urban sprawl engulfs the countryside, residents find some of the animals reluctant to vacate their domain. Skunks homestead under houses, woodpeckers drum their mating call on rooftops, birds chasing their own reflections crash into windows, and the chatter of baby chimney swifts sounds alarmingly like rattlesnakes. One man in a new subdivision west of Austin reported a large furry creature gnawing on his cedar deck. To his surprise, the mysterious beast was a porcupine. An inquisitive raccoon regularly climbed down one person's chimney and scavenged through the pantry.

Various callers wanted to know if armadillos dig up and eat tulip bulbs (they eat insects), if owls suck blood from chickens (no), and if birds abandon their nests if you touch the eggs. Apparently, most parents tell their children this myth to keep the curious youngsters from harming bird nests, so the fable passes from generation to generation. In reality, most birds cannot smell, so the human scent will not keep the parents away. When I studied the hatching success of cave swallows, I measured, weighed, and numbered hundreds of eggs and young in scores of nests without causing any harm.

Humans have more sympathy for baby birds than for almost any other animal. Each spring, visitors inundate the Nature Center with "abandoned" babies. After hatching, baby birds use all their energy to reach adult size, then begin growing their main body and flight feathers. When the partially feathered juveniles cannot fit into the small nest, they take to the limbs. Their cheeps for food ring through the bushes as their parents, who are always nearby, feed and protect them. Well-meaning people mistakenly assume these babies are abandoned and "rescue" them. The Nature Center usually receives more than 100 kidnapped blue jays, grackles, mockingbirds, and other "orphans" during the peak hatching season. Feeding the screaming youngsters requires an army of dedicated volunteers.

The serious concern of the public for injured wildlife

always impressed me, and sometimes added a touch of humor to my job. One worried person wanted to know the proper first aid for a pet frog that suffered from frequent strokes, and another asked how to resuscitate a lizard. Children, whose inquisitive minds have not been programmed to accept the world as it appears, often ask the most provocative questions. "Why does a baby deer have spots?" "Why do screech owls have feathers that look like ears?" "Why does a skunk have a white stripe?" In asking these questions, children assume a purpose in the world of nature that we adults often overlook—that the features of an animal are not accidental, but satisfy specific needs.

One of the least understood concepts, yet one of the most enthralling, is natural selection. Basically stated, natural selection means that those inheritable features that help an organism survive and produce offspring will be passed on to future generations. In each generation of animals, or plants for that matter, the individuals with the physical and behavioral characteristics best adapted for survival in their particular environment will live the longest, produce the most offspring, and pass more genes to the next generation. For instance, if brown rabbits in dark woods can hide from predators better than white ones, eventually most of the rabbits in the woods will be brown.

Natural selection is one of the driving forces of evolution. The fossil record indicates that life has existed on this planet for approximately three billion years. During that time, the weather fluctuated from ice ages to tropical extremes. Riding on the earth's magma, continents floated from arctic to tropical climates, oceans periodically rose and fell, covering and exposing vast continental land masses, and countless mountain ranges arched toward the sky and eroded away to flat plains. As these changes occurred through the millennia, the plants and animals either disappeared or slowly changed in response to the new conditions. Fossils preserve the history of periods when massive extinctions occurred, such as the annihilation of the

3

dinosaurs, as well as the gradual shift in a species' characteristics. Paleontologists, scientists who study fossils, trace the relationship of present organisms to those that long ago vanished from the earth.

The gradual shift in the characteristics of organisms as they adapt to the changing environment is called evolution. Instead of threatening our concept of the cosmos, evolution enriches it by demonstrating the creative force that governs the natural world. The chapters in this book describe how each animal has evolved to be uniquely adapted to live in its particular habitat. We can see how the size, color, food preference, hunting strategy, mating behavior, defenses, and every aspect of an organism's life are molded by the selective process of survival. The result is a world populated by life forms so diverse that they stagger the human imagination. Evolution is merely an organism's continual development to stay in alignment and harmony with an ever changing world.

The same diverseness found in the biotic world also occurs in the mineral kingdom. As a crystal grows, the laws of physics irrevocably bind every molecule in alignment with the surrounding structure. Yet, despite the rigid limitation of the physical laws, no two crystals develop identically. Crystals display a myriad array of colors, shapes, and combinations and awe us with their breathtaking beauty. Human hands have never sculpted works of art as intricate or imaginative as the crystalline structures formed by water and minerals deep within the earth. To study nature, whether animals, plants, or rocks, is to enter a realm of mystery and majesty, a world, though bound by natural laws, that remains unconstrained in the expression of diverseness.

Modern Americans, in the midst of an ongoing technological revolution, still suffer from environmental illiteracy. To many, the animals around us represent little more than names and general categories. The term "butterfly" covers the hundreds that dance on the Texas breezes, and "bird"

4

includes the 545 species that sing in the trees across the Lone Star State. Having such a narrow awareness of the world around us is like going through life classifying people only as men and women, never knowing their names or anything about them. As we learn more about our friends, they mean more to us and a valuable and fulfilling relationship develops that enriches our lives. Our relationship with nature can be the same. The more aware we become of the animals and plants around us, the more highly we value them both for their unique characteristics and for their contribution to our enjoyment of life. As we sample the richness of creation, we begin to visualize the larger picture in which every form of life has an intrinsic place, purpose, and value.

In the world of nature, the facts are often stranger than the myths. This book explores the lives, reports the folklore, and relates the habits of some of Texas' most interesting furry, feathered, and scaly creatures. Sometimes our views of an animal mingle facts with misconceptions and obscure the truth. We hear a bird singing and conclude it is happy, when in reality it is warning other birds of its species to stay out of its territory. Anthropomorphism, attributing human feelings and motives to animals, is at the heart of most folktales and prejudice against animals. We say turtles are patient when in reality they are just slow. We consider a wolf evil for killing a deer, but praise another predator, the worm-eating robin, for being industrious in its pursuit of food. Whether we like an animal usually depends more on the human characteristics we attribute to it than on any economic impact it has on our lives. Once we learn to resist applying human values to animals, we can see the beauty in all creatures. We can view bats as one of the most marvelous and interesting mammals alive, instead of considering them ugly and despicable. Many times in this book I describe an animal with adjectives that also may apply to human characteristics, but I am not attributing human feelings, understanding, or emotions to the creature.

5

Nature is full of the unexpected and bizarre, even in urban Texas. The mammals, birds, reptiles, and invertebrates of Texas are as interesting as any in some tropical hideaway, and a lot more accessible to you and me. Read this book and get to know some of your neighbors better!

The Great Texas Wildlife Auction: Going, Going, Gone?

What did Stephen F. Austin find when he brought his first settlers to the wilderness of Texas 160 years ago? Can you imagine the High Plains so thick with bison that a traveler could ride horseback for three days with the herd stretching continually from horizon to horizon? This is just one of the images painted by early Texans. Historical records quote accounts of prairie chickens so abundant that they darkened the sun when they flew over. Settlers in South Texas could see thousands of deer in a single day. The coastal bays and marshes teemed with a seemingly unlimited supply of ducks, geese, and shorebirds. Bighorn sheep, elk, grizzly bears, wolves, and pronghorn antelope lived in abundance in the mountains and deserts of the Trans-Pecos. Prairie dog towns, some as large as 25 miles in diameter, ranged across the western third of the state.

In addition to the oceans of bison, deer, and pronghorns, the vast grasslands stretching from South Texas to the Panhandle supported millions of longhorns and mustangs, compliments of the early Spanish explorers. After the Civil War, ranchers exploited the abundant wild cattle, brought millions of dollars into the bankrupted state, and forged forever the image of the American cowboy. While cattle became king and displaced wildlife from the Texas grasslands, farmers busted the sod of virgin prairies, and the lumber industry began chewing away at the towering forests in East Texas. The rich woodlands of the Big Thicket once supported the greatest diversity of wildlife in North America. Bears, cougars, bobcats, beavers, mink, otters, wolves, Carolina parakeets, passenger pigeons, and ivory-billed woodpeckers witnessed the arrival of early Texans.

John James Audubon reported that one flock of passenger pigeons passed overhead for three hours and contained more than one billion birds. Modern-day Americans cannot imagine the abundance of wildlife that this country originally supported.

With so much wildlife, early Texans felt no need for moderation in hunting. One hunter killed 1500 deer in one year, and commercial hunters killed millions of waterfowl. A trading post near Waco shipped 75,000 deer hides to New York between 1844 and 1853. In an effort to eliminate the major food source of the Indians, hunters, encouraged by the government, exterminated the vast herds of bison. While ranchers in the west decimated bears, wolves, and other predators, farmers in the east battled the ducks, geese, and Carolina parakeets, which feasted on grain and fruit crops. A few early writers expressed remorse over the drastic decline of wildlife, but the state was slow to pass game laws. Not until 1907 did Texas appoint a game department, and it did not begin issuing hunting licenses until 1909.

The story of the taming of Texas, and the entire continent, reflects the irreparable effect of humans on an unspoiled wilderness. With the explosive growth in population, small towns became large cities at the necessary sacrifice of our native grasslands, prairies, forests, and wildlife. The consumption of the environment continues today, unfortunately with all too little concern about preserving natural areas. Wildlife in South Texas loses about 17,000 acres annually as ranchers convert brushland to pastures. Only 1 percent of the Lower Rio Grande Valley has escaped cultivation.

Lumber companies in East Texas decimate hundreds of thousands of acres of prime wildlife habitat each year. In the last decade, clear cutting of the rich forests increased by 40 to 60 percent. As the 1980s began, lumbering, pine plantations, agriculture, reservoirs, and population growth already had destroyed 63 percent of the prime wildlife habitat in East Texas. But the greatest threat to wildlife and the environment is not the god of profit, nor the production and supply of necessary goods. Ultimately, it is you and I.

Rattlesnake roundups have become a tradition in West Texas, and high society demands fur coats. These are examples of how humans exploit animals for amusement. Our pioneer ancestors found a rich land, and to survive they had to use the resources close at hand. They valued the land and animals around them primarily as objects to make their lives easier. Unfortunately that pioneer ethic lives on today in our nonrecyclable consumer society. If present trends continue, the world will lose about one species of animal or plant for every hour between now and the year 2000. The same mentality that places no intrinsic value on the life forms that share this planet with us views the world, its resources, and its peoples as opportunities for personal pleasure and profit. If we are to survive on this earth, at some point in the evolution of human society we must learn to view ourselves as stewards and not as lords and masters.

Satellite photographs reveal that the insatiable appetite of urban sprawl takes the greatest bite out of wildlife habitat in Texas. The human population continues to grow at an explosive rate, and Texas has several of the fastest-growing metropolitan areas in the nation. Each year residential developments, shopping centers, and business complexes gobble up some 200,000 acres of open space in this state.

Today we must live within the constraints of the decisions of our forefathers, whether we like the situation or not, and tomorrow our children will wrestle with the problems we create. Traditional spray and flood irrigation, wasteful but more economical than water-conserving methods, and the growing demands of cities and industry use more of the state's vast supply of underground water than rain replenishes each year. The state's water supply is rapidly drying up. Some of the major springs, like Comanche Springs in Fort Stockton, have already disappeared. Comal Springs, the largest in the Southwest, and most of the others are expected to become intermittent by the turn of the century regardless of what we do now. San Marcos Springs, with a daily output of more than 100 million gallons, forms the San Marcos River, considered to be one of the unique aquatic ecosystems in North America. Two species of fish, one salamander, and a species of wild rice live in the river and nowhere else in the world. Most of the other large springs harbor their own endemic species, which will perish if the springs dry up.

We still must come to grips with our attitude toward the environment and recognize our responsibility to future generations. We no longer can see the bison, ivory-billed woodpecker, elk, mountain sheep, or black-footed ferret in the wild, but what about the bald eagle, brown pelican, peregrine falcon, ridley sea turtle, or the other 109 threatened or endangered species in the state? We are stewards of the only wild breeding flock of whooping cranes, every golden-cheeked warbler in existence, the remaining population of Atwater's prairie chickens, bat caves with the largest concentrations of mammals in the world, and a number of fishes, amphibians, reptiles, and plants that live in Texas and nowhere else on the planet.

The decisions we make today about the environment will affect the lifestyle, recreation, and profession of our children. At this late date, we must recognize the seriousness of the threats to the environment and make every effort to save as much of the remaining natural areas in the state as possible. Texas ranks 41st in the nation in the amount of state park acreage per capita. The State Parks and Wildlife Department, with the restrictions of a failing budget, now operates 102 parks, recreational areas, and historic sites totaling about 200,000 acres, with about 20 more parks planned for the future. Private organizations, like the Texas Nature Conservancy, have preserved almost as much land as the state parks system, although most is closed to the general public. The federal government operates two national parks, a national seashore, a national preserve, ten national wildlife refuges, two national recreation areas, four national forests, two national grasslands, and scores of lakes across the state. Yet, with 98 percent of the state privately owned, those parks and preserves represent too little to save the biological uniqueness of Texas. Powered by an anticipated population increase of 46 percent during the last two decades of the century, wild Texas continues to disappear at an alarming rate.

More than 20 million Texans flock to the state parks each year. A poll conducted by the Parks and Wildlife Department revealed that more than 80 percent of the park visitors come to the outdoors to relieve the mental stress and strain inherent in our modern lifestyle. But Texans gain more than mental relief from the state's wild areas. Hunters and recreationists spend more than $432 million annually. Wild areas are a profitable, but unrecognized, business, largely ignored by real estate developers, city planners, and most private landowners.

Hikers and hunters are not the only people who benefit from wildlife and wilderness preservation. Half of our modern medicines are derived from compounds first found in nature. Researchers discovered an enzyme in the saliva of vampire bats that inhibits blood clotting; someday it may be used to treat stroke victims. What makes opossums immune to rattlesnake venom and pallid bats indifferent to scorpion stings? How do hummingbirds slow down their metabolism at night? Who can guess at the number of undiscovered cures existing in the plants and animals around us? Plants rich in hydrocarbons someday may replace the nonrenewable petrochemicals so essential to our society. The majority of plants, especially in the tropics, have never been tested for their pharmaceutical or commercial possibilities, yet the rain forests, with their rich diversity of plants and animals, probably will have disappeared by the turn of the century.

So the loss of wildlife habitat affects, not just some obscure species of bird or fish, but every one of us, and our children as well. My children cannot experience the relaxation of hiking in a wilderness setting along Barton Creek near downtown Austin. Despite a scenic easement ordinance, condominiums, office buildings, and homes line the cliffs overlooking the beautiful stream. My camping spot in the Piney Woods near Beaumont is now an exclusive housing development. The story of lost wilderness is like one of lost innocence: once gone, it can never be regained. But by proper city planning and growth management, by preserving strategic natural areas, by realizing the indirect benefits of wild areas, and most of all by developing a perspective that values the plants and animals around us, we can retain some of the remnants of our environmental heritage.

Though the investment of preserving wilderness pays immediate psychological and economic dividends, the long-run ecological benefits far outweigh the short-term results. At stake is not merely a few species but the health of the entire environmental system that we depend upon for survival. When we act to preserve a species, the whole ecosystem benefits. Like an investment portfolio, diversity means stability and protection against bankruptcy, and a diversity of species in an ecosystem indicates a healthy and stable environment. The failure of vast numbers of species, as we witness today, indicates that serious problems exist in our system. We don't have to wait until lakes, rivers, and forests die from pollution and acid rain to determine that these problems threaten our own existence. We can observe the gradual disappearance of wildlife and plants and diagnose the problem. The symptoms of disaster now unmistakably cloud the atmosphere, shadow the rain forests, and wash ashore from the seven seas. As astronauts on this spaceship earth, we must recognize that our life-support system is rapidly failing. Now is the time to sound the alarm and unify our efforts to save ourselves from ourselves.

Mammals

Sperm whales dive into the ocean depths 10,000 feet beneath the surface, and Tibetan yaks climb mountain peaks 20,000 feet above sea level. The one-to-two-inch, 0.09-ounce Mediterranean pigmy shrew chases earthworms through their burrows, while the 110-foot, 26-ton blue whale plies the ocean waves. The cheetah can sprint 60 mph, yet the sloth hangs motionlessly upside down staring at the sky above its feet. At birth, ten opossum babies hardly fill a teaspoon, while a newborn elephant weighs 260 pounds. Humans, with an intelligence unmatched in the animal kingdom, have harnessed the laws of nature and modified much of the earth's surface to meet our needs. Despite the diverseness of these many animals, they all have something in common: they are mammals.

All mammals have hair and a four-chambered heart, feed their young milk, and regulate their body temperature at a constant level. Beyond these characteristics and other common anatomical features, the appearance, behavior, lifestyle, and diet of mammals differ in every imaginable way. They run, crawl, fly, swim, burrow underground, and live in trees. Some live one to two years, others in excess of a hundred years. These versatile creatures have exploited the most extreme environments existing on this planet. They inhabit the hottest deserts and the frozen arctic, the arid wastelands and the watery depths.

According to fossil evidence, mammals developed from primitive reptiles some 200 million years ago. Only a few fossilized teeth and jaw fragments remain of the earliest mammals. Another branch of reptiles, the dinosaurs, began developing about the same time and eventually became the lords of the land, air, and sea. Plant- and animal-eating dinosaurs from the size of a cat to the giant *Tyrannosaurus rex* dominated the earth for about 125 million years, while mammals remained insignificant mouse-size creatures. Finally, after spending eons on the sidelines, mammals got their chance to become the star performers.

During the late Cretaceous period, 65 million years ago, the large terrestrial, marine, and flying reptiles, as well as about 70 percent of all other animal species, vanished. The massive extinction of species has been attributed to a variety of causes, including changes in climate and vegetation, habitat destruction from mountain formation, and the cataclysmic impact of a meteor, the hypothesis currently most favored. The absence of the dinosaurs allowed mammals to begin a rapid development. A tremendous increase in mammal species occurred during the following 40 million years. Hooved animals developed, bats took to the air, whales and dolphins turned to the sea, and elephantlike animals with trunks appeared. The grazing animals diversified into a variety of sizes, and dog- and catlike animals became the major predators. The descendants of only a few of these ancestral families exist today. We know the rich mammal fauna of that time period primarily from studying the fossil remains.

Modern mammal families began to develop during the Miocene epoch, from 23 to 6 million years ago. Horses and camels originated in North America and dispersed to the rest of the world, and elephants, antelopes, and giraffes evolved in Africa. The explosive development not only of mammals but also of insects and birds is closely related to the variety and abundance of flowering plants that evolved during this period. The flowers and fruit provided a new and abundant source of food. Today 75 percent of the mammal families in the Northern Hemisphere date from the Miocene, and about 50 percent throughout the world.

Three types of mammals exist in the world today, each with radically different methods of reproduction. The most widespread are the placental mammals, whose young develop within the mother's body before birth. The babies are born live and may require extensive parental care before they become independent. The marsupial mammals have a pouch in which the young develop after an immature birth. The young crawl into the pouch and nurse until they have developed enough to emerge. Placental mammals have a relatively larger brain than marsupials, and generally displace marsupials when the two compete for resources.

About 3 million years ago, the Isthmus of Panama connected North and South America, allowing previously isolated animals to associate and compete with each other. The placental mammals from the north crossed the land bridge and displaced the predominantly marsupial mammals of the south. The opossum family is the only surviving marsupial family in North and South America. In Australia, which had no placental mammals until they were introduced in modern times, a diversity of marsupial mammals fill all the environmental niches that placental mammals occupy in the rest of the world. Australia is also home of the third class of mammals, called monotremes, which consists of two species, the duck-billed platypus and the spiny anteater. These bizarre animals lay eggs, but have primitive mammary glands.

What enabled mammals to assume such a dominant role in the world after the dinosaurs disappeared? Mammals developed, diversified, and covered the face of the earth because they could adapt, both behaviorally and physiologically, to environmental extremes and take advantage of new situations. Unlike reptiles, mammals maintain a constant body temperature independent of the climatic fluctuations. This permits longer daily and yearly periods of activity. Maintaining a constant internal temperature requires expending considerable energy. Therefore, food, more than temperature, limits the success of mammals and where they can live.

The development of hair is closely related to a regulated body temperature. Hair insulates an animal from cold, as well as performing other vital functions. It protects the skin from injury and increases the tactile sense. Rodents and cats have specialized whiskers to sense touch. In modified forms, hair provides an effective defense. Horns and claws are derived from hair, as are the protective scales on the pangolin and the shields on an armadillo.

A large brain gives mammals the intelligence required to discover and exploit new sources of energy in the environment, which has allowed them to diversify and fill every available niche. When a food source is particularly abundant and dependable, an animal can specialize, as the anteater does, and reduce its competition with other animals. Some mammals, like coyotes, take a smorgasbord approach and feast from a variety of sources, increasing the likelihood that some food will always be available.

Respiration and other bodily functions consume about 85 to 90 percent of a mammal's food energy, leaving 10 to 15 percent available for growth. An animal that grows large must have a plentiful supply of food; thus, the largest mammals dine on plants, the primary and most abundant source of energy available. A carnivore, or meat eater, lives on the fraction of food energy in the ecosystem that is stored in the bodies of its prey. With less energy available, carnivores tend to be fewer in number than the animals they eat and often prey heavily on much larger animals. Omnivores, like raccoons, bears, and humans, eat both plants and meat and are some of the most successful animals at survival because they rely on a variety of food resources.

From about 30,000 to 5000 years ago, a massive wave of extinction swept across North America and Europe, annihilating most of the large mammals. Creatures that had withstood the climatic rigors of four glaciations suddenly disappeared. The horse, camel, mastodon, woolly mammoth, giant bison, giant beaver, ground sloth, imperial elephant, dire wolf, sabertooth cat, and almost every other large animal vanished. Only a few medium-sized mammals survived on a continent once as rich in wildlife as the African savannahs. We may never know for certain what caused the demise of the large mammals, but since humans migrated into North America during this time, many scientists speculate that the animals were hunted to extinction.

Though we may speculate about the influence of humans on past extinctions, we have no doubt concerning the animals that disappeared in recent history. Between 1600 and 1900, approximately 75 species of mammals and birds vanished worldwide, about 1 every 4 years. Between 1900 and 1980, the rate averaged 1 per year, then accelerated to 1 to 3 per day during the early 1980s. If all animals and plants are considered together, the current rate of extinction has increased to approximately 1 species per hour. We may see 1 million species of plants and animals disappear during our lifetime.

Like the dinosaurs of the past, mammals are the lords of the present age. Today about 4230 mammals in 122 families inhabit the earth. Rodents comprise 42 percent of the species and bats 23 percent. We might like to think that mammals—especially one species, humans—are the most advanced animals on the earth. However, insects and other forms of life easily match the diversity and adaptability of mammals. Mammals comprise only about 10 percent of the vertebrates, or animals with backbones, and vertebrates only 4 percent of the animal species in the world. Humans may be the dominant species today, but, with all life linked together as partners sharing a common homeland, nature offers no guarantees about the future. The immediate fate of the human species, and perhaps of most life on the planet, depends on whether we can avoid a self-inflicted catastrophe surpassing the one that eradicated the last great lords of the earth.

The next 13 sections describe a selection of the 156 species of mammals that have been recorded in the state of Texas (and one fictitious creature). Most also inhabit the southern and western United States, and some range through Mexico to South America and north into Canada. Texas has 50 species of rodents, 30 bats, and about 18 marine mammals; 22 species are so rare that they have been sighted fewer than 5 times in the last 80 years. Though every animal has its unique features, and sometimes bizarre adaptations, I have chosen those that I think have the most interesting stories to tell, and whose lives have influenced and been influenced the most by humans.

The Armadillo: Texans' Newest Native Son

Nine-banded armadillo
Dasypus novemcinctus

The sign proclaimed in hand-painted letters "Armadillers for Rent." Curious people crowded in front of the pen of scampering animals at an "armadillo race" in Austin.

"Are they mammals or reptiles?" asked one puzzled onlooker.

"Neither," said the man renting the animals for the race, "they're just plain ol' dillers!"

Today people call them "dillers," but during the Great Depression folks referred to them as "Hoover's hogs." In the hard times, these unusual critters became a culinary delicacy, if not a necessity, for many people. In the past decade, Texans have rediscovered the lowly armadillo and enthusiastically adopted it as their native son. Roadside vendors and exclusive specialty stores sell armadillo hats, purses, belt buckles, and bumper stickers. Underground comic books and nationally televised beer commercials glorify the animal, and the Texas Legislature even designated the armadillo as the official state mammal. Scores of towns sponsor armadillo races, where, to the roar of intoxicated crowds, adults on hands and knees chase terrified animals across a finish line. Ironically, a society that fines and even jails people for mistreating a dog or cat is blind to the flagrant abuse of a native animal like the armadillo. The care and protection that the law affords and that society expects for our pets should extend to wildlife as well.

Why armadillos have become so popular with modern Texans puzzles even the most astute psychoanalysts. With pea-size eyes, a piglike snout, and the uncanny ability to get massacred on highways, armadillos do not exactly inspire

19

awe or project an image about which Texans can brag. If armadillos could brag, however, they would put Texans to shame. Long before humans migrated into North America, these animals homesteaded in what eventually became the Lone Star State. They have rooted through Texas soil for more than one million years, which makes today's animals 250,000th-generation Texans. Not even the most boastful native Texan can match that genealogy!

Armadillos are as independent as a West Texas rancher, and about as sociable as a cattle rustler. They have little or no interaction with their kin or other animals. They probably never noticed the Spanish conquistadors who claimed the land north of the Rio Grande, nor the Anglos who fought both the Mexicans and Indians. Armadillos just wiggle their piglike noses in the sand and contentedly let the world go by.

An armadillo can easily afford an unconcerned attitude about the changing world. Like its South American cousins, it wears the family armor that protects it from most predators and the thorny bushes through which it scampers. The armor is actually a layer of bony plates covered with horny tissue. Its scalelike skin adds to the armadillo's bizarre appearance, and gives this strange mammal a reptilian look. The protective shield covers its shoulders and hindquarters, and nine movable bands protect its back. With such an effective armor, the armadillo does not need speed, keen vision, or super intelligence for defense. Unlike its South American relatives, however, the nine-banded armadillo cannot curl into a ball to cover its unprotected abdomen.

An armadillo responds to danger in a manner opposite to the macho image of a brave Texan. When alarmed, it stands on its hind legs, holds its nose in the air, and squints its beady eyes. If truly frightened, an armadillo jumps straight up and comes down running. This strategy works well, except that the animal often forgets the danger in a few seconds and nonchalantly resumes its rooting activities.

20

Perhaps Texans secretly identify with the way an armadillo copes with existence. This unconcerned creature spends its life wandering aimlessly through the woods unaware of man or beast. A contented armadillo has its nose several inches in the soil sniffing and rooting for bugs. The only well-developed sense these nearsighted creatures require is smell, necessary for finding food.

Perhaps the one thing armadillos really have in common with modern Americans is that both travel far from home. Since early naturalists first mapped their range in 1890, these rambling creatures have spread from Central Texas into New Mexico and Oklahoma, and east to the Mississippi River. Armadillos purportedly cross streams in the most straightforward manner—by walking underwater—but they needed the help of a Marine sergeant to ford America's biggest river. After World War I, a soldier stationed in Texas took two armadillos across the Mississippi River to Cocoa Beach, Florida. Armadillos, the sergeant soon discovered, make miserable pets. He released the pair, which immediately began to populate the state.

Soon the tanklike creatures had invaded Alabama and Georgia. Armadillos are exceptionally good at populating. Females always give birth to identical quadruplets. Born with their eyes open, the babies can scramble after their mother in just a few hours. Only freezing weather seems to stop the unassuming emigrants' northward march. Temperatures below 50 degrees F cause these almost hairless creatures to shiver violently.

To protect themselves against cold weather, armadillos insulate their burrows, which they dig in great numbers, with leaves and other vegetation. How does an armadillo gather leaves? Just like you or I do—it rakes them into a pile and picks them up. With its front paws full, it hops awkwardly backward to its home. Skunks, snakes, mice, and other animals often make comfortable homes in the extra armadillo burrows.

A warm burrow and a leaf-covered forest floor meet an

21

armadillo's needs. These creatures spend the evening, and sometimes midday, hours rooting through the leaf mulch and soft soil for insects and other small critters. They grind up beetles, scorpions, spiders, and centipedes with 32 peg-like teeth. Armadillos eat many bugs highly destructive to crops and range grasses, yet a misguided rancher near Austin bragged that he had shot more than 500 in two years. Sportsmen sometimes contend that armadillos decimate the quail population by eating eggs. A four-year study, however, showed that invertebrates comprise 93 percent of an armadillo's diet. Armadillos damaged only 9.7 percent of the quail nests studied, a number too small to affect the bird population.

After enjoying a million years of peace, prosperity, and obscurity, armadillos face trials unforeseen by nature. Today these animals must contend with being kidnapped for armadillo races, attacked by four-wheeled predators, and considered nature's biggest joke. The armadillo's four genetically identical siblings are a boon for scientific and medical research that requires identical subjects for testing. Medical researchers have discovered that armadillos carry a leprosy virus similar to the one that infects humans. Between 5 and 12 percent of the armadillos within 100 miles of the Texas coast and in South Texas carry the virus. Only about 2 percent of the rest of the state's armadillo population tests positive for leprosy. The Federal Centers for Disease Control in Atlanta warn that, though it is extremely unlikely, humans may be able to contract leprosy from armadillos. At least one case, a man who used armadillo meat to make sausages, has been reported. Nonetheless, Texans are undaunted in celebrating their newest and most popular native son and universally ignore this danger.

Bats:
Mammals
of the Sky

Mexican free-tailed bat,
guano bat
Tadarida braoilicnoio

Texas has more bats and more species of bats than any other state in the nation. This fact would horrify the many people who rate bats along with rattlesnakes, cockroaches, and
tax collectors. When an Austin newspaper columnist solic-
ited letters on "squeamish" creatures, responses about bats
showed the most hysteria. Bats probably suffer more than
any other animal from an unwarranted reputation based on
folktales. At the sight of the winged mammals, normally rational people react with a fear born of superstition, prejudice, and misunderstanding.

Bats are harmless, extremely beneficial, and some of the
most scientifically interesting creatures on the earth, yet they
probably will never receive the widespread admiration they
deserve. We readily value koalas, baby seals, and pandas,
which live thousands of miles away, but not the furry creatures that catch flying insects in our own backyards. The
habits of bats perfectly combine the elements of myth and
superstition. First of all, they flutter through the night,
enough to scare the child in us all. Second, many have con-
torted faces, which we interpret as evil and sinister. Last but
not least, some members of the clan feed on blood. If the
vampire myth were not enough, the exaggerated rabies
scare in recent decades has guaranteed bats a bad reputation.

At one time Texans welcomed bats as honored guests,
and even built special belfries for them. In the early 1900s,
mosquito-borne malaria threatened much of Texas, and
health officials considered bats an effective mosquito control

23

measure. A San Antonio health inspector built 11 towers, each 50 feet high, to attract these tiny creatures with large appetites. With each bat catching at least 5 grams or more of insects per night, the Texas population of guano bats alone consumes approximately 144,000 tons of insects annually. Guano, or bat excrement, makes a rich fertilizer, and several million bats leave tons behind when they fly south for the winter. Ranchers with bat caves shovel up the remains and pocket a tidy Christmas bonus after the bats leave. During the winter of 1985, the owners of Bracken Cave near San Antonio extracted 150 tons of guano.

During World War II, bats stimulated the imagination of the military. The Air Force devised a devilish scheme to burn Japanese cities. According to the plot, bats with incendiary bombs attached to their bodies would be refrigerated until they went into hibernation. While in the torpid state, the booby-trapped animals would be packed in special boxes and dropped over the target city in slow-falling parachutes. If the plan worked, the bats would regain consciousness during the fall and immediately seek a dark refuge under the eaves of the Japanese buildings. When the bombs went off, the Japanese and the bats would never know what hit them.

The military finally perfected the technique, but only after thousands of failed bat bombs. The tiny kamikazes burned down a model Japanese city constructed in the desert, as well as an auxiliary air station near Carlsbad, New Mexico. But the Japanese never had to endure the suicide squadrons of flying mammals, for the atomic bomb proved much more efficient at death and destruction.

The primary occupant of the numerous limestone caverns and sinkholes of Central and West Texas is the Mexican free-tailed or guano bat, *Tadarida brasiliensis*. Guano bats outnumber all other bats in the state combined. Each spring, 100 million of the ⅓-ounce flying mammals migrate to Texas from the tropics to raise their families. Bracken Cave hosts 20 million, the highest concentration of mammals on earth. The bats from this cave consume 125 tons of flying insects nightly. Nine other caves attract from 4 million to 10 million bats each, and several smaller caverns boast populations of up to a half-million guano bats. These bats adjust to suburbia as well and roost under bridges, under eaves, and in attics. The largest urban bat colony in the world lives under the Congress Avenue Bridge over Town Lake in Austin. Three-quarters of a million Mexican free-tailed bats roost there, three times as many as live in Carlsbad Caverns, emerging at night to eat insects attracted to the city lights.

Most of the guano bats living in the caves and sinkholes from February to November are females and their young. The males live in separate caves or find roosting sites in cities. The giant nursery colonies fly from cave entrances like smoke curling through the evening air. The bats fan out and forage as far as 50 or more miles away. Air Force radar tracked the bats spiraling from Bracken Cave to an altitude of 11,000 feet before the flock dispersed, riding the high-altitude winds to their feeding grounds. A helicopter once followed a flock flying 60 mph.

Large nursery colonies of Mexican free-tailed bats may double their size with millions of infants in the summer. In mid-June, the females give birth to one baby. The young huddle together to keep warm while their mothers forage for insects. Amid the millions of returning females, the babies scramble for their mothers, who unerringly find their offspring. In general, bats have fewer babies than any other mammal their size. Nesting in large congregations and having only a few babies per litter make colonial bats extremely vulnerable to losses caused by human vandalism and disturbance.

Guano bats prefer the open, semi-desert habitat characteristic of the Southwest. They live from Houston west to the Pacific coast and winter in Mexico, Central America, and the Caribbean. They forage 15 to 100 feet or more above the ground catching their primary food, moths, and mosquitoes and any other insects that are available.

Texas has about 29 bat species. Not all bats live in large

colonies. The red bat, *Lasiurus borealis*, roosts singly and protects and nurses her one to three young under a leaf on a tree limb. Red bats live east of the Rockies from southern Canada to Mexico and into Arizona and California, and winter farther south. Besides the guano and red bats, the most common include the cave bat, *Myotis velifer*; Georgia bat, *Pipistrellus subflavus*; western pipistrelle, *Pipistrellus hesperus*; pallid bat, *Antrozous pallidus*; and hoary bat, *Lasiurus cinereus*.

The only vampire bat ever found in Texas did not live to see the light of the next full moon. Wrapped in its capelike wings, the creature lived in an abandoned railroad tunnel west of Del Rio. The vampire died, not by a stake in its heart, but in a researcher's preserving jar. Today, the blood-eating bat, a hairy-legged vampire, *Diphylla ecaudata*, sits on a museum shelf. These vampire bats typically inhabit tropical and subtropical forest land and lap, not suck, the blood of birds. Though other tropical species of vampires feed on mammal blood, they rarely choose humans as hosts.

Contrary to the popular expression "blind as a bat," these creatures of the night possess excellent eyesight, though vision is not their primary means of finding prey. Bats have the ability to locate objects by listening to high-frequency, or ultrasonic, echoes. They send out high-frequency beeps and read the reflected echoes like a radar screen. Though some shrews and rodents also use ultra-sound, none approach the sensitivity of bats. Bats can see with sound as well as humans see with vision. The parabol-ic shape of a bat's ears helps focus the echoes. Bats can detect large background objects 100 yards away, and dis-cern the size, shape, and even texture of closer objects.

The frequency pattern used by a bat depends on the ter-rain. Guano bats forage in open shrubland and high above the ground, and are not concerned about flying into trees or other objects. They search for prey using a constant fre-quency of about ten beeps per second, which indicates the presence of an object but not much else. When pursuing prey, the bat switches to a faster, frequency-modulated (FM) signal that reveals much more information about the object. Bats foraging among trees or other obstructions alternate their search signal between constant and modulated beeps.

Before high-speed photography, people generally assumed bats always caught insects in their mouths. Now we know that they frequently snare insects with the fingertips of their webbed wings, transfer them to the cupped membrane connecting their tail and hind legs, and eat them in flight. But not all bats eat flying insects. Some tropical species specialize in small mammals, fish, calling frogs, fruit, nectar, and crawling insects.

Bats in North America avoid the scarcity of flying insects in the winter by either migrating or hibernating. Most hibernating bats seek a cave or crevice deep enough to maintain a stable air temperature above freezing throughout the winter, but some, like the red bat, hibernate in trees. A bat's ability to lower its heart beat and metabolism (how fast its body uses food) is a marvel of adaptation. The tiny creatures drop their heart rate from up to 600 beats per minute to as low as 10 per minute. At an air temperature a few degrees above freezing, bats have the lowest metabolism of any mammal. If the temperature drops below freezing, bats must burn stored fat to generate heat, and at higher temperatures their bodies naturally use more energy. Bats that remain in Texas hibernate only a few months and may break their torpid state on warm days, but those in northern latitudes hibernate as long as eight months.

Instead of hibernating, many species of bats migrate south for the winter to areas with abundant food. Migrating Texas bats enjoy the tropical climate of Mexico, Central America, and the Caribbean islands from November to February. Marked guano bats flew as far as 800 miles from their Texas nesting site into Mexico.

Even when not hibernating, a bat has the surprising ability to lower its metabolism while sleeping during the day. As it placidly hangs in a protected retreat, its body temperature approaches that of the surrounding environment, usually 65 to 70 degrees F inside a cave. Most bat-size mammals live only 1 to 2 years, but bats have survived for 30 years. Scientists once thought the ability to slow down bodily functions on a daily basis might account for the unusual longevity of many species of bats. Recent studies, however, have shown that some tropical bats that maintain a high metabolism live more than 20 years.

The 29 species of bats in the Lone Star State live in almost every imaginable habitat. They inhabit the deserts, forests, mountains, plains, and cities. They hang upside down in caves, cracks, fissures, hollow trees, buildings, under bridges, and from branches and twigs. The Seminole bat, *Lasiurus seminolus*, roosts in clumps of Spanish moss. Some forage exclusively over water, others over grass, under the forest canopy, or above the treetops. Most pursue flying insects, but the pallid bat lands on the ground and catches beetles, grasshoppers, crickets, and scorpions. Surprisingly, the sting of deadly scorpions that can kill humans does not affect the tiny pallid bat. The Mexican long-tongued bat, *Leptonycteris nivalis*, feasts on nectar and pollen in the mountains of Big Bend. The agaves growing so abundantly in the desert depend almost exclusively on bats for pollination. Every species of bat has its preferred habitat, roosting sites, foraging pattern, and diet items. Such specialization enables many different species to inhabit the same area without competing with each other.

Even though bats live by the millions in Texas, many experts consider some species of the small mammals threatened with extinction. In recent years, their numbers have decreased at an alarming rate. The decline once was attributed mainly to pesticides and habitat destruction, but disturbance from cave exploration and vandalism appear to represent even greater threats. Bats have deserted caves that once hosted enormous populations. One thoughtless person could cause a million bats to abandon a nursery cave, leading to their untimely death. If disturbed during hibernation, a bat loses 20 to 30 days of fat reserves before it can return to its deep sleep. Several disturbances during a winter could doom the entire population of bats in a cave.

Bats in Texas enjoyed a beneficent image and were protected by state law from 1925 to 1957. As the state became urbanized, attics, eaves, and buildings proved to be alluring substitutes for the disturbed caves. The greater contact with humans increased the chance of infection from a sick bat, and a paranoia worse than the vampire superstition gripped the populace. The fear of rabies brought these beneficial animals out of favor, despite the fact that many more people are injured by pet dogs and cats than by bats. In 1985, 1000 people suffered from dog bites in Austin and Travis County, and one child died. Only two people, both researchers knowingly taking unusual chances, have died from bat-borne diseases in Texas.

The first bat I saw as a child was wrapped in a cloak of wings, hanging from a twig just above my tree house. It was probably a red bat, which commonly roosts in trees across the state. How wonderful, I thought as I plucked it from its perch and ran inside to show my mother. She shrieked as though I were holding a rattlesnake, and she made me wash my hands for at least ten minutes. For days she watched me to see if I was foaming at the mouth.

Recent advances in identifying rabies have shown that each animal species carries a different strain of the virus. Tests can determine exactly which animal has transmitted the disease. Bats seldom spread the dreaded virus to other animals. The state health department reports that no rabid animals tested in Texas (as of 1986) contracted the disease from bats. In other states, only a cow and a cat have been infected by sick bats. Bats accounted for only 16 percent of the rabid wild animals tested statewide in 1984. Scientists working with bats or spending time in bat caves often take rabies immunization shots as a precaution. Probably less than one tenth of one percent of the bat population has rabies, so bats pose little threat to the public, as long as the obviously weak and unhealthy ones are avoided. If a bat can be caught, it is probably sick and should not be handled.

Because of the worldwide threat to bats, Bat Conservation International was founded to educate the public, prevent extinction and habitat loss, and to ensure survival of viable populations. Members of the organization receive a newsletter and educational materials—including backyard bat houses—and can participate in special programs and outings. The BCI address is P.O. Box 162603, Austin, Texas 78716.

The Cougar:
The Reclusive Cat

Mountain lion, cougar, panther
Felis concolor

Startled passengers in passing cars stared at the four of us crammed in the cab of the pickup truck. A policeman pulled up and momentarily considered stopping us but changed his mind. Three of us were a little nervous ourselves about the fourth passenger, an adult mountain lion. Though declawed and defanged, it could have killed us all in a matter of seconds. Fortunately we all survived the trip to the television station, where the lion starred in a local talk show. By appearing on TV, we hoped to dispel some of the common misconceptions about this docile, but powerful, cat.

Mountain lions are the most widely distributed land mammal in the world, yet one of the most misunderstood. These 8-foot, 180-pound beasts strike terror in the hearts of people from the Yukon to the tip of South America. Most consider cougars blood thirsty killers that scream in the night and silently stalk human victims, yet since colonial times these cats have killed fewer than a dozen people. The only recent attack in Texas occurred in the Chisos Mountains of Big Bend National Park in August 1984. A family of hikers came upon a juvenile that had no fear of humans and appeared to have once been a pet. When one of the children screamed and began to run, the cougar attacked with the instinctive pursuit response to running prey. The lion severely injured the eight-year-old child and would have killed him if his father had not wrestled him loose. The next day, rangers tracked the cougar with dogs and killed it. Despite the proximity of lions and park visitors, a cougar had never before attacked anyone in the park, which has 18 to 20 lions in its 1100-square-mile boundary. In the spring of 1986, cougars attacked two children in California. Since mountain lions normally prey on animals the size of small children, preschoolers naturally stimulate the lions' chase and kill instincts.

Until the last two or three decades, even the National Park Service considered mountain lions worthless vermin and exterminated them. Only in 1970 did the last western state repeal its bounty laws on these cats. Today, Texas alone offers no protection to cougars; all the other western states classify them as game animals with a regulated hunting season. Ranchers hate pumas, panthers, cougars, or whatever they may be called, and kill them whenever possible.

Despite their evil reputation, mountain lions would rather flee than fight. In a lifetime of tracking, killing, and capturing 668 cougars, a famous western hunter saw only one lion that had not been treed by dogs, and he never heard the animals scream. The nocturnal shrieks usually come from owls, or bobcats in heat. Cougars detest barking dogs, and they will climb a tree to avoid a single hound, even though they could easily kill the canine. Trained dogs track the lions and hold them in a tree until the hunter arrives.

The unbelligerent, reclusive nature of these large cats contributes to the myths and half-truths repeated from generation to generation. While some Indians elevated cougars to representatives of the deity, early explorers considered them diabolic. Any animal so secretive must be hiding its evil intentions, so they reasoned as they stared into the night and told imaginative stories based on fear and conjecture. Humans justly should fear these powerful cats that can kill with a single slap—a cornered lion will fight to the death. But cougars are threatened more by humans than we are by them.

The pioneers moving west across the continent pushed the mountain lions before them, replacing the wilderness with farms, ranches, and cities. Hunting and loss of habitat eliminated the lions from most of their historical range, which originally included every state. In North America, the large cats survive primarily in the deserts and mountains of the West; the only breeding population east of the Mississippi lives in Florida.

Once common from shore to shore, these adaptable felines lived in mountains, forests, prairies, plains, swamps, and deserts. Their range corresponded to the distribution of their primary food—white-tailed deer in the East and mule deer in the West. As predators, cougars played an important role in keeping the deer population in balance with food resources. Decades of study have shown that the lions invariably kill the sick, feeble, and surplus young deer in the herd, leaving the healthy and strong animals to breed and care for the young.

The beneficial relationship between prey and predator was illustrated on the Kiabab Plateau on the north rim of the Grand Canyon. In an effort to "manage" the deer herd, the government systematically killed all cougars and wolves. With no natural controls, the deer population rose from 4000 in 1907 to 100,000 17 years later. Finally, with the forest abused and overgrazed, the starving deer died in great numbers until less than the original number survived.

An adult mountain lion kills between 35 and 100 deer annually, usually closer to the smaller number; these opportunistic hunters also will eat anything available. They savor porcupines and kill the quilled animals whenever they find them. Cougars eat mice, raccoons, and other small mammals, as well as insects and grass. In the deserts, they regularly hunt javelinas. Hungry cougars hunt by searching and stalking and by waiting and pouncing. They prefer country with heavy cover to conceal their movements and precipitous terrain with rocky ledges and escarpments so they can lie in ambush.

When a deer gets within range, the cat leaps toward the prey and pulls it down by grasping its shoulders and biting its neck. Cougars can bound with lightning speed for several jumps, but they do not have the endurance to win a race and seldom chase prey. The prey often dies instantly with a broken neck from the lion's powerful assault. The lion then drags the animal to a secluded spot and eats its meal. When full, the cat covers the carcass with leaves. It may return the next day to feed again, but mountain lions will not eat rotten meat. Coyotes, bobcats, eagles, vultures, and other less picky eaters dine on the leftovers.

A hungry cougar, like any opportunistic hunter, eats the food most available and easiest to catch, whether mice and deer or sheep or goats—thus, the eternal conflict between stock raisers and large predators. Ranchers also despise mountain lions because the cats occasionally kill much more than they can eat. The multiple attacks result not from a sadistic love of killing but from an instinctive reaction. A cat pounces on and kills prey, not in response to hunger but in response to the fleeing action of the prey. Wild animals naturally run and scatter to safety, but a herd of sheep, bred for high productivity of meat and wool, may mill around in confusion. As long as the stimulus is present, the lion will kill. If you encounter a cougar in the wild, do not run like the child in Big Bend, but slowly retreat.

Cougars are highly specialized hunters, superbly equipped to kill large animals. They have stereoscopic vision, necessary to judge distance when stalking and attacking, and their large eyes are adapted for night vision. Their canines can slash deep wounds, and their jaw muscles can crush bones. Their retractable claws can disembowel a deer or elk with one slash, and their powerful leg muscles break the prey's neck with one blow. Yet despite their deadly weapons, most cougars pose less of a threat to humans than a bull that charges any person entering its pasture.

Mountain lions prefer a life of solitude and associate only when mating. The male stays with the female during the two to three weeks that she is in heat and drives away any intruding males. Sometimes vicious fights occur, with the dominant male winning the right to father the cubs. The female chooses a shallow den under a ledge or log to have her one to six kittens. The black spotted cubs open their eyes in about ten days and nurse for two to three months. After weaning, they accompany their mother on hunting trips, and in the course of the next two years learn the hunting skills necessary to survive. During their second winter, the young leave their mother, who is ready to breed again, and strike out on their own. The juveniles may establish a home range from six to ten miles away or wander for a hundred miles until they mature and establish their own territory. The transient juveniles replace lions that have died or been killed.

Cougars mark their home range, which differs from a true territory because home ranges often partially overlap. Within that area, the cat maintains a small resting range for its exclusive use and a larger hunting range that it may share with its neighbor. The cat scrapes together a pile of leaves along a well-traveled trail and marks it with urine. Any wandering lion respects the No Trespassing sign and turns away to avoid conflict.

One morning I woke up in my desert campsite in Big Bend National Park and discovered mountain lion tracks within a few yards of my tent. Later that day, I found the lion's fresh scrape on a ridge overlooking the camp and Terlingua Creek. The cat had scraped a three-foot circle with a pile of dirt and an old rag in the center. I would have loved seeing the lion silhouetted in the moonlight along the ridge.

Wildlife researchers know little about the status of the mountain lion in Texas. Breeding populations exist in Big Bend and Guadalupe Mountains national parks, and ranchers regularly encounter the animals in the Trans-Pecos and south of the Nueces River. Scattered sightings occur in the Rolling Plains and Cross Timbers areas in North Texas and on much of the Edwards Plateau. In the early 1980s, one was seen repeatedly near Lake Travis. Most of the sightings represent transients, some probably driven from Mexico by increasing hunting pressure. The depressed economics of sheep and goat ranching have favored the mountain lion in the last decade. With fewer livestock on the range, the pressure to control the predators has decreased. Though the number of Texas cougars is undocumented because of lack of research, more of these magnificent cats may exist now in the state than in recent history.

The Coyote:
The Midnight Minstrel

Coyote
Canis latrans

A startled jackrabbit raced from the bushes as we bounced down the dusty road to our camp at Terlingua Abaja in Big Bend National Park. Suddenly, from out of nowhere a coyote appeared, and the chase began. The rabbit shifted into high gear and crested a low hill with the coyote a breath behind. A few seconds later, the panting canine trotted off empty-handed, like its cartoon counterpart, Wile E. Coyote. The coyote probably knew it didn't have a chance, but what could be better sport than chasing a rabbit?

Coyotes seldom overlook anything, especially if it relates to food or danger. Their keen vision, hearing, and smell keep them tuned in to their surroundings. At the Mule Ear Peaks overlook, one came trotting over a rocky bluff a hundred yards from my car. It instantly stopped to inspect the human invaders in its desert domain. A cautious nature has saved more than one coyote from human ill will. We stared at each other for a while, I with my binoculars, he with his sharp yellow eyes. As soon as I took out my telephoto camera lens, he melted into the underbrush. A minute later the coyote was a quarter mile away, resuming his daily rounds.

A coyote loping across the open desert seems a natural part of the rugged surroundings. Adults make long migrations, and the young often disperse as much as 100 miles from their parents' territory. These lean and lanky animals can jog at a comfortable gait of 10 to 12 mph for hours without tiring. They can run 25 mph with bursts of speed up to 40 mph. Coyotes will lead hunting dogs on an all-day chase if given the chance. A pack of hounds once pursued a coyote 50 miles before they dropped from exhaustion.

I found a coyote den in a sandy river bank near San Vicente, a Mexican village just across the Rio Grande from Big Bend National Park. Coyotes can dig like miners, but would rather use an old badger hole, rock crevice, or other protected place to rear their young. No one was home, but I could imagine the four to seven frisky puppies rolling in the sand, attacking each other, and tugging on mom's and dad's ears. The parents bring food to the young when they start eating solid food, after about three weeks. By nine months, the juveniles reach adult size and soon after leave the family.

Coyotes are easily satisfied. When they are tired, any shady or protected spot within their home range serves as a bedroom. A pair maintains a home range from one to ten square miles, and in some instances aggressively protects this domain. Yet these social animals often greet visitors with the same friendly tail wagging and sniffing ceremony common among neighborhood dogs. Coyotes usually run in pairs, though you often see only one at a time. Many mate for life, some only for the season, and others live in solitude. They also may run in a pack when food, especially carrion, is abundant.

Coyotes invented country-and-western singing long before cowboys rode the range. The Aztecs called them *coyotl,* or barking dog. Even their Latin name, *latrans,* refers to their frequent moonlight serenades. Coyotes' music must be heard to be appreciated. The barking, yodeling song alternately sounds like a lonesome wail and the frenzied greeting of old friends. Once in Big Bend a predawn chorus of yaps and howls sounded like a dozen excited animals. But at first light a single pair came trotting through the campgrounds checking the garbage cans just like city mutts.

A coyote's disharmonious howling, the signature of the Old West, now echoes through the night in every state, including Alaska and most of Canada. In taming the West, humans killed the coyote's major competitors, gray wolves and mountain lions. Without these larger animals to limit its expansion, the adaptable coyote soon spread throughout North America and now ranges south to Costa Rica.

Coyotes seldom receive the credit they deserve. Contrary to Hollywood's Wile E. Coyote, a bumbling idiot who can never catch the roadrunner, these canny canines employ ingenious hunting techniques. Two coyotes may form a relay team to catch a fleet-footed jackrabbit. One rests while the other pursues the rabbit, which invariably runs in a large circle. At the end of each revolution, the fresh partner continues the chase.

Coyotes allegedly cooperate with badgers to catch rabbits in burrows. The badger works digging out the victim while the coyote waits at the exit tunnel. When the trapped animal tries to escape, it lands in the jaws of the coyote. By the time the badger realizes the burrow is empty, Mr. Coyote is long gone with a full belly. What some call cooperation, others call thievery.

Stockmen, like the badger, unintentionally cooperate with coyotes. The predators do not mind at all that ranchers stock the range with animals that have had their defensive behavior bred out. The opportunistic coyote accepts livestock as gifts, or perhaps as tribute, from the humans usurping its domain.

Never a gourmet, a coyote will eat the most easily accessible food. Its diet includes anything edible, plants or animals, dead or alive. Seasonally, berries and fruit (including melons) comprise a large portion of the desert dog's diet. It preys heavily on rodents, rabbits, and ground squirrels in areas where they are abundant. Dead animals, especially along highways, are a standard food item.

Rabbits and mice represent by far the major portion of a coyote's diet. One hundred field mice, about a two-week food budget for a coyote, consume as much forage as a growing lamb. The rabbits on a section of ranchland can easily eat as much grass as six sheep. By helping to control these destructive range animals, coyotes help the rancher.

Ignoring a coyote's contribution to controlling rats, mice, and rabbits on the range, humans have hated and slandered coyotes since the first cowboy rode the range. Naturally ranchers can be expected to turn their fury on any animal that kills their livestock, and coyotes can be expected to prey on sheep and goats. Ranchers traditionally consider coyotes ruthless villains that should be exterminated, but in reality coyotes kill only a small percentage of livestock lost each year. Individual coyotes, however, sometimes do become stock killers and inflict heavy losses.

Coyotes prey more on lambs and angora goat kids than on any other livestock. In 1983, lamb mortality on Texas ranches was 11 percent, with 4.5 percent attributed to coyotes. The kid mortality was 14.8 percent, with coyotes responsible for 5.1 percent. Coyotes killed 57 percent of the total number of lambs and kids lost to predators. Decades of studies show that about twice as many deaths of adult sheep and goats result from disease and other causes as from all predators.

Some control of coyotes inevitably is required in ranching areas. Trapping, poisoning, and shooting may remove problem individuals and reduce local populations. Unfortunately indiscriminate use of poison devastates all meat-eating species, guilty and innocent, harmful and beneficial. Western states yearly expend considerable sums of money attempting to eliminate predators. In 1983, state, federal, and private agencies in Texas spent $4 million to control predators, rodents, and other animals that cause economic damage. Livestock losses amounted to approximately $3.5 million. According to the Texas Animal Damage Control Program, the total benefits of the overall control program exceed the costs by a factor of four.

Despite the concerted efforts of state, federal, and private sectors and the urbanization of its range, the coyote is more widespread now than ever before. The U.S. Wildlife Research Center in Denver reports that almost every major western city has a resident population of coyotes. While practically every other predator has succumbed to the pressures of modern society, the coyote has learned to take advantage of the food habits of civilization. The omnivorous diet and elusive nature of this adaptable canine enable it not only to survive but also to thrive in a modern world.

Deer: Texans' Favorite Game Animal

White-tailed deer
Odocoileus virginianus texanus
Sierra del Carmen white-tailed deer
O. virginianus carminis
Desert mule deer
O. hemionus crooki

Texas is the deer capital of North America. With almost 3.5 million white-tailed deer and 250,000 mule deer, the Lone Star State has the highest deer population in the country. No wonder many Texans take deer hunting seriously. To hunters, the opening day of deer season in mid-November is as traditional as the Super Bowl, Thanksgiving turkey, and the Fourth of July.

With the first nip of autumn, hunters begin to see visions of a mule deer silhouetted against the setting sun with its giant ears straining to pick up the slightest rustle— or of a white-tail with its nose in the breeze and flaglike tail straight up, a sure sign it is about to bound away. This malady common to hunters is called buck fever.

Texans should not brag about the abundant number of deer in the state. Texas has too many deer. Finding enough food poses a real problem for the animals. Most rangeland suffers from overgrazing by sheep, goats, and cattle. Without a protective cover of vegetation, the soil washes away with the rain. Weedy plants with low nutritional value invade the abused areas and become established. After a century of overgrazing, the state's most productive deer habitat, the Edwards Plateau, does not have enough annual protein available for healthy deer. As a result, deer seldom reach their full size, and large numbers starve during dry summers and severe winters. The South Texas Brush Country is the only area in the state with sufficient nutrition for deer consistently to reach their full genetic potential for size and antler development.

For 100 years, ranchers and farmers have killed the wolves, coyotes, and cougars that historically kept the deer from overpopulating. The predators removed the old, sick, and surplus juveniles from the breeding population, leaving only the healthiest animals to reproduce. Despite blinds, high-powered rifles with telescopic sights, and a hunting tradition as old as the state, Texas hunters do not kill enough deer, and they insist on killing the wrong ones. Each year, a half-million hunters take to the woods and kill 300,000 deer, about 150,000 short of the annual harvest required to maintain a healthy deer herd through most of the state.

Since hunting is the only way left today to limit the state's deer herd, hunters need to kill more does. Hunters want trophy bucks with a rack to hang on their den wall, but shooting a buck does little to decrease the population. Most of the bucks killed are inexperienced yearlings, which leaves the mature animals to breed with all the females. Each year about 80 percent of the antlerless deer permits go unclaimed. The deer population will not diminish until the number of females is reduced. On the Edwards Plateau, home of half the deer in Texas, hunters need to kill three times as many does to bring the population in balance with the available food supply. State biologists feel that 20 percent, or 360,000, of the adult does should be removed annually. If hunters killed only does, the deer population would approximate the healthy number for most of the state.

Texas averages 3.5 white-tailed does for every buck, with an average of 1 fawn for 2 does. A healthy female with plenty of food generally conceives twins, and white-tails sometimes have triplets. White-tails usually give birth in May and June, and mule deer from June through August. Food availability, both for the pregnant and nursing female and for the baby after weaning, has the greatest influence on how many fawns survive the first year. Disease and predation, especially from dogs, also take their toll. As many as 75 percent of the fawns may die during stressful years, yet infant mortality alone is not checking overpopulation.

The classic Disney movie *Bambi* has formed an enduring impression for Americans. The helpless condition of the dappled fawns fills us with compassion, sometimes to the point of rescuing "deserted" young. But the fawns are far from deserted or helpless. Their spots camouflage them in the mottled light that filters through the trees as long as the fawns remain motionless, which they instinctively do. The mother feeds only a short distance away and returns several times daily to nurse the young.

When the fawns are two months old, the mother allows the yearlings to rejoin the family. White-tailed deer are moderately gregarious, and family members forage together during most of the year. In areas with abundant food, several family groups may feed together, giving the appearance of a large herd. Mule deer are more gregarious and form herds before, during, and after the breeding season.

As November approaches and restless hunters start showing signs of buck fever, the mature bucks begin suffering from a different kind of fever. Their thoughts turn to the does. White-tailed does come into heat from late October through November, and mule deer about a month later. Their scent attracts bucks like ants to a picnic. Though normally shy and reclusive, bucks become bold and fearless during the rut, or breeding season. With polished antlers they battle saplings and bushes, anticipating actual combat with bucks that may invade their territory.

Deer have small home ranges and seldom wander more than a mile. White-tailed bucks mark their territory by pawing up a patch of ground under an overhanging limb. They urinate on the ground and rub the scent glands near their eyes against the limb. These "scrapes" are sure signs that a buck is in residence. A buck also leaves his calling card by rubbing the musk glands on his hind legs on saplings.

Bucks do not limit themselves to the females in their territory; they will chase the scent of a doe with wanton disregard into the territories of other deer. The clash of antlers echoes through the woods as males spar vigorously with intruders. Hunters take advantage of the bucks' obsession and rattle two old antlers together to sound like a fighting pair. Often the reigning buck in the area comes running to investigate the suspicious sound.

The bucks tend to disregard the dangers of a hostile world during the rut, but the females become even more secretive and solitary. They even drive away their yearling offspring. Despite the many paintings depicting a buck, doe, and fawn, mothers with young rarely tolerate the presence of other deer, including fathers. The males breed with as many females as possible and have no family ties or parental responsibilities.

Unlike cattle, which graze on grasses, deer browse on leafy herbs, fruit, acorns, leaves, and twigs. In the desert, mule deer favor lechuguilla stalks, sotol, mesquite beans, juniper, and leafy plants. Deer consume very little grass, even in times of extreme food shortages. They do not compete with cattle, but they do eat the same foods as sheep and goats.

Dinner time for deer comes just before dawn and again at dusk. Although they usually bed down in a protected location for the day, they may be active at any time. Deer are more active on windless nights when their acute sense of smell can best alert them of danger. They have sharp vision, but like most animals of the night they're color blind. The bright orange vest worn by a hunter looks dull gray to a deer. Despite their acute vision, deer have difficulty discerning the details of stationary objects. Many times I have had a deer approach to within a few yards before it caught my scent and bounded away.

Since deer feed mainly on low-growing plants and have no reason to fear owls or hawks, they seldom look skyward. Hunters take advantage of this characteristic and construct blinds in trees or elevated on poles. These usually overlook a clearing that deer frequently cross or that has been baited with corn.

Mule and white-tailed deer are biologically, ecologically, and behaviorally distinct. The common names hint at the major differences in appearance. Mule deer have large ears, 11 inches long and 6 inches wide, that they cock when alarmed. When the white-tail senses danger, it holds its bushy 10-inch tail straight up. The dark tail has a snow-white underside that flashes like a flag as the deer runs. Mule deer hold their tail down when running. Until a mule deer matures at three or four years, its antlers resemble the white-tail's. At maturity, white-tails have four or five points growing from the main beam without any branching, while each beam of a mule deer's rack divides into two equal branches with two points per branch. Generally mule deer weigh 15 to 20 pounds more than white-tails of the same age.

The desert mule deer of the Trans-Pecos favor a different ecological habitat from the white-tails'. Mule deer live in steep, rugged, open terrain and never inhabit flat prairie and plains country. White-tails prefer heavy brush and dense woodlands. The animals' flight behavior corresponds to their different habitats. In open country, mule deer can keep a watchful eye on anything threatening and will run a safe distance and stop. On the other hand, woodland-dwelling white-tails cannot see what danger lurks behind the bushes, so they do not feel safe until they have put considerable distance between themselves and the threat. A running mule deer has a high, bounding gait necessary to clear boulders and cacti, while a white-tail runs in a low gallop to avoid overhanging branches. A mule deer once was clocked at 38 mph for a short burst, then it slowed to 23 mph.

White-tails live in all but 3 of the contiguous 48 states. This highly adaptable animal is divided into 16 subspecies that range north into Canada and south through Mexico to South America. The Sierra del Carmen white-tail, a mountain subspecies, lives only in the high mountains of the Big Bend area and Mexico. In the rest of the Trans-Pecos, white-tails favor mountain foothills with a heavy cover of thick brush.

Seven subspecies of mule deer live from central Mexico to coastal Alaska. They are found in the semi-arid deserts and mountains of the western United States and Canada and the badlands of the Great Plains. In Texas, desert mule deer live in the Trans-Pecos and the canyons and rugged terrain of the High Plains.

The Dolphin: Delightful Mammal of the Deep

Bottlenose dolphin
Tursiops truncatus

Do dolphins save drowning swimmers? Do they chase away sharks and surf in the waves beside humans? Questions buzzed around the boat as the curious tourists crowded the railing and scanned the waves in anticipation. The captain of the excursion boat had just announced that he had turned on his fish finder to attract dolphins. As though on cue, two dolphins burst through the ship's wake, rode the waves while everybody cheered, then disappeared beneath the waters. Such scenes are frequently reenacted along the Texas coast as dolphins play escort service for boats.

Dolphins, also called porpoises, have thrilled and mystified humans for thousands of years. As opposed to the fish with the same name, dolphins are sea-dwelling mammals. They breathe air, feed their babies milk, live in groups, and interact with humans in ways unexpected for animals. Countless stories recount how dolphins have helped swimmers, towed boats, and played with children. Today trained dolphins at amusement parks add to the mystique. They jump through hoops, walk on water, and propel their 600-pound bodies 16 feet out of the water to pluck fish gracefully from the trainer's hand.

Thirty-two species of the family Delphinidae ply the oceans of the world. Some live in the shallow zone along the continental shelf, while others prefer deep waters. The species found in Texas waters is the bottlenose, the most common dolphin in the Gulf of Mexico and the star performer in oceanaria around the world. Texas dolphins hunt a variety of fish in the shallow bays and channels, but mostly eat striped mullet. Seldom do they venture farther than 12 miles from shore. A 1978–79 survey counted about 2 bottlenose dolphins per mile along the Texas coast, one of the highest populations in the Gulf of Mexico; Aransas Bay had highs of 104 dolphins in October and 281 in January.

Dolphins may thrill us with their tricks, but they fascinate marine scientists for other reasons. A dolphin's skeleton shows traces of hind limbs, and its front flippers have the same bone structure as the human arm. Their close relation to terrestrial mammals indicates that dolphins lived on dry land before they inhabited the sea. Fossils indicate that mammals colonized the ocean about 58 million years ago, probably filling empty niches caused by the mass extinction of reptiles.

Though vastly different from fish, dolphins are equally well adapted to a watery lifestyle. Powerful swimming muscles propel these streamlined animals through the water as fast as 22 mph. Their flexible, torpedo-shaped bodies and oily skin secretions reduce drag and turbulence. Most species feed on fish in shallow waters or near the surface, but some can dive 2000 feet. Human divers must carefully regulate their ascent from even moderate depths to prevent the nitrogen absorbed in their blood from expanding and causing the painful and deadly sickness called the bends. Dolphins never get the bends. When dolphins dive, the water pressure squeezes the air out of their lungs into bronchial passages where no gas exchange occurs. Some species can remain underwater for as long as one hour. Their muscles contain a large amount of myoglobin, which combines with oxygen and stores it for later use. Where is a dolphin's nose? Not at the end of its snout, but on top of its head so it can breathe when it floats on the surface.

Dolphins live about 30 years, and take 5 to 10 years to mature. Like humans, dolphin young have a long learning period. Many of the dolphins seen cavorting alongside ships are mothers with their offspring. The males live in separate groups, or pods. Pods in Texas waters average 5 to 6 dolphins, depending on food availability, among other things. Several pods may join to form a large herd. Dolphins stay in a loosely defined home range, but may switch from pod to pod. As researchers learned about the dolphins' complex social structure, they realized that many of the tales about these friendly animals were based on facts, not imagination.

For dolphins, cooperation is an important facet of survival in the deep. They group around a female giving birth and help the baby to the surface for its first breath. Dolphins with vulnerable young drive away sharks, but if not threatened usually ignore the predators. Sometimes one female will baby-sit the pups while the others hunt. Dolphins often cooperate while hunting. A pod surrounds a school of fish and forces it into a compact cluster; the animals take turns rushing in to feed while the others prevent the fish from scattering. They also corral fish in shallow water. Occasionally, they flush a school onto the shore then swim out of the water to catch the floundering fish. In Africa, fishermen have learned to take advantage of these natural hunting strategies. They wade in the surf and call dolphins by slapping the water. The dolphins herd fish into their nets and get an easy meal in exchange. Texas fishermen report that dolphins respond to the shift in a shrimp boat's engine noise and to the whine of the net winches hauling in a catch. The clever animals follow along and feed on the discarded fish.

Helping fishermen, saving drowning humans, and playing are extensions of a dolphin's natural behavior. Two dolphins will swim on either side of an injured companion, keeping it afloat until they get it to shore. One dolphin even pushed a mattress onto a beach. Dolphins love to play. They spring from the water, race boats, and surf in the waves. The tricks they learn to perform at oceanaria may entertain us, but the tricks they learn by themselves astound us more. A dolphin in a large aquarium saw a diver cleaning the inside glass. The dolphin began to imitate the diver and even made noises and bubbles like the scuba tank. From then on, the dolphin took over the job of cleaning the glass. In another aquarium, a visitor blew a puff of smoke at a baby dolphin. The baby immediately swam to its mother and got a mouthful of milk, then returned to the visitor and puffed the milk at him. The milk made a white cloud in the water like smoke in the air.

Though dolphins have been held in captivity since 1914, scientists did not discover that they used ultrasound for echolocation until 1958. By sending out a stream of 1000 clicks per second, dolphins can read the ocean floor like a road map. This sense is so sophisticated that they can tell the difference between various types of metal, or if a fish has a hook hidden in its body. A research vessel placed a fence of metal pipes across a narrow channel used by a pod of dolphins. The dolphins detected the fence from 1000 feet away. A scout went ahead and investigated, then returned to report to the others. The biologists recorded the dolphins' excited conversation before the animals ventured around the barrier.

While hunting, playing, or traveling, dolphins stay in constant communication with whistles, beeps, belches, and grunts. One experiment tested the ability of dolphins to communicate with each other. Two were trained to get food by pressing a paddle when a light came on. Then they were placed in a tank separated by a curtain with the light on one side and the paddle on the other. The dolphin with the light quickly learned to signal its partner to press the paddle when the light came on. Scientists recorded the conversation, but were unable to decipher it.

Communication, cooperation, and a complex social structure all require a high level of intelligence. A dolphin's brain is larger and has more convolutions than a human's, but has fewer layers of neurons. The ability of dolphins to communicate excites marine scientists, such as Dr. Louis M. Herman at the University of Hawaii. He has trained one dolphin to understand arm gestures and another to understand computer-generated sounds. The animals are forcing us to redefine our beliefs that only humans can comprehend words and sentences. The dolphins understand that words are symbols for objects and that the order of words in a sentence changes the meaning ("take boat to ball" vs. "take ball to boat," for example). Diana Reiss at Marineworld/ Africa USA near San Francisco gave dolphins an underwater keyboard. Each of the nine keys has a different meaning and sound. The dolphins press the keys and imitate the sounds when they want an object. Someday this kind of research may develop an artificial language that will enable humans and dolphins to understand each other. If that happens, we may discover that these smiling creatures want to teach us a few tricks.

Foxes: Clever Canines

Red fox
Vulpes vulpes
Gray fox
Urocyon cinereoargenteus
Kit fox
Vulpes macrotis
Swift fox
Vulpes velox

"I was afraid they would kill my cows, so I shot the parents," the gruff-looking farmer said. Then he softened. "But I couldn't kill the pups. Can you take care of them?" Expecting coyotes, I took the box and looked at the five squirming, woolly babies with their eyes barely open. To my surprise, they were red foxes. The misguided farmer had thought that a diminutive fox, not much bigger and no more dangerous than an alley cat, posed a threat to his cattle.

Unfortunately, the fox still carries the tainted reputation that Aesop depicted some 2600 years ago: a clever, cunning animal, but always the villain. We call a person who is a sly rogue a "fox" and say we've been "outfoxed" when we are deceived. Too often, the fox is appreciated only as an animal that provides a sporting chase or has a valuable pelt. Other than that, many consider it vermin.

I grew up with a more positive image of this remarkable animal. Early in the year when the swelling buds promised spring, the red foxes' yapping echoed through the woods surrounding our house, a sign that mating season had arrived. Once, a pair chose the old stone fence in our backyard as a denning site. That ancient wall stemmed the flow of trees and vines trying to reclaim the fertile East Texas soil. It marked the end of manicured lawn and the beginning of wildness. We heard but seldom saw the secretive family of foxes. Only once did I catch a daytime glimpse as a bounding, bushy tail disappeared into the brush.

Like most members of the canine family, all foxes make good parents. Since they cannot dig well, the pair prefers to remodel an abandoned den—a burrow for the red, kit, and swift foxes, but often a rocky crevice or hollow limb high in a tree for a gray fox. The male fox brings the female food while she nurses the litter of three to five pups. The babies open their eyes in 8 to12 days and can walk in 3 weeks. In 6 months the young are fully grown, and the adults and juveniles disperse to claim their own separate territories.

Though the rock fence that served as a fox nursery ended a few feet behind our chicken coop, the wild canines never molested the chickens. As every fox knows, a fat mouse or a tender cottontail makes the best gourmet meal. But foxes are not too picky to dine on chicken, or any other food that comes easily. Foxes are survivors—opportunistic omnivores. An adult red or gray fox must catch about five pounds of food per week. It dines on grasshoppers, beetles, and crickets in the summer, berries and other wild fruit in the spring, earthworms that cover the ground after a rain, and carrion whenever it is available. Despite some hunters' contentions, foxes do not prey on bird nests frequently enough to have an adverse effect on pheasant and quail populations. Mice and rabbits are too easy to catch for a fox to waste time looking for nests. An observer once saw a grouse successfully fledge a nest just a few yards away from a fox's den.

A fox spends its nights, and often part of the day, trotting along at 4 to 5 mph searching for food. Its tireless gait inspired a ballroom dance, the fox trot. While hunting, a fox keeps its ears cocked, listening for the slightest rustle in the grass or the soft squeak of a mouse. Its sensitive nose constantly samples the breeze for the faintest aroma of anything edible. A foraging fox zigzags through fields and may stand up on its hind legs for a clear view through the grass, then almost effortlessly pounce on a mouse, gopher, or field rat.

In a bounding chase, the fox uses its long, bushy tail to help maintain its balance. The furry tail serves another purpose on cold nights—the animal curls it around its face as a nose warmer.

The fox's keen senses of hearing and smell make it an efficient predator of small mammals and equip it well for survival. A rancher in South Texas once encountered a gray fox heading straight toward him. Thinking the animal rabid since it showed no fear, the man shot it. To his surprise, he found the fox perfectly healthy, but blind. Because of its sharp senses, the sightless fox had been able to survive in the unpopulated countryside. Other than humans and automobiles, a fox has only to fear coyotes, bobcats, and an occasional eagle.

The red fox has rightfully earned its stereotypical "foxy" image. Like a riverboat gambler, it is always ready to match its wits with any challenger. Since a red fox cannot win a race with the hounds by stamina alone, it must rely on instinctive and learned survival skills. Herein lies the charm of the chase for the hunter. A red fox will double back or crisscross its trail, run along the top of rock fences, backtrack through streams, and circle behind the dogs. Members of the European nobility donned red coats, had the kennel master fetch their pedigreed hounds and the stable master their horses, and made a day of tea and chasing the wily creature. The fox cooperated by leading the riders and baying dogs for a merry romp through the woods. The noble tradition lives on in America. Backwoodsmen sip home brew and listen in anticipation as the howls of ol' Blue and the other hounds disappear in the distance. Will the fox outfox the dogs?

Fox hunters disdain the unsporty manners of the gray fox. After a short run, it inevitably heads for the closest rocky den or climbs a tree. Unlike any other member of the dog family, gray foxes climb with the agility of a cat. They hook their claws in the bark of the straightest trunk and shimmy right up to the first limb. They may stand in plain view just above the frenzied dogs or hide in the leafy crown of the tree. In any event, the thrill of the chase is too short-lived to satisfy a devotee of the classic fox hunt.

Four species of foxes live in Texas: the red, gray, kit, and swift fox. Each has its distinct habits and habitats. The red fox occurs north of San Antonio, except for the Trans-Pecos and the Panhandle. With its characteristic white-tipped tail, it haunts the edges between forests and meadows, woodlots and fields. A diverse habitat with mixed hardwoods, rolling cropland, brush, and pasture makes an ideal home. In contrast, gray foxes are more shy and retiring and avoid human occupation. They range throughout the state, except for the Panhandle north of Palo Duro Canyon. They prefer dense woods, swamps, thickets, and chaparral—areas with a thick understory of vegetation. The brush country of South Texas and the scrub vegetation and rocky outcrops and canyons of Central and West Texas provide ideal hunting, hiding, and denning sites. While the red fox dines on succulent dewberries, wild grapes, plump meadow mice, and cottontails, the gray fox relishes juniper berries, cactus fruit, mesquite beans, kangaroo rats, and jackrabbits.

No one knows for sure whether the colonists found red foxes in North America or brought them with them, or both. Red foxes were introduced into East and Central Texas for hunting. Fossils found in Pennsylvania indicate the gray fox has called America home for at least 25,000 years. Possibly because of the cold climate of the Ice Age, foxes disappeared from New England and did not return until the last century. Now the gray fox lives throughout the United States, except for the northern Rocky Mountains, and south into Central America. Except for the desert regions, the red fox covers the North American continent, and roams across Europe and Asia as well. Northern red foxes have several color phases: black, silver (black with white guard hairs), cross (dark across the shoulders and back), bastard (bluish gray), and Samson (no guard hairs). Foxes with the silver coloration bring the highest fur prices and are commercially raised.

The two other foxes that live in the Lone Star State, the kit and swift, are much smaller than their cousins and rarer. The kit fox lives in the deserts of the Trans-Pecos, the western United States, and northern Mexico. The swift fox occurs in the grassland prairies that range from the Texas Panhandle north into Canada. The only other fox occurring in North America is the arctic fox, *Alopex lagopus*, an inhabitant of the polar regions.

One night while camping in the desert at Big Bend National Park, I was visited by an inquisitive kit fox. No larger than a cat, but sporting oversized ears, the little critter smelled an empty tuna fish can in my trash sack. Twice it came and prowled around my car while we sat quietly a few yards away. Looking for the source of the enticing aroma, it almost jumped into the car. In hushed wonder we watched the little creature prancing back and forth in the moonlight like a phantom from a world where animals have nothing to fear from humans. Finally, it disappeared into the night to search for a more traditional dinner.

The closely related kit and swift foxes are the smallest, yet fastest, foxes in North America. For 100 yards, they can outrun any prey or predator that they might encounter. Whether in pursuit of a rabbit or trying to escape a coyote, they can change directions at lightning speed. Such an effective defense probably explains why they act so fearlessly and without caution. Lacking the wariness and suspicion of the red and gray foxes, these innocent canines have suffered greatly from coyote and other predator control programs that distribute poisons. As a result, they have been eradicated from large areas in the United States where they once thrived. Fortunately, with the curtailment of predator poisoning campaigns, the swift fox appears to be returning to its original range. Perhaps the kit fox will also return.

Trappers in Texas harvested 50,459 gray foxes in 1986–87 and 7,298 red foxes. At the going rate of twenty dollars per pelt, trapping foxes is more than a million dollar per year industry in Texas. State laws classify foxes as fur-bearing animals and prohibit hunting or trapping without a license. A fox that escapes hunters and trappers usually lives 4 to 5 years, though foxes have survived 15 years in captivity.

The worldwide distribution of the fox has brought it in close contact with humans for untold thousands of years. As it trod through time, this remarkable creature left its imprint on human folklore and language from the Mediterranean to North America. Unlike many wild animals suffering depletion of numbers and loss of habitat, the red fox has benefited from human interaction. Hunters, instead of diminishing its population, have expanded its distribution across three continents and recently transported it overseas to Australia. So, because of its appeal as a game and fur animal, the red fox has managed to extend its range in modern times. A pretty foxy maneuver, huh?

The Javelina: Prickly Pear Gourmand

Javelina, collared peccary
Dicotyles tajacu angulatus;
formerly *Pecari tajacu* (Linnaeus),
Tayassu tajacu, Pecari angulatus

One dark night in the Basin campground of Big Bend National Park, I heard a rustling noise in the bushes near my tent. Critters frequently invade the camp, but the grunting, munching, and lip-smacking sounded like a monster from outer space devouring helpless earthlings. Fortunately the ten eyes that reflected the light of my flashlight belonged instead to five javelinas pigging out in a prickly pear patch. Eventually these four-legged gluttons wandered on to the next gourmet course of their progressive dinner.

Javelinas have the table manners of hogs, and many people confuse them with domestic pigs gone wild. In reality, they are related only distantly to our familiar porkers: both belong to the order of hoofed animals. Fossil records of their ancestors in America date back 22 million years. When the Spanish introduced swine to the New World in the 1500s, javelinas ranged from Argentina to Texas and even into Arkansas.

Javelinas retreated south as ranchers converted most of Northeast Texas into open pastures, but Texas still has more javelinas than any other state. They favor areas with heavy undergrowth and plenty of prickly pears. Much of the state remains prime habitat, especially the Brush Country of South Texas and the deserts of West Texas. Their range extends westward along the southern border of New Mexico into Arizona, and south through Argentina.

These roving garbage disposals eat almost any vegetable matter. Contrary to tales of hunters and ranchers, javelinas

61

do not eat snakes, eggs, birds, rabbits, baby sheep and goats, or any other animal matter. Just give them prickly pears, lechuguillas, sotols, mesquite beans, acorns, and century plants. Since javelinas eat little grass, they do not compete with cattle for food. Prickly pears are essential to javelinas, not only for nutrition, but also for water. They devour the thorny pads and fruit with complete disregard for the spines. Javelinas can go six days without water, and months if their diet includes prickly pears. Three pounds of the cactus a day will keep an adult from becoming dehydrated. Prickly pears are so important that javelinas seldom live in locations void of the plant.

Javelinas have adapted perfectly to life in the hot, arid Southwest. When they are stressed by lack of water, physiological changes reduce water loss from respiration by 68 percent and from urination by 93 percent. Javelinas also adapt their daily activities to conserve water. During the hottest times of the year, these hardy animals forage through the desert only in the cool of the morning, evening, and night. Even in the winter, temperature strongly influences the javelinas' activities. They forage during the warm afternoons, and freezing temperature causes them to huddle together for warmth.

Touching is a way of life for these gregarious animals. Of the 31 behavior patterns observed among herd members, 17 involve touching. Javelinas groom each other more than any other social interaction. Two animals stand close together and rub their noses on each other's hindquarters. Javelinas have a navel-like gland located just above their tail that exudes a musky liquid that helps them identify each other. Grooming and touching probably help maintain the social bond among the individuals of the herd. Besides body language and scent, javelinas communicate with a vocabulary of at least 15 signals. They vocalize to indicate aggression, submission, alarm, and other reactions. A javelina chatters its teeth not from cold, but to threaten its neighbor.

From the viewpoint of a cactus, javelinas are ruthless,

vicious animals. They attack prickly pears without hesitation and voraciously consume the plant. But when alarmed by a human or animal, they scatter in all directions. An inexperienced hunter once froze when a herd of the startled, grunting animals seemed to charge him. One actually brushed his pants leg as it scampered by, unaware of the exact location of the human intruder.

The scatter response, typical of herding animals, confuses the predator and makes attacking a single animal difficult. But humans interpret the flight of fear as the attack of savage animals. After scattering, the nearsighted javelinas may wander about nervously woofing and popping their teeth together, unsure if danger still exists. More than one excitable hunter has sought refuge in a thorny mesquite thinking these timid critters were circling for the kill. Only when defending itself does the javelina bare its two-inch canine teeth and become a serious threat.

The millions of generations of Javelinas that have survived through time have developed the senses necessary for survival and lost those that were unnecessary. Javelinas do not need keen vision to search for plants in dense underbrush, but acute hearing and smelling are essential to their social life. Their complex vocabulary keeps the herd close together while foraging through heavy cover, and individuals recognize other herd members by scent, a necessity for social animals.

An equal number of males and females make up the herd, but only the dominant male breeds with the females. Pregnancy lasts for 145 days, and twins are common. The young can walk and follow their mother after the first day, and mature in about 48 weeks. Adults weigh from 25 to 60 pounds, stand 20 to 23 inches tall, and are 34 to 38 inches long. The size of an animal, more than its sex, determines its place in the pecking order.

In Texas, herds average from 15 to 17 animals, depending on the amount of food available. Herds remain stable, but they often have several subgroups of about 6 that may eventually break off to form new herds. All members defend the territory—about 400 to 585 acres—against intruding javelinas. The animal's short legs and stout body were not built for travel, but for scampering through the underbrush. A javelina seldom ranges more than a square mile during its decade-long life.

Even though the javelina was elevated to a game animal in 1939, Texas hunters and ranchers have traditionally considered it vermin. Ranchers dislike this not-so-innocent critter because it tends to slash up the cow dogs that search thickets for stray cattle. Hunters sometimes have the same problem with their bird dogs. Javelinas have a natural animosity for dogs, probably because coyotes kill javelina young. They do not have tusks like wild boars, but their two-inch canines can inflict a serious wound. Any cow dog or bird dog attacking a javelina usually requires an emergency trip to the veterinarian for stitches.

Today many stockmen value javelinas primarily because they can help increase profits. By eating prodigious amounts of prickly pear, the animals do more to control cactus than many range-improvement programs. Many ranchers who sell hunting leases now view these creatures as a money-maker along with deer. But whether or not the javelina has the approval of the ranchers, this animal has a rightful place on the range along with the more appreciated denizens of the Southwest.

The Longhorn:
The First King of Texas

When the Civil War broke out, almost every man of fighting age left Texas to defend the honor of the South. As he was leaving, many a father told his oldest boy, "Son, find a cow with a calf and tie it up in the corral till it's tame enough to milk. Then mother will always have milk for the children while I'm gone." The cow that the young lad dutifully chased out of the thorny thickets, lassoed, and tied to a post in the family corral was the wild longhorn. A longhorn, especially a mother with a calf, would just as soon gore a horse and rider as swat pesky flies with its bushy tail.

"Texas was born of hide and horn," goes an old frontier poem. The hide and horn belonged to what settlers considered the toughest, meanest, sliest, most independent critter that ever called Texas home—the longhorn. These ornery bovines became legendary long before they became cash on the hoof at Kansas railheads. Big game hunters from Europe considered them the fiercest animals in North America. With six-to-nine-foot horns and a disposition that made a bear seem mellow, longhorns challenged the bravest hunters from the continent.

After the war, the returning men found their state bankrupt and in the depths of a depression. The only salable commodities were the hides and tallow of the longhorns that had run wild for centuries. Like bison on the prairies, the cattle were shot and skinned and their carcasses left to draw flies. Then the railroad reached Kansas and made the hungry East only a trail drive away. A $3 cow in Texas brought $40 in Abilene, Kansas. Large ranches formed in South Texas, and cattle became king of the economy. With so many men lost in the war, ranchers had to employ adolescents to herd the cattle, giving birth to the term "cowboys."

The cattle that blessed Texas bankrolls were gifts from the Spanish conquistadors and padres. Christopher Columbus brought the first cattle to the New World on his second voyage, and in 1540 Coronado, searching for the fabled golden cities of Cíbola, took the first herd north of the Rio Grande. By 1600, hundreds of thousands roamed free in Mexico. Spanish missionaries brought the first breeding cattle into East Texas in 1690. By 1770, a herd of 40,000 grazed the grassy plains that surrounded the Mission Espíritu Santo. The mission is now a state park at Goliad. Unlike bison, longhorns refused to graze in large herds across the prairies. They preferred the protection of impenetrable thickets and cedar brakes. During 200 years of running wild, a breed of rangewise cattle that Texas could call its own had developed.

As longhorns spread across the state, they had to survive disease, drought, scorching heat, and freezing weather. In the winter, they pawed through ice for food and browsed bushes like deer. Besides the natural calamities, wolves, cougars, and other predators culled out the weak. Only the hardiest, fleetest, most resourceful creatures lived to produce offspring. Like a potter molding clay, natural selection shaped a breed with a survival instinct that no improved breed can match. The endurance and stamina of the longhorn made possible the perilous trail drives destined for the future.

By the mid-1800s, millions of longhorns hid in the chaparral country north of the Rio Grande. They ranged north to the Red River, east to Louisiana, and west to the Brazos River. These cautious animals hid in the brush by day, grazed by night, and would flee at the first sign of a rider. Early settlers tried in vain to tame them, but even the captive calves grew into outlaw cattle. Longhorns, though numerous, proved so difficult to kill that in times of famine the pioneers resorted to killing mustangs, which also ran wild across the state.

The wild longhorns bore no brands, and any rancher could round them up and burn his sign on their flanks. The first cowboys in South Texas had to "pop the brush" to drive out the reluctant longhorns. Their rugged ponies, themselves products of the brush country, bounded through the thorny growth like a bronco at a rodeo. The rider dodged and ducked for his life, fighting to stay on his horse while he roped and threw the cow. Without his hat, jacket, leather leggings, boots, and gloves, the South Texas cowboy would have been skinned alive by the thorny vegetation. Later, cowhands on the vast ranches in the Panhandle had the luxury of chasing cattle across open prairies, unimpeded by brush or thorn.

Both the longhorn and the cowboy adapted to living in the wildest part of Texas by becoming tougher than the rugged, unforgiving environment. Although the cowboys proved tougher, it was not by much, and not all the time. Both became legends, and rightly so, because pushing a herd of longhorns 800 miles up the Chisholm Trail had to be one of the hardest jobs ever demanded of man. The cowboys managed the greatest human-controlled migration of animals in history. During the 1870s and 1880s, they "trailed" ten million head of cattle to the northern railheads.

The era of the cattle drive brought wealth to Texas and gave the world a rich and enduring legend, but it lasted only a brief 25 years. By the 1890s, railroads spanned the Lone Star State, and barbed wire dissected the open ranges. Though at first bitterly opposed to fencing the range, ranchers found that confining cattle allowed them to breed more profitable stock. The very characteristics that had made longhorns king of the open range almost doomed them to extinction.

By the turn of the century, cattlemen wanted beef, not brawn. They wanted uniform animals that would fatten up at a predictable rate. An even disposition in a fenced pasture mattered more than survival in the wild. Longhorns had a natural independence and an uncanny ability for eluding fences. A 1500-pound steer could leap like a deer, bust through a fence, and even swim underwater to get into the next pasture. Stories abound of freedom-minded outlaw steers that dropped dead at the sight of a cattle pen, or that lay down and died before being dragged into a herd. So, after 25 years of stardom, exit the longhorn and enter the Hereford and other more manageable breeds. The next quarter of a century saw the fabled longhorn fade like a western sunset.

In West Texas, a few old mossy-horned steers survived in the rugged Glass Mountains after ranchers had converted to Herefords. Windmills dotted the arid Big Bend country, and high-class Herefords roamed the range. The longhorns would come down to the water tanks and gather a herd of a thousand yearling Herefords. At the first sign of a rider, the longhorn steer, as fleet as a coyote, would lead his herd in a mad stampede for the hills. The cowboys spent days rounding up their stock. In time, the young Herefords became lean and wild like the longhorns, and the devil to manage. Finally the frustrated foreman of the ranch mounted his fastest horse and hunted down the last of the noble longhorns like vermin.

By 1920, only a few hundred survived in the remote areas of the Brush Country. Western author J. Frank Dobie, an old South Texas rancher himself, loved the lore of the West and began assembling a herd of the rare animals. Dobie's longhorns eventually became the official state herd, which now numbers about 125 and is kept at Fort Griffin and other state parks. In 1927, Texas congressmen introduced a bill that established a herd in Oklahoma's Wichita Mountains National Wildlife Refuge. Officials inspected 30,000 Texas cattle but found only 20 cows, 3 bulls, 4 calves, and 3 steers that they considered purebred longhorns.

Two hundred years of life in the brush molded other distinctive characteristics into this vanishing breed besides horn size. The longhorns' heavy forequarters make their front legs appear shorter than the rear. Their horns crown a long, wide head topped with a thatch of hair. A lean look, swayback, and hump just above the tail give these rangy critters an unsightly appearance. Steers have the longest horns, followed by cows and bulls. The wide color variation of a longhorn makes every individual unique. The technicolor tones range from red to blue and black to white in abstract splashes, speckles, streaks, and spots.

When the Longhorn Breeder's Association formed in 1964, about 1500 head existed. Now 62,000 graze in state, federal, and private herds. Among the 2500 registered breeders, individuals pay as much as $60,000 for a premium cow. Cattlemen buy longhorns for more than nostalgia, show animals, or investments. With the price of ranching steadily increasing, an animal completely self-sufficient on range grass and one that can survive the hardships of disease and climate represents a genetic gold mine. The fertile longhorn cows reproduce for 25 years, while other breeds stop calving after 8 years. Stockmen are attempting to breed the survival characteristics of the longhorn into the better beef-producing breeds. So the legendary longhorn is assured of a lasting place in Texas, not just in relic herds but also in the genes of future breeds of premium cattle.

The Opossum: America's Strangest Animal

Opossum
Didelphis virginiana

"It has a head like a Swine, a taile like a Rat, and the bignesse of a Cat." The bizarre little animal we call the opossum astounded Captain John Smith and the other Pilgrims of the early 1600s. But long before the colonists set foot on the new continent, the opossum had made its mark on Europe. The Spanish explorer Vicente Yáñez Pinzón discovered the strange "monkey fox" in about 1500. The conquistador presented the lowly opossum to the royal court of Spain, where Queen Isabella slipped her jeweled fingers into the animal's marsupial pouch and marveled at the extraordinary creature from the New World.

The opossum, or possum as it is usually called, baffled the first explorers with more than its strange looks. The more they became acquainted with the opossum, the more they considered it one of nature's strangest jokes. It grins and salivates like an idiot, but has an IQ higher than a dog's. It has opposable thumbs like a human, yet hangs from limbs by its tail like a monkey. It carries its babies in a pouch like a kangaroo until they are old enough to cling to its back or hang from its tail. It has poor vision and cannot run or climb fast enough to escape a predator. Its most famous peculiarity is its tendency to play dead when frightened. These characteristics ensured it a prominent place in southern folklore.

Since the days of the Pilgrims, the opossum has gained more recognition than it would have liked. The 1644 botanist Georg Marcgrave described opossum tail soaked in water as a "wonderful remedy. . . . in all of New Spain there is not to be found another remedy so useful in so many cases." Possum tail reportedly "cured inflammation of the kid-

71

neys, constipation, coughing, and if placed on a wound would draw out any ailment of flesh and bone."

The opossum's culinary reputation, however, soon eclipsed its medicinal contributions to society. Possum and taters became a meal time favorite in the South. (Not knowing that "taters" in this case means yams is a sure sign of Yankee ancestry!) Late-night hunting trips with baying hounds and moonshine whiskey became a southern tradition.

The sex life of the possum has aroused more speculation than a soap opera. According to widespread rumors, the male possum copulates with the female's nose and she blows the fetuses into her pouch. The possum's unusual reproductive organs account for this preposterous misunderstanding. The male's penis has two heads to match the twin canals of the female's uterus. The unusual anatomy gave the opossum family its scientific name, Didelphidae, Greek for "double womb."

The female reinforces the myth by her activities just before giving birth. She sticks her nose in her pouch, not to blow in the babies but to lick a path to help guide the young from vagina to pouch at birth. The half-inch babies are born after only 12 days, the shortest gestation of any North American mammal. At birth the babies, hardly more than embryos, weigh only $1/175$ of an ounce. An entire litter of 10 to 20 can fit in a teaspoon. The tiny young have strong front legs equipped with claws for crawling the 3 inches to the pouch, but they lose the claws soon after attaching to a nipple. Safe and secure in the pouch, as many as 13 begin the slow process of maturing.

At two months, the mouse-size young begin leaving the crowded pouch between meals to climb onto their mother's back. They cling tenaciously to her fur as she ambles on her nightly foraging trips. Weaned by three months, the juveniles may stay with the mother for another month, and they reach sexual maturity in eight months. Possums usually have two litters per year.

The possum's naked tail has inspired numerous folktales. According to legend, a possum stealing corn near a cemetery saw a ghost. The poor critter was so frightened that all the hair fell off its tail. Another misleading account credits fire with causing the hairless condition. The stories vary, but no one disputes the fact that possums make good use of their tail. Besides helping them balance when running and climbing, they use the prehensile organ as an extra hand to cling to limbs or to carry nesting material.

Possums belong to the ancient order of marsupials, animals with a pouch in which the young develop. While most marsupials occur in Australia, the possum has lived in North America for over one million years. No other marsupial lives north of Mexico, but 65 different species live in Central and South America.

Until the early 1900s, possums ranged north to Pennsylvania, Ohio, Indiana, Illinois, and Iowa. Since then they have moved into Vermont and southern Canada. Extreme winters limited their northern range expansion until human settlements provided warm dens and winter food. Because these nocturnal creatures eat almost anything, including carrion, they do not mind having humans as neighbors. With dog food and garbage providing gourmet dining at night, possums feel as at home in exclusive neighborhoods as in the deepest woods. In Texas, possums favor deciduous woodlands, but they occur in almost every county. In the prairies and arid West Texas, they live along wooded streams and rivers. The residents of Upshur County in East Texas call their county the Possum Capital of the World. If you happen through the small town of Rhonesboro, stop by the International Possum Museum, housed in the general store.

A possum makes its home in a hollow tree, in an empty burrow, or under a house. For a soft, warm den, it bundles up leaves and carries them in a downward curl of its tail. To protect its naked tail and ears, a possum avoids extreme cold. Even in Central Texas it often suffers from a frostbitten tail and ears. In the winter it packs its den entrance tightly with leaves and sleeps through the cold spells. But it will not hibernate; it will emerge as soon as the weather warms.

A possum does not need much space in either a wild or urban setting. Its home range varies from 4 acres in rich woodlands to 50 acres in habitats with less abundant food. It lives alone and wanders only far enough to fill its belly. Two studies in East Texas reported that about 70 percent of a possum's diet consists of insects, worms, and plants. Mammals, primarily cottontails and rodents, accounted for about 10 percent of its food, and reptiles for about 7 percent. In the fall, possums like to eat persimmons and the red fruit of the holly *Ilex decidua*, commonly called possum haw because of its popularity with the animal.

Possums view snakes from a totally different perspective from most other animals. Instead of fear, they exhibit an innate desire to eat them. They eagerly devour rattlesnakes, copperheads, and cottonmouths with no ill effects from even repeated bites. Possums injected with venom from North American and foreign pit vipers, including cobras, showed no tissue reaction or organ damage. Though possums are immune to the venom of pit vipers, the neurotoxin from a coral snake bite is deadly for them.

Possums have neither sharp claws nor speedy legs to protect them from predators, but no animal is defenseless. By human standards, possums look stupid; learning and discrimination tests, however, indicate they are smarter than man's best friend, the dog. The marsupials may appear inept, but they have a few tricks to get them out of tough spots. A threatened possum snarls with lips curled back exposing all 50 teeth: it has more teeth than any other American mammal and no compunction about biting the hand that offends it. Angry hissing and copious salivating accompany the show of teeth, an act that discourages most predators. I once saw a possum stand its ground against a 75-pound German shepherd, who finally gave in and let the snarling beast scamper away. Although the hissing, salivating animals may appear rabid, possums seldom contract rabies.

If the ferocious bluff fails, these animals have one final, and famous, defense: feigning death. They roll over and go limp, with their tongue hanging out and eyes closed. They often discharge a greenish, foul-smelling liquid that helps repel an attacker. "Playing possum" is not a clever trick, but an innate survival response. The animal enters a catatonic state triggered by a brain reaction to fear. It may recover rapidly, but can return immediately to its deathlike trance if danger still threatens.

A possum's bluffing works well. This defenseless creature seldom becomes the meal for its major enemies: dogs, coyotes, bobcats, and great horned owls. Besides human hunters, the other serious threat to the possum is that four-wheeled predator, the automobile. Possums have survived a million years of climatic and environmental changes and have even adapted to urban life, but modern-day traffic may be this enduring animal's greatest test for survival.

The Pronghorn: Home on the Range

Pronghorn
Antilocapra americana

"Where the deer and the antelope play," sang the cowboys as they rode across the broad open range. The antelope in the lyrics was the pronghorn, a native of the rolling prairies and brushlands from Canada to Mexico. Before the cowboys' time, 500,000 pronghorns roamed the prairies with the bison. Settlers romanticized pronghorns in song and legend, but eradicated them and the bison from most of their range. The creatures suffered from massive slaughter by hunters and found their range crisscrossed with barbed-wire fences. Unlike deer, pronghorns never learned to jump even a three-foot fence. Fences block their movement unless they can crawl underneath. By the 1920s, only about 12,000 of these free-spirited animals remained.

Most ranchers had the mistaken idea that pronghorns competed with cattle for food. Any animal that cut profits became the enemy, preferably viewed through the sights of a high-powered rifle. Stockmen hunted and trapped wolves, mountain lions, coyotes, and pronghorns to extinction where possible. Eventually ranchers discovered that pronghorns do not usurp the cattle's grasses but primarily eat shrubby plants and succulent forbs (herbaceous plants other than grass). Once pronghorns gained the favor of ranchers and the protection of state laws, their numbers began to increase. Most of their ancestral range has been farmed, ranched, and overgrazed, but state wildlife departments have reintroduced this magnificent animal wherever possible.

Living almost a million years on the open prairies has adapted pronghorns perfectly to their expansive habitat. For safety, they depend on sight, speed, and their herding instinct. Their large eyes can detect the slightest movement across the treeless landscape. The location of their eyes on the sides of their heads provides a wide field of view, which makes sneaking up on them almost impossible. If a predator does surprise them, they can bound away faster than any other North American mammal.

A pronghorn's body is an engineering marvel designed for speed and endurance in the roughest terrain. Pronghorns gulp air while running; their hearts, lungs, and windpipes are much larger than those of other animals their size. The deep breathing enables the heart and lungs to circulate oxygen-rich blood to the straining muscles. These graceful animals can run at speeds approaching 55 mph.

A thick, cartilaginous pad on their hooves prevents lameness when bounding among rocks and boulders. The tendons, ligaments, and leg bones fit so well together that these rugged animals seldom suffer a sprain. Their front hooves, which hit the ground with the most force, are a half-inch larger than the rear hooves, another adaptation to increase surefootedness.

Herding behavior also helps protect pronghorns in their short grass, shrubby environment. These alert animals constantly look up to scan the horizon while grazing. Many eyes can detect danger faster than a single pair, and the first one sighting a potential threat signals the rest of the herd. If danger is imminent, the herd bolts but stays close together, a typical escape pattern for plains-dwelling herbivores. The movement of the herd confuses a predator and makes selecting an individual victim more difficult—the herd can run together at speeds of 47 mph.

Pronghorns use 31 behavior signals in communicating with each other. A puzzled or suspicious pronghorn raises the tan hair on its back and the black hair of its mane. It walks or trots stiff-legged. If danger threatens, the animal flares the long hairs on its large white rump and dashes away.

Equipped with an unusual curiosity, pronghorns will

investigate any small moving object that they do not recognize. Hunters through the ages have taken advantage of this by tying a rag to a bush or lying down and waving a handkerchief. Often the inquisitive animal can be lured within range, whether it is an Indian's bow, photographer's camera, or hunter's rifle. Texas now has enough pronghorns to have a hunting season. Each year approximately 800 are killed from almost 20,000 in the state.

When you drive through the western half of the state, look for pronghorns grazing across the countryside or near a water tank. Common, though scattered, they range from the Panhandle to South Texas. They usually stay far from the road, but I once saw a herd of ten adults and juveniles grazing near a fence. As soon as the car stopped, the animals nervously stared in my direction and hesitantly pranced away. Finally the dominant male decided the threat was too great and began to herd the others in a forced retreat. He ran back and forth until all had run a safe distance. With their protective coloration, the agile animals seemed to disappear into their surroundings.

From March through the breeding season, from midsummer to October in Texas, a male establishes his territory and collects a herd of from 2 to 14 females. The buck vigorously defends his territory and harem from intruding males and greets trespassers with a hard stare and a snorting and wheezing warning. If the challenger does not retreat, the dominant male chases him; horn clashing and combat, however, rarely occur.

The females have their babies in February and March in South Texas and from May to June in West Texas. They usually have twins and nurse them in separate locations for protection against predators. Within a week, the youngsters can run about 20 mph. The fawns group together in nursery herds, and the mothers return several times daily to nurse their offspring. By the time the male juveniles are weaned in September and the females in November, the young males have established a lifelong hierarchy within their age group.

The young of all mammals like to play, but pronghorns enjoy playing all their lives. Their favorite game is running. They race, charge, circle, and chase each other at the least provocation. Racing is such a thrill that they seem to delight in challenging automobiles and even trains, and frequently dart in front of a vehicle once they pass it.

All this running, both for play and defense, takes a lot of energy, and pronghorns eat literally day and night. They eat at dawn, rest, have lunch, rest during the heat of the day, eat until dark, rest, and continue the cycle through the night. With stomachs half the size of a sheep's, they must eat highly nutritious foods. Succulent forbs comprise about 60 percent of their diet, shrubs about 25 percent, and grasses about 15 percent. Flowers and fruit seldom escape their attention. Pronghorns, perfectly adapted to the food in their habitat, eat large quantities of locoweed and other plants that can kill domestic livestock. Their liver and kidneys, larger than those of domestic animals, can metabolize the toxic elements in the plants.

The horns of this unusual creature make it unique in the animal kingdom. Pronghorns have true horns, like cattle, made of a hairlike structure covering a bony sheath. But unlike other horned animals, the pronghorn sheds its horns annually, the way a deer sheds its antlers. The horns end in a slight hook curving backward. A prong, which gives the animal its name, faces forward. Both males and females have horns, but the females do not have prongs. The males' horns begin growing at two months of age, but the females' delay until their second year and reach about 10 inches in length. The record trophy, a buck with 20-inch horns, was killed in 1899. Today hunters consider 12-to-14-inch horns a good trophy.

Rabbits:
Hippity-hopping
across Texas

Black-tailed jackrabbit, California jackrabbit
Lepus californicus
Eastern cottontail
Sylvilagus floridanus
Swamp rabbit
S. aquaticus
Desert cottontail, Audubon cottontail
S. audubonii

One chilly spring afternoon, I stopped for gas at the only store in Dew, Texas, population 71, and got a fill-up, a candy bar, and two unusual passengers. The store was the old-fashioned type—the only kind that could survive in this dot-on-the map town since Interstate 10 had diverted the Houston–Dallas traffic ten miles west. The superheated interior from a big space heater and the cold stares of two elderly domino players greeted me as I pushed open the rickety door. My entrance interrupted not only their game but also the conversation between a young girl holding an old cigar box and the lady behind the candy counter. The girl had something, apparently alive, in the box and appeared puzzled about what to do.

"Anything else?" asked the proprietor as she came over to the cash register. My curiosity would not let me leave without knowing what was in the box.

"Maybe a candy bar," I said, and nonchalantly stepped over to the candy counter. To my surprise, the girl had two baby cottontails not more than a few days old nestled in the cigar box. "Where did you get those?" I inquired as I looked at the squirming, almost naked bunnies. "They hardly have their eyes open!"

"My dog killed their mother, and I don't know what to

81

do with them." A few minutes later, I left the store, got into my car, and handed my surprised wife an Almond Joy and a box of bunnies. We named one Dew and the other Tex, after their birthplace.

For the next week, our lives revolved around holding our two babies in the palm of one hand and feeding them milk with an eye dropper. Rabbits grow fast, and within two weeks they refused to stay in their box. Dew and Tex had an insatiable curiosity and explored every nook, corner, and closet. They jumped on our bed in the middle of the night, got trapped inside a trash basket, and left their pellet-size calling cards in our shoes, on chairs, and under furniture.

Nights, the active time for rabbits, became a real adventure around our house. No more quiet evenings. Our guests bounded through the rooms chasing each other, zigzagging, and jumping from one hiding place to another. We discovered the importance of their play when we tried to catch them. They had perfected the evasive maneuvers necessary for escape and knew the exact locations of all the hiding places. Six weeks after our providential stop in Dew, I released our two wards in some nearby woods.

Rabbits are ingrained in the culture and folklore of our society. When the lights go out after an Uncle Remus story of Br'er Rabbit, children cuddle their stuffed bunny for warmth and security. Peter Rabbit, with his narrow escapes in Mr. McGregor's garden, and Bugs Bunny, with his adventures with Elmer Fudd, are among a child's first folk heroes. The Easter Rabbit even shares the glory of one of Christianity's most revered holy days.

The mythical creatures characterized by Hollywood and commercialized by Madison Avenue exhibit little of the true nature of cottontails and jackrabbits. Far from being witty, brave, and aggressive, rabbits crouch in a protected hiding place by day and venture out to feed only as the day fades into evening. But to survive in what to them is a hostile world, rabbits must be alert, cautious, and quick to respond. Besides human hunters, their primary threat, rabbits have to contend with hungry hawks, owls, eagles, coyotes, foxes, bobcats, raccoons, dogs, cats, and rattlesnakes. So many animals depend on bunnies for food that only one out of six adult rabbits lives to see its second year.

Rabbits cope with such extreme predation in a very simple way—they have lots of babies. In South Texas they breed year-round, and in other parts of the state they have a 9-to-10-month breeding season. A short gestation period, 27 days for eastern cottontails and 41 for jackrabbits, and only 1 to 2 weeks of postnatal care allow every mature female to have as many as seven litters per year. An average litter consists of two or three young, though five to eight are not unusual.

Eastern and desert cottontails dig five-to-ten-inch burrows and line their elaborate nests with soft fur. Swamp rabbits construct their nests above ground, concealed in a tunnel of dead weeds with a side entrance. The babies, helpless and almost naked at birth, open their eyes in about 7 days and leave the nest in 12 to 14 days. Juveniles mature sexually in 4 to 6 months, so those born in the early spring sometimes breed before their first winter. Adult females average about ten surviving babies per year.

Jackrabbits, members of the hare family, do not need the cozy nests necessary for cottontails. Newborn hares enter the world fully furred, with open eyes, and frisky as fleas. They leave the nest, a shallow depression under a bush or other protection, within 24 hours. After a week, the litter scatters and the young are on their own. They mature in about 8 months. Approximately 14 young for every jackrabbit female survive each year.

Rabbits as a species depend on a high birthrate to prevent extinction, but the individual rabbit relies on sharp hearing and keen vision to spot danger, and speed to escape. At the first sign of danger, a rabbit perks up its ears and scans like a radar antenna to detect the slightest sound. The rabbit cautiously hops to safety if the threat is far away. If danger is near, the rabbit drops its large ears, squats close to the ground, freezes, and relies on its brown color to help it blend in with its background. If the predator approaches too closely, the rabbit darts away with evasive zigzags and jumps. Cottontails can sprint 15 to 20 mph, while jackrabbits reach 35 mph and cover six to nine feet with a single jump.

Predators probably exert the greatest influence on the size of local rabbit populations, but land use determines whether a local population survives or disappears. In the last 50 years, habitat destruction by agriculture and ranching has greatly reduced the number of almost all wild animals, including rabbits. But rabbits can adapt to such a wide variety of habitats that they remain one of our most common wild animals.

Grasslands and fields interspersed with brushy refuges provide the best habitat for cottontails. These cautious animals seldom venture far from cover. The farming practices of the early pioneers, with wood lots and brushy fence rows, ideally suited the cottontails, and their numbers increased significantly. But when large-scale, intensive farming cleared vast acreages of pastureland, woodlots, and thickets, cottontails had no safe refuge, and their numbers diminished.

The eastern cottontail is the most widespread rabbit, living from southern Canada southward beyond Mexico. Its range includes the eastern United States from the Atlantic to the Rockies and into New Mexico and Arizona. In Texas, this cottontail occurs in every county except the extreme western counties of the Trans-Pecos.

The swamp rabbit favors floodplains, bottomlands, marshes, swamps, and estuaries, and it seldom ventures further than 1.5 miles from a major body of water. Its numbers are decreasing due to the draining of lowlands, clear cutting of forests, and flooding of riparian woodlands by impounded rivers. Its range extends through the southeastern United States and into Texas west to San Antonio and south to Aransas Bay.

The desert cottontail lives in the arid Southwest, where it favors brushy ravines, thickets, and brambles. It lives in deserts, dry mountain slopes, creosote flats, and arid shrublands from the high deserts of Montana south through the western half of Texas and into Mexico. It is the only rabbit known to climb sloping trees and bushes, and is so common in prairie dog towns that it is sometimes called the "prairie dog rabbit." In Texas, its range is west of a line from Wichita Falls to Brownsville.

The black-tailed jackrabbit bounds across the arid regions of the Southwest and inhabits Texas west of a line from Houston to Dallas. It prefers open, short grass areas where its keen vision and hearing are unimpaired. Jackrabbits thrive in desert shrublands, pastures, and cultivated areas. They survive extreme desert temperatures by crouching in the shade all day and by radiating body heat through the many blood vessels in their large ears. Also, their body temperature can rise between five and seven degrees F during the day without ill effects. At night, the stored heat is released and their temperature returns to normal.

Besides their high reproductive rate, the rabbits' cosmopolitan diet helps them thrive in widespread areas. During the growing season, they eat grasses and almost any herbaceous or succulent plant. In the winter, they survive on shrubs, bark, twigs, and woody plants. In large numbers, rabbits can have a significant impact on crops and range grasses. According to one report, 148 jackrabbits eat as much as 1 cow, or 6 as much as 1 sheep.

A contented rabbit requires only a safe refuge for hiding and a patch of grass for dinner. With these conditions satisfied, it has no reason to travel. In prime habitats, the home range of a cottontail may be less than 5 acres, while a jackrabbit requires about 40 acres. The size of a home range varies according to the abundance of food and cover. Several individual ranges may overlap, with many rabbits congregating on roadsides, in cultivated fields, or in other feeding areas. Rabbits follow well-beaten trails and know the exact location of every hiding place within their home range. When frightened, a running rabbit tends to circle within its range, a habit that hunters, both human and coyote, use to their advantage.

During the breeding season, the males travel freely, while the females remain in their home range and drive away other females. Males develop a well-defined hierarchy, with only the dominant individuals mating. After the breeding season, the juveniles disperse to establish their own home ranges. The broad dispersal of the young, their high reproduction rate, adaptability to a variety of habitats, and a universal diet enable rabbits to be one of the most abundant yet most preyed upon animals in North America.

The Raccoon:
The Masked Bandit

Raccoon
Procyon lotor

Almost everyone who spends much time outdoors encounters a particularly brazen animal that wears a mask like a bandit—the raccoon. The dark eye patches and banded tail are the tradomarks of this nocturnal prowler. The midnight clamor of upset trash cans announces the raccoon's presence, and the unerring stare of its eyes, reflecting red or green in a flashlight, attests to its boldness.

Raccoons play their role as lords of the night with gusto, and they reluctantly give up the part when the curtain of dawn ascends. Early risers may see a raccoon busily foraging along a stream bank, probing under rocks in the water searching for its favorite food, crayfish. Bits of colorful shells accompanied by long-toed tracks in the mud show where a raccoon enjoyed its dinner.

Though ranging from central Canada through Mexico, and equally at home in deserts, forests, farmlands, and suburban areas, raccoons seldom stray far from water. Aquatic invertebrates comprise an important year-round portion of their food. In East Texas, half of their annual diet consists of crayfish and acorns, supplemented by plants, insects, and rodents. Berries and fleshy fruit take them through summer and fall, and acorns sustain them through the winter. Wild plants make up most of their diet, but the opportunistic feeders never overlook carrion, garbage, corn, orchard fruit, or any other easily obtainable food.

These fearless foragers are famous for washing their

food. Captive raccoons invariably dunk their meal and then play around with it in their water dish. I once saw a raccoon in a zoo try to wash a snowball. This stereotyped behavior gave them their Latin name, *lotor,* meaning "the washer." Raccoons in the wild, however, show no compunction about eating either dry or dirty food. The food washing of captives is merely a substitute for their normal aquatic feeding.

As winter approaches, raccoons become butterballs, and their waddling gait only adds to their obese appearance. A raccoon gorges all summer on berries, grapes, persimmons, wild plums, crayfish, and whatever corn, grains, rodents, birds, and fish it can find. By fall, it may have doubled its weight, but unlike that of humans, the raccoon's fat serves an important purpose. When food becomes scarce in the winter months, the stored body fat tides the animal through until the next spring. In northern latitudes, where deep snow covers the ground all winter, raccoons may sleep for four months. Unlike true hibernating animals, though, a raccoon's metabolism and body temperature remain normal, and the animal wakes up anytime the temperature warms. In the Southwest, raccoons remain active throughout the year and become dormant only during protracted cold spells.

A raccoon's varied diet and widespread distribution hint at its intellect. A highly intelligent and keenly discerning animal can take advantage of a greater choice of habitats and food sources. To survive in new situations, an animal must learn rapidly what is safe and what is dangerous. Laboratory tests place raccoons halfway between cats and rhesus monkeys in speed of learning, and equal to cats in visual discrimination.

Raccoons have keen vision, both during the day and at night when they are most active. They have sensitive hearing and pay particular attention to unusual noises. A highly developed sense of touch and long fingers on their forepaws give them remarkable dexterity. They can catch flying insects and darting crayfish and can pick up minute morsels. In tests, raccoons do as well as humans in distinguishing between objects of different sizes and textures.

Anyone with a pet raccoon soon discovers that its alert, curious nature and manual dexterity often spell trouble in the home. After a young raccoon passes through the cuddly stage, common to all mammal babies, its insatiable curiosity drives it to explore cabinets and empty boxes, and to spread out sewing kits, jewelry, and tools all over the floor. Wild juveniles are equally inquisitive, with object manipulation occupying a major part of their play.

When a pet raccoon reaches adulthood, it becomes more than a nuisance—it can be a terror and a threat to human safety. Companionship plays an important role in the learning and development of babies and juveniles, but they become solitary creatures when they mature during their second year. Solitary animals never develop the social behavioral restraints that govern gregarious animals like dogs. As a result, a pet raccoon may tell you it does not want to be stroked by chewing off your fingers. The Texas laws regulating fur-bearing animals prohibit keeping raccoons as pets.

Whether in the home or in the wild, a raccoon that loses its fear of humans can become a major menace. Wildlife rehabilitation groups have difficulty reintroducing them into the wild once they have become accustomed to human care. When released, one female yearling who had outgrown her human parents soon found the nearest ranch. She raided trash cans and even tore through a screened back porch to get dog food.

For years park engineers have tried to design a raccoon-proof trash can. Big Bend National Park once placed a new design at the campgrounds near Santa Elena Canyon. The can had a five-pound lid with a six-inch-wide steel border welded around the edge. The border overlapped the sides so that the heavy lid had to be lifted straight up. Shortly before midnight, a crescendo awakened me, and in the beam of my light a raccoon nonchalantly sifted through the refuse.

It sauntered to the next can, stood in the handle conveniently located on the can's side, and lifted the lid straight up. The carefully engineered, guaranteed animal-proof trash receptacle was child's play, no challenge at all for the adroit raccoon.

Trash cans are like credit cards to campground and suburban raccoons. Unlike their country cousins, these freeloaders seldom have to work for their meals. They may never wander more than a half-mile from home. The home range for urban raccoons covers about 12 acres, while their country counterparts require 40 to 100 acres to meet life's needs. The size of a raccoon's home range varies according to its age and sex, season, quality of habitat, and population density.

For raccoons, a good denning site makes a home complete. They will use a variety of shelters but favor a hollow tree for their winter bedroom and spring nursery. In the absence of a suitable tree, raccoons will snuggle up in brush piles, abandoned buildings, caves, crevices, or another animal's old ground burrow. As subdivisions engulf the countrysides, expectant mothers sometimes may set up house in attics and garages.

The mother raccoon has from three to four babies in April or May. Their eyes open in 18 to 24 days, and by 4 to 6 weeks they begin walking. By 7 weeks, the frisky babies run and climb. The mother raccoon has all the family responsibilities: she stays with the babies during the day and forages for food at night. After 11 weeks the young travel with the female on her nightly rounds. The young stay with her until the autumn, when they disperse. Sometimes the juveniles den with their mother for the winter and disperse the next spring. They reach their full size the second year.

The family foraging trips play an important role in preparing the young raccoons for life. Their instinctive knowledge equips them well for survival, but their mother's example shows them how to cope with the everyday problems of finding food and avoiding dangerous situations. Once while sitting on the banks of a bayou in East Texas, I heard a low whining growl interrupt the solitude. A movement at the water's edge caught my eye. A raccoon nervously paced back and forth crying under her breath. Wondering why she did not run away, I looked around and discovered three babies hanging motionless on a nearby tree trunk. The mother's distress calls had alerted the naive juveniles that danger was near.

Raccoons communicate by body language, as well as by vocalizations. An agitated raccoon lashes its tail, and when threatened it bares its teeth, lays back its ears, stands on its hind feet, raises its shoulder hackles, and arches its back. Many a hound has learned to respect these not so subtle signals from a cornered raccoon.

The ingenuity of a hunted raccoon has inspired and frustrated hunters since they first unleashed "coon hounds" in the woods. The baying call of the hounds sends the raccoons scampering. The normally slow-walking creatures can run surprisingly fast for considerable distances, climb as well as a squirrel, and swim like a duck. A pursued raccoon will try to get the dogs off its trail by climbing a tree, running along the limbs, and jumping out some distance away. Another trick is to head for water. Even the largest dog meets its match if it dives in after a raccoon: the raccoon will climb on the dog's back and hold its head underwater. Many a hunter has lost his prize hound to a swimming raccoon.

Raccoon fur has been popular since Davy Crockett wore a coonskin cap. During World War II, raccoon coats became the rage, but in the fluctuating world of fashion and furs, they dropped from view in the 1950s and 1960s. A revival in fur demand, especially overseas, brought the value of a raccoon pelt from a low of $1 to the present $15 to $30. Trappers catch more than three million raccoons each year in the United States. Animal furs support a $16 million per year industry in Texas. Our pioneer ancestors had to kill animals for food and clothing, but today we have other alternatives. I prefer to shoot raccoons with my camera and enjoy the antics of these entertaining creatures in the wild.

Fossil records indicate that raccoons have called North America home for more than one million years. Despite the increased pressures from trappers, hunters, and urban sprawl, these adaptable creatures are as numerous now as in pioneer times. If you live near water and woods, you probably have one of these enduring critters as your neighbor.

The Skunk:
The Animal with a
Chemical Defense

Striped skunk, polecat
Mephitis mephitis

What animal in North America, though the size of a house cat, does not fear any creature, large or small? All animals, tame or wild, respect the skunk, and usually let it pass unmolested. Skunks pay little attention to bears, mountain lions, wolves, or even humans. The bravery of this independent creature results not from brute strength, claws, or cunning, but from its ability to irritate.

Skunks have a chemical spray guaranteed to cause an attitude adjustment in an attacker. A direct hit with the spray leaves an indelible impression on the memory of the unfortunate victim. The noxious odor discourages most predators, but no defense is perfect. I have known dogs that regularly harassed and sometimes killed skunks. Usually the painful experience and the lingering odor remind animals to avoid future encounters with this harmless-looking animal.

A skunk's spray is as potent as Mace, as blinding as tear gas, and as noxious as rotten eggs. Powerful muscles around the pair of scent glands on the skunk's posterior eject the sulfur-based spray as far as 15 feet. When threatened, a skunk stomps its front feet, raises its tail, arches its back, and even prances on its front feet. Any animal that has encountered an angry skunk understands the warning and backs off. To spray its scent, the skunk looks over its back, raises its tail, and aims at the aggressor. My dog once challenged a skunk under our house. The barking ended abruptly with a yelp, and we heard him hit every floor beam as he blindly raced away. Moments later we evacuated our house.

Skunks seldom miss adversaries within nine feet. They can direct the musky liquid over an area of 30 to 45 degrees behind them, and vary the spray from a fine mist to rain-size drops. A sprayed animal, with eyes burning, lungs bursting for fresh air, and stomach retching, turns tail and runs. The only consolation to humans is that the symptoms eventually diminish and disappear.

If sprayed, you can remove the musk odor from clothes by several washings with detergent and household ammonia. Deodorize pets by bathing them with tomato juice or, more effectively, with neutroleum-alpha, a compound available from hospital supply houses. Use it in mop water to remove the odor from garages and basements.

The contrasting black and white back of a skunk makes it the most easily recognized animal in North America, both by humans and by other animals. That is exactly the purpose of the bold markings. As dusk settles across the countryside, skunks emerge from their dens as part of nature's night shift. Most nocturnal animals seek safety under the cloak of darkness, but not the skunk. Its warning colors advertise its presence to all. The white stripes reflect the fading glow of twilight and the light of the moon like a bright beacon warning others to stay away. While the colors of many animals help them blend in with their surroundings, secrecy is unnecessary for skunks. They have chosen to advertise their presence openly, mind their own business, and take what they want.

Because of their potent chemical defense, skunks have a dauntless attitude and aggressively pursue their every want. A naturalist at Big Bend National Park related that once, while he sat in a photo blind, a skunk ventured by. The hungry animal smelled the naturalist's fried chicken and invited itself for dinner. The unexpected guest received the greatest of courtesy. A skunk once interrupted my camp breakfast and devoured a carton of eggs mistakenly left on the ground.

Skunks waddle through the woods rooting for insects, spiders, small mammals and reptiles, fruit, nuts, and carrion. With short legs and a fat body, skunks avoid a chase or even a long walk. Lacking speed to pursue fast-moving animals, they lie in wait and slowly stalk mice, moles, ground squirrels, and other scampering animals. With a diet so easily satisfied, these animals seldom travel further than 1.5 miles from their dens. Rooting by starlight requires neither sharp vision nor a keen sense of hearing. Skunks depend on smell, their only well-developed sense, to find the insects and other small bugs that comprise 90 percent of their diet.

A skunk's smelly defense is not unique in the animal kingdom. Many beetles, one of its favorite foods, discharge foul-tasting secretions. Undaunted in pursuit of a tasty morsel, a skunk rolls the beetle in the dirt until it has exhausted its supply of chemicals. Just as skunks ignore the beetle's smelly protection, the great horned owl ignores the skunk's potent spray. Like most birds, owls cannot smell, and an airborne surprise attack gives a skunk little chance to establish its defensive position. Only owls and other large birds of prey regularly eat skunks.

As May approaches, female skunks begin searching for a protected den for their nursery. Though skunks root and dig with the five long claws on each forepaw, they prefer to use a natural or deserted den rather than digging one. The mother-to-be makes a nest of grass under a rock, in a thicket, in a dense stand of cacti, or in an old fox or badger den. By mid-May, from three to seven blind and helpless kits snuggle up in the safety of the den. After two to four weeks, the young have opened their eyes and are armed for action.

After two months, the kits accompany their mother on her nightly excursions. At first they follow single file and remain close to the parent, but quickly become adventuresome and wander further away. The young skunks have a short-lived home life, and by the end of August are rooting on their own.

Baby skunks look like adorable striped kittens, and at one time, de-scented kits were a popular item at pet stores. But skunks never quite become tame, and owners find they have to contend with a cantankerous, unpredictable wild animal in their home. The state regulations for fur-bearing animals now strictly control the killing and commerce of skunks. Keeping a live skunk requires a special authorization.

As a skunk matures, it becomes strictly antisocial. It never develops the manners and inhibitions of gregarious species, like dogs, that must learn how to get along with others. Except for mating and in communal dens, the adults do not interact. In Texas, skunks generally remain active all year, but in northern climates as many as ten may den together for the winter. At any time, several skunks may share the same sleeping den.

Skunks live in a variety of habitats, including urban areas. Their nocturnal habits and omnivorous diet enable them to coexist with humans. I have seen striped skunks on the University of Texas campus in Austin, and one has lived under my house in San Marcos, along with an opossum and my cat, for the past two years.

Suburban skunks sometimes cause problems. Besides occasionally spraying a dog or human, they may transmit dangerous diseases. They carry rabies more than any other mammal, with about 500 rabid skunks reported in the state each year. Outbreaks of the disease sometimes occur with a high percentage of skunks in an area becoming infected. Sick skunks may bite dogs or other animals and spread the deadly virus. A high percentage of skunks also carry leptospirosis, a bacterial disease that causes fever, muscle pain, and jaundice, as well as parasites harmful to humans.

In the wild, skunks are more beneficial than harmful. They eat prodigious amounts of insects harmful to range and agriculture, such as army worms, cutworms, bud worms, potato beetles, grasshoppers, squash bugs, and sphinx moths. They also eat large numbers of mice and rats, especially around farms. The fur industry considers the thick, durable, glossy fur of the striped skunk a favorite. Trappers catch thousands each year, especially in the colder climates that produce thicker pelts than Texas.

Striped skunks live in every Texas county, and range from northern Mexico to Canada. The twin white stripes from head to tail distinguish them from the other five species in the state. The smaller eastern spotted skunk, *Spilogale putorius,* and western spotted skunk, *S. gracilis,* have six broken stripes on their backs and sides. The eastern species lives east of a line approximately from Amarillo through Abilene to Austin and south to Laredo. The western spotted skunk lives west of a line approximately from Big Spring through Abilene, San Antonio, and McAllen.

The hooded skunk, *Mephitis macroura,* with markings similar to the striped skunk, has a distinct ruff, or hood, of longer hair on its upper neck. It occurs in the Big Bend region of the state and into Mexico. The hog-nosed skunk, *Conepatus mesoleucus,* has a single broad white stripe down its back. Its triangular range in Texas extends south of a line from Midland to Beaumont and back to Laredo, and into Mexico. The Gulf Coast hog-nosed skunk, *C. leuconotus,* lives along the coast from Aransas Pass south to Brownsville and into Mexico.

The Mysterious Jackalope

An animal so bizarre lives in the barrens of West Texas that most people deny its very existence. Only a lucky few have witnessed a jackalope bounding across the rugged West Texas plains, and many, like those who have seen UFOs, only reluctantly discuss their experience. Most people, especially in the scientific community, contend that such a strange creature cannot exist. But through the years enough evidence has accumulated to warrant a serious investigation of the facts. Unlike UFOs, jackalope sightings appear to have a regularity, both seasonally and diurnally. Sightings of these fantastic critters continue to increase as more people discover the salubrious climate of forsaken West Texas and retire to such sagebrush resorts as Terlingua, Lajitas, and Study Butte. Before I present previously unrecorded evidence supporting the existence of this alleged native unique to the desolate wastes of the Lone Star State, let me describe its physical appearance.

Fortunately we know exactly what jackalopes look like, which is more than you can say about Nessie the Loch Ness Monster, the Abominable Snowman, or Big Foot. The remains of jackalopes have been preserved by taxidermy, and are proudly displayed in homes and commercial establishments across Texas. Except for the trophy-size antlers crowning their heads, jackalopes bear an amazing resemblance to ordinary jackrabbits. Males apparently commonly display 10- and even 12-point racks. Unfortunately, to the chagrin of wildlife biologists, live specimens invariably elude all attempts at capture.

99

The antlers naturally make a jackalope immediately recognizable. If they wore such sporty headgear all year, they would probably be considered as common as sandburs. From an intensive study of all available accounts, written and oral, I have concluded that jackalopes, and just the males at that, have antlers only during the mating season, which lasts for a brief two weeks. During the rest of the year, the male's appearance is identical with the jackrabbit, and the female is indistinguishable at all times. Because of this, scientific studies have never determined the true population density, habitat requirements, demography, and social behavior of this chameleonlike species.

Many scientific studies have documented mimicry of one species by another. After all, butterflies copy each other's looks as much as the English copy the Queen's. The viceroy butterfly discovered that it paid to look royal, and copied the monarch's colorful pattern. Birds that eat monarchs get a stomachache that Alka-Seltzer can't touch, so the viceroy hides safely concealed in its royal garb. Once the reader fully understands the adaptive significance of mimicry, the advantages of the jackalope's deception are readily appreciated.

While photographs of Big Foot and the other mystery creatures invariably show blurred images of poorly exposed subjects disappearing in the distance, photographs of the jackalope show every detail in stunning clarity. The pictures render in sharp focus every hair on its sleek body and every bump on its rugged antlers. Jackalope photographs aren't hidden away in some dusty archive, either. Look for them at truck stops, souvenir shops, and cafes from El Paso in West Texas, to Orange, 855 miles to the east. Wherever postcards are sold, you can purchase jackalope photos for three for $1.

As I mentioned earlier, jackalope sightings occur regularly in the vicinity of Terlingua. The recent rebirth of Terlingua and the surrounding area is the fulfillment of a dream of the famous Union soldier General Philip Sheridan. He once said that if he owned Texas and Hell, he would rent out

Texas and live in Hell. Texas entrepreneurs have gotten rich hawking parched hillside ranchettes in the hottest spot in the nation to retirees trying to escape the arctic winters up north.

Another boon for Terlingua and jackalope documentation is the World Chili Cook-off held each year in the ghost town. Thousands of chili gourmets converge there, reminiscent of days of forgotten glory when the town boomed with frenetic activity. Once again music plays long into the night and more beer flows than water in the nearby Rio Grande. Most jackalope sightings occur after midnight, usually by a chili cook trying to find his camper.

That type of sighting corresponds with the second most frequent sighting of this elusive animal: near roadside taverns shortly after the 2 a.m. closing hour. Numerous studies have attempted to correlate jackalopes with roadside habitats; however, no statistically significant trend could be established, other than that they are nocturnal creatures. Recent Terlingua sightings completely discredit the roadside theory and reveal the startling details of the highly speculated, but never before reported, sex life of the jackalope. Once the animal's sexual behavior was understood, its entire life history fell neatly into place.

As previously mentioned, the male jackalope grows antlers only during its two-week rut, or breeding season. While in rut, the behavior of the normally docile, gregarious herbivore radically changes from Dr. Jekyll to Mr. Hyde. The males become bitterly aggressive, and vicious battles between rivals echo through the night. With antlers forward, the males charge each other at speeds exceeding 55 mph. About five feet before impact, they leap high in the air propelled by their powerful hind legs. Some accounts report that the midair collision is so violent that sparks ricochet from the antlers. The competing males repeat this charge-leap-collision pattern until the weaker is thrown backward with such force that its brain is addled. The bewildered animal loses his antlers and thinks he is a jackrabbit for the rest of his life. This behavior effectively removes the weaker animals from the breeding population.

The schizophrenia overcoming the male jackalope during rut affects more than his personality. The diet of this incredible animal undergoes phenomenal changes. During the brief period when they have antlers, the males become vicious predators and eat only meat. Their favorite food is coyote hearts, and they hunt the cunning canines with a passion. Terrified coyotes tuck tail and run, but they have no chance of escaping the speed demons chasing them. Is it revenge, or an increased caloric need for high-energy meat that drives jackalopes to pursue coyotes relentlessly? Only further research will tell.

The coyotes near Terlingua have gained a reprieve from the meat-crazed jackalopes. The enticing smell of exotic chili wafting across the desert distracts the ravenous jackalopes. They disdain coyote meat in favor of the gourmet concoctions that made Wick Fowler's name a household word. Only when observers realized that the roasting chili attracted the jackalopes were the hidden secrets of these mysterious animals finally discovered.

The territorial dispute between male jackalopes neatly answers a question that has puzzled children for centuries: how can Santa's reindeer fly? From my first memory, I couldn't enjoy Santa Claus because I knew deer couldn't really pull his sleigh through the air. But jackalopes leap with such powerful bounds that they could easily carry Santa's sleigh from house to house. When the truth is known, everything has a simple explanation.

If you ever have the mind-numbing experience of spending a day driving across the unfrequented deserts of West Texas, study the monotonous landscape for unusual-looking critters. Look closely at every jackrabbit you see, especially any that chase coyotes. For as sure as Big Foot lives in the California mountains, Nessie swims Loch Ness, and the Abominable Snowman treks across the Himalayas, jackalopes bound across the desolate West Texas plains.

Birds

Few groups of animals can match the diversity, flamboyance, and distribution found among the 8600 species of birds. They come in a rainbow of colors and vary in size from the two-inch, $1/10$-ounce bee hummingbird of Cuba to the 8-foot, 300-pound ostrich. In North America, the 5-foot whooping crane stands the tallest, and the 25-pound trumpeter swan and Canada goose weigh the most. The wandering albatross has the longest wingspan, 11.5 feet, of any living bird, while an extinct relative soared on wings stretching 20 feet from tip to tip. Birds exhibit an amazing diverseness even in flight. Some swifts, proving their name, can fly 200 mph, and acrobatic hummingbirds can hover, fly backward, and turn somersaults. Though strong fliers, ducks spend most of their lives floating and diving in the water, and roadrunners prefer dashing through thick vegetation chasing lizards. Forsaking the air, some birds have given up flight altogether. Penguins swim underwater using wings that have evolved into flippers. Other birds, like the kiwi and ostrich, prefer walking and running. Yet, despite the immense differences, all birds have one thing in common: feathers. Any animal, fossil or living, with feathers is by definition a bird.

Birds have mystified humans since the dawn of history. They appear in Stone Age art, Greek mythology, superstitions, folklore, and as ancient and modern religious symbols. Earthbound humans have considered birds messengers from the spirit world, representatives of God, and omens—for both good and evil. The popularity of birds continues unabated today, and they are perhaps the most loved of all wild animals. What accounts for this ageless love affair of humans with our feathered neighbors?

First of all, birds have the power of flight, an ability that humans coveted and eventually emulated at Kitty Hawk, North Carolina. Second, birds are exhibitionists. They flaunt their spectacular colors and remarkable singing talents at every opportunity. The brilliant pigmentation of a bird's feathers and the ringing melody it sings cannot fail to attract our attention and capture our imagination.

Scientists, trying to decipher the secret of flight from the feathered beasties, discovered that the ability to become airborne had not come without extreme specialization. Every feature of a bird's body has undergone remarkable modifications to adapt the animal for flight. Hollow and honeycombed bones replace the heavy, solid bones of the skeleton, and a lightweight bill substitutes for a mouthful of teeth. The flight muscles attach to an enlarged keel or breastbone, and bones in the arms, wrists, and fingers are fused and transformed into a wing. From head to tail, a bird's streamlined shape reduces drag, and the curve of the feathered wing creates the highest possible lifting force. Small feathers on the shoulder reduce the turbulence of air flowing over the wing, which would decrease the lift, and feathers on the wingtips act as tiny wings that enable the bird to fly at slower speeds without stalling. A bird's body, externally and internally, represents an engineering masterpiece of flight design.

Flight demands so much energy that birds must have special digestive, circulatory, and respiratory systems to supply food and oxygen to the wing muscles. Birds have the highest heart rate, body temperature, and metabolism of any warm-blooded animal. A bird's heart may pump between 600 and 1000 beats per minute to circulate blood, which contains twice the sugar content of human blood. Its stomach digests and assimilates food so rapidly that it must eat frequent meals throughout the day. Small birds daily may consume food equaling one-third their body weight, making nonsense of the expression "eating like a bird." Air sacs in their body cavity connect to the lungs and circulate air to increase oxygen absorption and to assist cooling.

Birds possess one of the most amazing features of any animals, a unique skin covering, feathers. Feathers, like fur on mammals, probably evolved not to enable flight but to conserve body heat for the warm-blooded bird. Fossils indicate that gliding, common today in many nonflying animals, preceded true flight. Feathers provide a waterproof coat and a highly insulating layer for warmth. To stay warm, a bird fluffs out its feathers to capture a thicker air space around its body, the same effect as putting a feather comforter on the bed. For their weight, feathers are the strongest, most durable objects found in nature.

Birds have two basic types of feathers. The pennae have a stout midrib lined with hundreds of tiny barbs. Barbules line the edges of each barb, allowing the bird to zip up the barbs much like a zipper. A bird can clean and repair a ruffled feather by passing it through its bill, an activity called preening. The flight feathers on a bird's wings, the tail feathers, and major outer body feathers are pennae. The down feathers, or plumulae, cover the bird's body and provide insulation. These fluffy feathers have only a short midrib and no barbules to hold the barbs together. The number of feathers on a bird's body varies with its size and the climate. A diminutive ruby-throated hummingbird has about 940 feathers, while 25,000 feathers cover a whistling swan. A bald eagle's skeleton weighs only 9.5 ounces, a fraction of its 24-ounce coat of feathers, illustrating the importance of feathers to a bird.

Besides providing a protective covering and enabling flight, feathers perform another vital function: they color the bird. Most birds have dappled brown, black, and white patterns for camouflage. Some, usually the males, sport brilliant colors designed to attract attention. The male's color and song warn other males of his species to stay out of his territory. The female, to increase her odds for rearing a successful family, chooses the male with the best territory. Some males have special feathers, like the peacock's flamboyant tail, for sexual display. Once the breeding season passes, the males usually molt and lose the nonfunctional feathers that decrease their ability to fly.

Flight has given birds a mobility unequaled by any other animal. On an ounce-by-ounce comparison, human flight and navigational technology cannot match the accuracy and flight capabilities of birds. Without map or gyroscope, many birds migrate thousands of miles twice a year. The whooping crane flies 2600 miles from Canada to the Texas coast, while the arctic tern flies 11,000 miles between its summer and winter homes with unerring accuracy. The ruby-throated hummingbird, weighing less than an ounce, flies 500 miles nonstop across the Gulf of Mexico.

The mobility of birds has allowed them to populate the earth and diversify like no other vertebrate. Birds have colonized every island and inhabit every continent, including Antarctica. They have adopted every imaginable lifestyle: birds eat seeds, sip nectar, catch flying, crawling, and burrowing insects, dive for fish, scavenge carrion, and kill other animals. These highly intelligent creatures even use tools, and some communicate with complex vocabularies: crows have 23 distinct vocalizations. Crows and blue jays sometimes use twigs to retrieve food just out of their reach. The woodpecker finch on the Galapagos Islands carefully prepares a stick to extract grubs from decaying trees. The dexterity of their bills and feet makes birds master architects in the animal kingdom. To protect their delicate eggs, birds weave intricate nests, usually single-family dwellings but sometimes multifamily condominiums.

Like a detailed résumé, the beak and feet of a bird reveal how it makes its living and where it lives. Seed-eating birds, such as sparrows and cardinals, have short, thick bills to crush the hard seeds, while insectivorous birds, like warblers and wrens, have slender bills to probe under bark and leaves. A woodpecker's skull and bill are designed to jackhammer holes in limbs, and its feet allow it to hang vertically on the sides of trees. The purselike bill of a pelican enables it to net schools of fish, and the webbed feet of waterfowl allow them to paddle and swim. The bill and long legs of a wading bird permit it to stalk the shallows for fish. Raptors have powerful talons to kill prey and hooked beaks to tear flesh. The vast diversity of avian beaks and feet illustrates the remarkable ability of birds to adapt to a multitude of environmental conditions.

Today approximately 8600 species and 28,500 subspecies of birds inhabit the earth. About 650 occur in North America, and 545 in Texas. Paleontologists can trace most of the modern families of birds back 11 million years to the Miocene epoch. Fossils of birds related to herons, flamingos, kingfishers, geese, and several others date back 60 million years. The oldest fossil showing feathers was found in Germany in 150-million-year-old limestone. The crow-size bird, named *Archaeopteryx,* had a small keel, indicating that the wing muscles probably were strong enough for gliding but not for sustained flight.

Fossils reveal that *Archaeopteryx,* which has no living descendants today, retained many features of its reptilian ancestors, who may have been some type of tree lizards. It had teeth, a long tail, and claws on its wingtips. *Archaeopteryx* lived during the same time period as the giant pterosaurs that dominated the skies but was not related to them. Though insignificant in comparison to the flying reptiles, birds survived the ages, while only the stones record the evidence of the once great pterosaurs. Fossils of the largest flying reptile yet discovered were found in Big Bend National Park. The creature, called the Texas pterodactyl, had a 35-to-40-foot wingspan and may have weighed 135 to 180 pounds. Scientists recovered about 200 bone fragments of the right wing, but none from the body.

Like most animals in the world, birds have suffered since humans began crossing the seven seas. About half of the more than 75 species of birds that have become extinct since the 1600s disappeared because of human hunting and habitat destruction. About 2 percent of the living bird species are in danger of following the dodo, passenger pigeon, and Carolina parakeet into oblivion. Observers have recent sightings of only one or two individuals of more than 80 rare species. Texas, with a diversity of habitats ranging from desert to seashore, mountains to prairies, and forest to brushlands, harbors more birds than any other state, including its share of rare, threatened, and endangered species. The Texas Parks and Wildlife Department currently considers 10 birds in the state as endangered and 18 as threatened with extinction. The following 11 sections describe the impressive capabilities, bizarre behavior, intriguing folklore, and human interactions of some of the most interesting birds in the Lone Star State.

Eagles:
Masters of the Sky

Golden eagle
Aquila chrysaëtos
Bald eagle
Haliaeetus leucocephalus

In 1969, a voice rang out to all the world from 250,000 miles in space. Tension mounted as the Lunar Module used its last few seconds of fuel looking for a landing site on the cratered surface of the moon. Finally the dust settled and the triumphant astronauts radioed, "The *Eagle* has landed!"

What more appropriate name for the first spaceship to land on that distant moonscape than the bird that soars in the rooftops of the sky? From the time that ancient Persians and Romans carried eagles into battle, these majestic birds have symbolized courage, strength, and bravery. In 1782, Congress chose the bald eagle as the national emblem, despite an outcry that it had despicable habits. Bald eagles are infamous for forcing an osprey to drop its fish, and then catching it in midair. This thievery enraged early colonists who wanted a more respectable bird for the national emblem. But the bald eagle won the vote, and today it perches on the back of our one-dollar bills and adorns the Great Seal of the United States.

As aerial hunters, eagles are the undisputed masters of the sky. Nothing escapes their attention, even when they are soaring thousands of feet high. Their eyes see detail with five to six times the resolution of a human's. A human can discern a one-inch object at 30 yards, but an eagle can see it clearly from 200 yards. Such visual acuity enables these birds to spot a rabbit from almost 2 miles away.

The wings of such mighty birds are an engineering marvel for efficient gliding. Eagles can spread the tapering feathers on their wingtips to form many tiny winglets that reduce turbulence, increase lift, and prevent stalling at low speeds. A small feather, the alula, on the leading edge of their wing forces the wind smoothly over the top surface and prevents eddy currents from forming.

With a grasp far stronger than a human hand, an eagle's talons have legendary power. An eagle uses its powerful hind claw to kill small prey instantly while the three forward claws hold it securely. When a baby golden eagle sank its talons into a Montana scientist's arm while he banded the bird, his partner had to use pliers to loosen the eaglet's crushing grip. Similarly, an injured golden eagle in the care of a Texas wildlife rehabilitation group pierced its keeper's heavy hiking boot like an ax splintering kindling. The eagle's powerful bill complements its deadly talons; the upper beak has a four-inch hook to tear the flesh of its kill.

An adult eagle requires only about $8\frac{1}{2}$ ounces of food per day, and it often gorges at one feeding and fasts for the next several days. These 9-to-12-pound, three-foot birds use different hunting strategies. The golden eagle hunts while soaring high above the ground. With a seven-foot wingspan, it glides on the rising thermals for hours without flapping, looking for its primary food, rabbits. A nest study in the Panhandle by the Texas Parks and Wildlife Department found 92 percent of the golden eagle nests contained the remains of black-tailed jackrabbits, 25 percent contained prairie dogs, and 21 percent contained the cracked shells of ornate box turtles. True to legend, eagles do drop turtles from great heights to break open their shells.

The bald eagle employs a perch-and-pounce method of hunting. It surveys its domain from high in a tree. When it spots a fish at the water's surface or a rabbit in the grass, it dives for the kill. Bald eagles usually have eaten sufficiently by 10 a.m., and then spend the rest of the day soaring effortlessly.

When Anglos first settled in Texas, the bald eagle nested in the coastal marshes and along river systems as far north as the Panhandle. With a diet primarily of fish, it lives close to the ocean, rivers, and lakes. Golden eagles, the sacred war birds of the Comanches and other American Indians, once nested across much of West Texas. These birds prefer the mountain peaks of the Trans-Pecos and the rugged canyons that dissect the rolling plains of the Panhandle. This cosmopolitan eagle inhabits desolate areas in North America, Scandinavia, Europe, North Africa, and parts of Asia. Because of the golden eagle's worldwide citizenship, our founding fathers favored the bald eagle, which is restricted to North America, for the national emblem.

Our national bird and its relative have not fared well with the taming of the continent. Believing that bald eagles, not the fishing industry, were depleting the rivers of salmon, the territory of Alaska placed a bounty on the magnificent birds in 1917. Within ten years, hunters killed more than 41,000. Before the bounty was removed, 100,000 bald eagles had died. Not until 1940, and 1952 in Alaska, did the slaughter of our national symbol cease and the birds receive protection under federal law. Today about 1000 pairs of bald eagles nest in the contiguous 48 states. The total population in North America, and the world, numbers less than 100,000, with some estimates as low as 35,000.

Golden eagles have fared no better. By the middle of this century, sheep and goat ranching began increasing rapidly throughout the Southwest, especially in areas overgrazed by cattle. The eagles found their habitat overrun with lambs and kids, and ranchers determined to protect their defenseless livestock. An eagle can easily kill a young lamb, and to most stock raisers, the only good predator is a dead predator.

Using airplanes, Southwestern ranchers gunned down 20,000 eagles in 20 years. One Texas pilot bragged that he had killed 400 eagles. Federal law protected bald eagles, classified as an endangered species, in all states, but the golden eagle received protection only under migratory bird laws and no state laws. Finally, in 1962, Congress passed the Golden Eagle Protection Act, which extended federal protection to the bird.

Though expert hunters, eagles never pass up a free meal. These opportunistic raptors care not if their meat is fresh or rotten. The mighty hunters feed on a dead carcass just as common vultures do. The habit gains them an unwarranted bad reputation in sheep country. Ranchers lose about 10 percent of their lambs each year, averaging 5 percent to natural causes, 4 percent to coyotes, and 1 percent to other predators. The sight of an eagle at a carcass does not prove that the bird killed the animal. Certainly eagles occasionally kill lambs and kid goats, and ranchers can be expected to want to protect their herds. But eagles have little or no impact on the sheep and goat industry. During the winter of 1982–83, the U.S. Fish and Wildlife Department Animal Damage Control Division in Texas received only eight complaints against eagles, and could confirm no losses of stock to the raptors. Yet many ranchers still hate eagles and shoot them on sight.

Coping with hunting pressure is only half of the struggle that eagles face in our modern world. The widespread use of DDT and related pesticides that began after World War II decimated the bald eagles more than the hunters' bullets ever could. The fat-soluble poison washed into the rivers and became concentrated in aquatic organisms. The poisons accumulated in the bodies of fish-eating birds until they could no longer reproduce; the pesticides killed the embryos and caused thin-shelled eggs that easily broke. Finally laws were enacted that prohibited pesticides that did not break down into harmless compounds, but not before bald eagles disappeared from much of their native range. Only now are these noble birds beginning to make a comeback.

Eagle populations recover slowly from loss because the birds take about five years to reach breeding age, and 75 percent of the young die before maturity. A pair of nesting eagles requires an average of ten years to produce two mature birds to replace them. In 1980, Texas Parks and Wildlife found 95 golden eagle nests in the state and 15 bald eagle nests. Each year about 85 golden eagles and 8 bald eagles fledge. Texas does not have many breeding eagles, but fortunately the population seems to be stable.

Eagles mate for life, and they may use the same nest, or aerie, for years, adding to it each season. Golden eagles favor ledges on sheer cliff faces in their mountainous habitat, and may alternate from year to year between several nests within their territory. Bald eagles nest in treetops along undisturbed waterways. One bald eagle nest measured 10 feet across and 20 feet deep and weighed two tons. Eagles begin nesting in February and March, and the female incubates the eggs for 40 to 45 days. After 9 to 11 weeks, by mid-June in the Panhandle, the eaglets can fly. In 1980, golden eagle nests in the Panhandle produced 1 fledgling per nest, and in the Trans-Pecos the birds averaged 0.8 young per nest.

Eagles usually lay two eggs, but the babies have a peculiar Cain and Abel relationship. The female eagle begins incubating the first egg as soon she lays it. She lays the second egg two to four days later, so it hatches two to four days after the first. The 3.5-ounce eaglets grow and develop rapidly each day. The four-day-old chick is already active and screaming for food when its helpless nestmate breaks through its egg shell. Even when the parents bring enough food to the nest for both, the older chick often pecks the younger to death. Puzzled scientists have never adequately explained the advantages of this homicidal behavior.

A growing threat to eagles, and all predators, is the inevitable urbanization of our countryside. Texas cities gobble up about 200,000 acres of open space each year. To survive, eagles need large expanses of rugged country. A nesting pair requires from 20 to 60 square miles of hunting territory for use exclusive of other eagles. Timbering, clearing for agriculture, flooding for lakes, and real estate developments continue to preempt large amounts of habitat from eagles and other wildlife.

As winter approaches, eagles from across the continent head south for warmer climates and more abundant food. Texas hosts the largest winter concentration of golden eagles in North America. About half of the population wings its way to the Panhandle, Trans-Pecos, and Central Texas. Between 500 and 1000 bald eagles winter in the eastern two thirds of the state, primarily along the coast, lakes, and rivers. You can see bald eagles wintering on Lake Buchanan (18 in 1985) by taking the Vanishing Texas River Cruise from November through February.

A New World for the Cattle Egret

Cattle egret
Bubulcus ibis

How often was America discovered? The Vikings arrived about 1000 A.D., Columbus in 1492, and the cattle egret in 1877. The pioneering attempts of the Vikings failed, but Columbus and the cattle egrets soon established a firm foothold in the New World. Both the human and the feathered explorers had strayed off course when they stepped onto the American shore. Columbus had set sail for India, and the egrets that landed in South America were flying across Africa. Presumably, a storm or strong easterly trade winds blew the migrating flock 2000 miles across the Atlantic. Like the helmeted conquistadors before them, the egrets, with reddish plumes adorning their heads, immediately began their conquest of the Americas.

Colonization was not a new concept to these airborne explorers. They probably originally called Africa home, but their inherent wanderlust drove them north across the European continent as far as the British Isles. The travelers flapped across Southeast Asia and island hopped to claim Australia as egret territory. Before they could call themselves true world citizens, however, they had to conquer one final continent. After that first flock reached landfall in Suriname, America was theirs.

The cattle egret is the only bird that has become naturalized on every continent, except Antarctica, without the help of humans. Excluding songbirds, it is the only bird that apparently has expanded its range during this century of human progress. What qualities enabled these amazing birds

115

to spread around the world while most other animals diminished or survived only in a limited range?

As wanderers, cattle egrets can find new places, or habitats, with food and safe nesting. Humans, by converting forestland into expansive pastures, industriously create vast new homelands for these insect-eating birds. Unlike other egrets and herons that wade for their meals, cattle egrets prefer to dine high and dry in these man-made grassy fields. While other wading birds require the secure seclusion of swamps and coastal marshes, cattle egrets boldly march in step with cattle, horses, pigs, water buffaloes, rhinoceros, elephants, and even tractors. Wading birds suffer from the widespread pollution of estuaries and rivers, but cattle egrets feast alongside cattle in protected pastures safe from harmful poisons.

To colonize the new areas they discover, cattle egrets must reproduce in large numbers. Courting begins in April when the two-foot bird dons a wardrobe of cinnamon feathers that crown its head and accent its snow-white breast. Its bill, legs, and eyes change from yellow to scarlet, and they remain so until the eggs are laid. Large colonies of egrets build their nests in trees and bushes near water. Both sexes incubate the two to five eggs and meticulously care for the young. One adult always stays with the nest and quickly returns if frightened away, thus protecting the eggs and young from predators. With usually abundant food, they can double their population every year. The youth are the most prone to wander, and before the first breeding season often strike out on their own, seeking new lands to conquer.

By 1942, the relentless march of the cattle egrets had carried them through Central America, the Caribbean islands, and into Florida. With a "Westward, ho!" these pioneers advanced along the Gulf Coast to California, and north to Canada. They now breed as far north as southern Ontario, but retreat to the Gulf and further south in the winter. One was sighted 200 miles off the coast of Newfoundland. Perhaps it was an envoy to Greenland, still virgin territory for cattle egrets.

These indomitable birds reached the borders of the Lone Star State in 1955 and produced the first native Texan cattle egrets three years later. Those early homesteaders began rearing their families near Galveston. In 1959, only 11 pairs nested in the state, but the visitors liked their new home and six years later Texas boasted more than 20,000 breeding pairs. The total population exceeded 100,000 by 1972. Within a decade after they appeared in Texas, the V-shaped pattern of a flock of egrets silhouetted against a colorful sunset was a common sight along the Gulf Coast.

Cattle egrets have a feeding territory that they defend from intruding neighbors. Unlike the territories of most animals, their territory moves. The snow-white birds prance alongside a grazing cow, dart between its legs spearing grasshoppers, and sit on their benefactor's back. As many as ten birds jointly claim all insects flushed by their hooved ally. They take their positions around a cow like miniature cowboys and follow the animal as it moves through the pasture.

Cattle egrets eat more grasshoppers and crickets than any other food. Range-damaging invertebrates comprise 99.8 percent of their diet, along with occasional lizards, frogs, worms, and spiders. The easily satisfied birds even dine in garbage dumps when the opportunity arises. Since they eat no fish, they do not compete with other egrets, herons, or wading birds. Unlike starlings, house sparrows, and other animals spread by humans, these beneficial immigrants have no harmful effects on native bird populations.

One of the main secrets of the success of the cattle egret, besides wandering long distances and being opportunistic feeders and excellent parents, is the tolerance to humans these intrepid birds have developed. Some of their largest nesting colonies occur within sight of major highways. One of the first breeding colonies occurred along the shoreline around the busy Baytown Tunnel under the Houston Ship Channel. Cattle egrets nonchalantly forage along roadsides just a few yards away from speeding traffic. They even adopt tractors as their associates and follow the four-wheeled vehicles as they would a four-legged bovine. I have often seen the birds on the Clear Lake City golf course dodging balls and following golfers through the rough. These prolific birds, unlike most other wildlife, find the environmental practices of humans to their advantage. By converting the planet's woodlands into grassy pastures, we are creating a paradise on earth for the adaptable cattle egret.

Hummingbirds: Nature's Fanciest Fliers

Ruby-throated hummingbird
Archilochus colubris
Black-chinned hummingbird
A. alexandri

In the ironic world of nature, smallest sometimes means strongest. The hummingbirds, the second largest family of birds, have the double distinction of being the smallest warm-blooded (homoiothermic) creatures and the strongest fliers. The $\frac{1}{10}$-ounce black chinned and ruby-throated hummers zip through the air with a wingbeat of 50 to 75 times per second. During a courtship flight, a ruby-throat may beat 200 times per second! The English colonists, amazed at the buzzing sound of the tiny bird's wings, coined the name "hummingbird." In Spanish-speaking countries, these New World residents are called *chupaflor*, "flower sucker," *picaflor*, "flower pecker," and in Brazil, *beija-flor*, "flower kisser." My daughter excitedly called them "honey birds" when she was young.

The ruby-throated and black-chinned hummingbirds are the most common hummers in Texas. The black-chin breeds in the dry plateaus and deserts of the western half of the state. The ruby-throat, preferring the moist woodlands of the eastern half of Texas, is the only hummer that nests east of the Mississippi River. Their ranges overlap and both sip nectar in Central Texas. Six other hummers breed in Texas, and five regularly migrate through the state.

Despite their small size, hummingbirds migrate long distances. In the spring and fall, rufous hummingbirds migrate 2000 miles between Mexico and Alaska. Ruby-throats migrate 500 miles non-stop across the Gulf of Mexico. Contrary to folktales, the tiny birds do not hitchhike on the

119

backs of Canada geese. They increase their weight 40 to 50 percent in stored fat prior to migration, and average 25 mph during the 26-hour flight.

Many birds can fly faster than hummingbirds, but none can match their maneuverability. Hummers can hover, spin like a top, and fly backward, sideways, and even upside down. When they hover, they beat their wings back and forth horizontally in a figure-eight pattern. On the back-stroke, they turn their wings completely over so the bottom is facing up. They remain stationary because their back-stroke is as powerful as their forward stroke. Other birds have a one-way power stroke, but not hummers. They get twice as much lift and propulsion from each wing beat. Of all birds, hummingbirds have the largest flight muscles in proportion to their bodies, equaling 20 to 30 percent of their weight.

If not speeding from flower to flower, these unique birds try to dazzle each other with aerial acrobatics. The ruby-throat and black-chin males loop the loop trying to attract females. Like a giant pendulum, they race up and down in the air in front of a female sitting on a perch. Often the male orients his power dive so the sun shines directly on him as he zips by his lady love. With each pass, he raises his irides-cent feathers and flashes their brilliant colors. The lady seems to pay scant attention to the display, but who are we to say what she is thinking? If another male intrudes, the performer madly chases away the interloper.

Despite the sparkling red colors, hummingbirds have no bright red pigment in their feathers, only rufous, cinnamon, brown, and purple-black. The ruby-throat's glimmering scar-let throat comes from the way microscopic platelets in the feathers reflect and bend the light. Like prisms, platelets of different thicknesses and air content produce the gorgeous colors. When in the shade, a ruby-throated hummer appears dull gray. Thus, the male is camouflaged except when he displays in the sun.

The females of these two species have drab colors with

only a touch of green on their backs. Plain colors help them sit concealed in their thimble-size nests, hidden from predators. These birds build the smallest nests and lay the smallest eggs. A half-inch hummer egg is 7000 times smaller than the six-to-eight-inch egg of the ostrich. Hummers reinforce their two-inch nest with spiderwebs, which make it elastic enough to expand as the young birds grow. They line the inside with soft plant down, and decorate the outside with lichens. The two pea-size eggs hatch in about 15 days. After 2½ weeks, the babies can fly, but the mother feeds them for another 2 weeks until they learn where to find food.

The female does all the work raising the family, while the male busies himself flashing his iridescent feathers and chasing other males out of his territory. The brilliant throat and head feathers sparkle in the sunlight like warning beacons. The pugnacious male also fights vigorously for sole possession of a sugar-water feeder: when one has established a feeding territory, no other hummers enter unchallenged.

Hummingbirds have an avid curiosity and fearlessly investigate new objects. This probably helps them find new sources of food. To sustain their powerful flight, hummers require regular meals of sugar-rich nectar. Extracting the high-energy food from flowers requires hard work and specialized tools. Hummingbirds have a long bill to reach into deep-throated flowers, and a tubelike tongue with a fringed tip to sip the high-calorie liquid. Some tropical flowers, depending exclusively on hummers for pollination, are shaped and colored to attract the birds.

The color red universally attracts North American hummingbirds. Perhaps they find more red flowers while migrating. But hummers are creatures of habit—if most of the flowers in an area are blue, blue attracts them more than red. Hummers must eat about half their body weight in sugar daily. To stay healthy, they also catch flying insects. Captive hummers soon die if fed only sugar water.

To supply energy to their powerful flight muscles, hummingbirds have the highest rate of metabolism of any warm-blooded creature. Even at rest, they have a metabolism 50 times higher than a human's rate. These minuscule dynamos burn about 1000 calories daily. If humans burned energy at the same rate, we would have to consume 320 pounds of potatoes or 130 pounds of bread daily.

A hummer burns energy so fast that its system must slow down at night to conserve energy. Otherwise it could use so much energy staying warm that it might starve before morning. If its night temperature falls below about 93 degrees F, it usually enters a torpid state called noctivation, similar to hibernation. Its body temperature drops to near the air temperature. When its temperature falls to 60 degrees F, it burns only 1/60 of its normal energy. North American hummers take about 10 to 15 minutes to warm up and can fly when their body temperature reaches 86 degrees F. Their normal temperature is around 108 degrees F, depending on the species.

Hovering in front of a flower places tremendous physiological demands on the tiny bird's heart. Even at rest, the organ must pump 615 times per minute to supply enough oxygen-rich blood. When active, the heart may beat as high as 1260 times per minute. A hummingbird's heart represents 20 percent of its body weight. No other bird has a heart that large in proportion to its weight.

Small animals usually have a short life span, and one with the high-intensity heart beat and metabolism of a hummingbird could not be expected to live long. Yet both free and captive hummers have lived more than ten years. Perhaps noctivating contributes to a long life. Their exceptional flight skills certainly help them avoid predators: hummers fearlessly harass owls, hawks, and other nest-threatening animals, darting in much closer than other birds dare.

Once a hummingbird finds a rich source of food, it visits it regularly. It can even remember favorite locations from season to season. One spring, a female black-chinned hummer appeared outside our kitchen window hovering expectantly at the exact location of the previous year's feeder. We hurriedly filled and hung the jar, and to our delight she soon returned and feasted.

These tiny creatures often demonstrate their intelligence and ability to recognize who feeds them. The following story sounds like a fairy tale, but was reported in a scientific treatise on hummingbirds. A California artist convalescing from a serious illness in a sanatorium hung a hummingbird feeder in the window by his bed. Soon a male rufous hummingbird, a species ranging from Texas westward, claimed the feeder for his exclusive use. The artist delighted in seeing the feisty bird daily sipping the sugar water and chasing away uninvited guests. When the man was able to venture outside in a wheelchair, the grateful bird zoomed around his head and hovered directly in front of his face. This friendly greeting became a daily ritual. When the artist eventually returned to his country home by car, eight miles away, the faithful bird somehow managed to follow.

The artist took daily walks to build up his strength, always accompanied by his little friend. The rufous would wait for the slower human, and show him interesting sights he would have otherwise missed. His observant tour guide pointed out baby skunks, a covey of quail, and even a rattlesnake just off the trail. At last the day came when the man was well enough to return to his home in the city. After a month's absence, he returned, and stepping out of his car was greeted immediately by his feathered friend.

Within their feeding territory, hummingbirds have a regular circuit of nectar-rich flowers. You can be included in the bird's daily rounds by hanging a feeder with four parts water to one part sugar. Better yet, plant the bird's favorite flowers. Trumpet vine, honeysuckle, sweet pea, lantana, nasturtium, rose of Sharon, delphinium, and scarlet sage supply hummingbird cuisine. If you supply the food, you can enjoy the antics of these delightful birds all summer.

The Purple Martin: America's Favorite Bird

Purple martin
Progne subis

In some parts of the United States, the groundhog rates as the star performer of the winter season. According to legend, if it sees its shadow in early February, the winter chill gets another curtain call. But while people in the North search for groundhog shadows, people in the South gaze skyward eagerly anticipating the arrival of the purple martins.

Purple martins are the first migrating birds to arrive in Texas. Though weighing less than two ounces, these members of the swallow family fly to the United States and Canada from their winter home in the Amazon Basin of Brazil. They typically arrive in Central Texas around February 10. In warmer years, they may arrive several weeks earlier, and cold weather usually delays them. While some stay to nest in Texas, others move farther north, reaching New England by mid-April.

An advance guard of older males arrives first. These scouts often return to the same birdhouses that they used the previous year. By the time the females and younger males arrive several weeks later, the scouts have chosen a suitable home and are ready to set up housekeeping. After a week or so of relaxing in their summer home, both sexes begin constructing their nest. Martins do not build fancy nests, just a crude assemblage of twigs, string, and other scraps. Sometimes the birds line the nest rim with mud.

Martins originally nested in tree cavities, but since urbanization and modern timbering practices have made these scarce, they have adapted to city life. Like many people, these feathered suburbanites exchanged country living for an apartment lifestyle. Their penthouse must meet their specifications, though. A nest box at least 15 feet high and away from nearby limbs and buildings gives them security from nest predators. Their front doors should be from 2 to 2¼ inches in diameter and 1½ inches off the floor. Martins have learned that invaders can get through larger holes. An 8-by-8-by-8-inch room with ventilation holes seems ideal. The gregarious birds like to flock together, and prefer houses with at least six compartments.

Particular about their neighbors, martins avoid houses with nesting starlings or house sparrows. These two imported species aggressively drive away many of our native hole-nesting birds, including martins, bluebirds, and wrens. I saw a single pair of house sparrows destroy every egg in a colony of about 20 cliff swallows, and nest in one of their covered mud nests. You must continuously monitor martin houses in the early spring and remove the nests of unwelcome intruders before they become established. Sparrows and starlings tend to fill the nest compartment with grass, while martins mainly use sticks. A telescoping pole and hinged doors simplify matters greatly. Keep the nest entrances plugged until about a week before the martins arrive (a tennis ball fits the hole perfectly).

Once a martin family moves in, the birds busily swoop around their home catching food. They flap vigorously while chasing flying insects, then glide in long graceful dives. The males have a metallic blue-black back and front, while the females have a duller back and whitish belly. Like other swallows, martins prefer drinking on the wing. These agile birds even bathe while flying by dunking their rear quarters as they zip over the water, then shaking like a dog as they fly off. When not practicing their aerial acrobatics, the adults perch on the house and nearby wires and sing with a gurgling call. The delightful twittering song sounds like rushing water. In the morning, the whole flock joins the chorus to greet the dawn.

In Texas, martins begin nest building by late March or early April and lay their four to six white eggs from mid- to late April. Occasionally birds delay nesting until midsummer. The birds incubate the eggs an average of 16 days. A colony generally has babies hatching from mid-May to early June with parents busily zipping in and out feeding the hungry youngsters. Before the young fledge, they sit on their front porch and noisily beg for bugs from their foraging parents. One intrepid birdwatcher counted how often a pair fed their young between dawn and dusk. During the 16-hour period, the industrious parents made 205 trips! Martins need calcium in their diet and will eagerly feed on broken eggshells left near their home.

The young learn to fly in June and July, and the parents take them on increasingly longer foraging trips until they become independent. As the young fledge and begin spending their days foraging with the adults, the birds spend less time around the birdhouse. In July, the family packs up and leaves for winter retreat in Brazil. Like their spring migration, the birds set a leisure pace during the winter trip, with no hard and fast timetable. Once the martins leave, their house should be thoroughly cleaned and the entrances closed for the winter.

Bird enthusiasts love purple martins for their social nature, their airborne antics around their apartment birdhouse, and their voracious appetite for mosquitoes and other flying insects. Flying consumes so much energy that one of these active birds may eat 2000 insects a day. The residents of an eight-compartment martin house will consume about 32,000 insects a day, which is bad news for pesky mosquitoes.

The Western Electric plant in Kansas City used purple martins to solve its mosquito problem. Insecticides could not be used at the plant because of the delicate electronic parts being assembled, so the company installed martin houses around the buildings. The birds ate mosquitoes all day while the employees worked in insect-free comfort, and production increased significantly.

Despite the favor and protection of humans, purple martins have plenty of adversaries. Their chief foes are the starlings and house sparrows that usurp their nesting sites. Even though these two invaders can displace them, martins courageously defend their home against crows, hawks, and other predators. Screaming their loud alarm call, they mob any threatening intruder. Rat snakes can climb wooden poles and eat the eggs and young. For this reason, always place a section of sheet metal around the pole several feet below the house. Mites and other parasites can infest the nests and kill the young. Painting and sealing the inside of the house so the mites have no place to hide alleviates this problem. Occasionally, a screech owl may raid a martin house and snatch the birds right out of their nest. Proper construction, placement, and management of the house eliminates most of these problems, and experienced purple martin landlords often report that 100 percent of the babies survive.

Purple martins adapt well to city life and have delighted humans for centuries. The American Indians erected gourd martin houses in their villages. The colonists followed suit and constructed elaborate apartment dwellings for the friendly birds. Welcoming the purple martins is a 148-year-old tradition in Greencastle, Pennsylvania. Martin houses have lined the town square and streets since 1840. Increased interest and modern technology have in part repaid our debt to these displaced birds. Today purple martins are the favorite birds for neighborhood birdhouses. Gaily painted wooden structures and aluminum birdhouses especially designed for these much-loved creatures have sprung up across the country. The purple martin truly rates as one of America's most popular and beneficial birds.

The Mockingbird: The State Bird

Northern mockingbird
Mimus polyglottos

Our founding fathers may have given us the Lone Star flag, the cowboy, and other symbols associated with Texas, but the women of the state gave us the mockingbird. In 1927, at the urging of the Texas Federation of Women's Clubs, the Legislature declared the mockingbird the official state bird. They could have chosen the golden eagle, which winters across the western half of the state, or the cardinal that flashes his flaming red colors and greets the dawn with his ringing "whet-cheer." Of all the eligible birds, the women chose the mockingbird, and for good reasons. Perhaps no other bird in Texas is as well known and easily recognized, not because of dazzling colors, but due to its swashbuckling personality.

Never has a more fearless, defiant, belligerent, aggressive bird flitted through the treetops than the mockingbird. Nothing intimidates these indomitable birds. They will land at your feet to snatch up a grasshopper, or dive-bomb a cat. A mockingbird fears nothing that walks, flies, or crawls. One observer saw a mocker attack a diamondback rattlesnake until it pecked out the snake's eyes.

Let me tell you about the testy behavior of the JSC Mockingbird. When I worked at the Johnson Space Center, the antics of a mockingbird regularly amused the people in our office. She had declared the hedges bordering the walks outside our window her private domain. The mocker revealed her true personality in the spring when she nested. Most people passed within feet of her nest without noticing the drab gray bird hidden in the shadows of the leafy branches. On one occasion, a man wearing a hat saw the nest and pulled the limbs back for a better view. He might as

129

well have disturbed a wasp nest. Luckily his hat protected him from the furious assault, but from then on, the fiery bird peppered anyone that passed wearing a hat. People generally tried to ignore the first few swoops of the feathered assailant, but soon discovered she meant business. Executives, politicians, and even astronauts ducked and ran unglamorously from the relentless barrage.

In the winter, the mocker raged constant battle against the cedar waxwings that invaded her privacy. The hungry birds wished only to feast on the juicy yaupon berries, an important ingredient of the mocker's winter diet. As soon as a flock landed in one end of the hedge, our feathered mascot streaked in like a Minuteman missile. The flock would scatter and reassemble at the other end, only to be pursued by the tireless defender.

Mockingbirds have the same bellicose attitude toward the hordes of robins that invade their territory every winter. Roy Bedichek, in *Adventures with a Texas Naturalist,* recalls the mocker that kept his hackberry tree free of robins when every other tree in the block overflowed with the noisy birds. Against such odds, other birds might have given up, but not the mocker. It sat on the highest branch and dived on any invading bird.

Most birds, and people, learn to avoid the wrath of these antisocial birds. The resident mockingbirds at JSC had divided the campuslike grounds of the Space Center into a patchwork of home territories. They did not tolerate trespassing. Once a crow came slowly flapping over just above the rooftops. As soon as it entered a mocker's airspace, the smaller bird attacked. Despite the dive-bombing, the crow maintained its course and leisurely pace. Each mocker would drop back when the crow left its territory and let the next resident resume the battle.

Despite their antagonistic attitude, mockingbirds mate for life, or at least for many consecutive seasons. In the winter, each has its exclusive and mutually respected territory. Come spring, the pair rejoins to rear its family. The male sings and protects the territory while the female incubates the three to six eggs for about 13 days and broods the babies. The beautifully colored eggs vary from pale to greenish blue with brown spots and blotches. Both parents energetically feed and protect the young. After they leave the nest in 11 to 13 days, the chirping cry of the hungry juveniles echoes through the bushes. I once found a baby mocker in the street a block from my home. I placed the almost fully feathered baby in an old grackle nest and set it on a rabbit hutch in my backyard. Within an hour, an adult, presumably its parent, found the baby and began feeding it.

Though the pugnacious mannerisms of the mockingbird make it conspicuous, its claim to fame rests not with its behavior. More likely, the women of Texas presented it to the Legislature in recognition of its lovely voice and remarkable ability to sing. Of all the birds in the United States, mockingbirds are the prima donna songsters. Other birds may have prettier songs, depending on your opinion, but none sing as long and intensely as our state bird. The mocker's ringing melodies fill the air from early spring into late fall, from daybreak until late into the night, especially during a full moon.

Despite the numerous poetic verses giving human emotions to the mockingbird's serenades, mockers, and all birds, sing for a more utilitarian reason: to warn others of their species to stay out of their territory. A mocker's singathons match its intense personality. Whether in song, in defense of nest, or in pursuit of insects, it acts with authority and assertiveness.

The intricate lyrics of the mockingbird's song have thrilled the human ear since the Indians first settled North America. The birds may incorporate as many as 35 bird songs into their own, and every mocker has its personal collection. The screaming "kee-ahrr" of a red-tailed hawk, the piercing "kill-dee" of a killdeer, the whistling "peter-peter" of a titmouse, and the honking "yank-yank" of a nuthatch may belong to the mocker's repertoire.

The mockingbirds' scientific name, meaning "many-tongued mimic," reflects their remarkable talent. Mockingbirds do not mimic in the sense of trying to fool other birds. That would neutralize the purpose of their singing. Their song tells other mockingbirds, "I'm the boss mocker, and you better stay away!" They certainly don't want other mockingbirds to think that they are a titmouse, chickadee, or a helpless baby bird, a call frequently used.

Numerous scientific theories and folklore attempt to explain why mockingbirds borrow so liberally from the melodies of other birds. One theory couples the many hours per day that a mockingbird sings with its expansive selection of tunes. If the bird sang the same tune repeatedly for hours, the competing birds of its species would become bored and ignore the defender's warnings. So, of necessity, the mocker spices up its act by singing eight to ten different tunes per minute.

An Indian legend presents another explanation of why mockingbirds use other birds' songs. At one time, only the mockingbird could sing. None of the other birds could make a sound, not even a peep. Naturally the other birds were intensely jealous. Finally the Great Spirit came and asked the mocker to teach his song to all the birds. The proud bird refused. The Great Spirit then asked him if he would teach each bird one verse of his song. The mockingbird agreed and did so until each bird had a melody, but some of the birds forgot their tunes. That explains why the birds sing only a part of the mocker's song, and some just quack, squawk, and caw.

The mocker's renditions of other birds' songs are not usually good enough to fool a careful listener. Some naturalists even claim that the similarity to other birds' songs is totally coincidence, but I'll stand by the belief that mockers have the remarkable ability to remember and repeat sounds. One study reported a bird that changed its tune 137 times in ten minutes, singing 43 songs. Another documented a hand-raised mockingbird that could sing 42 songs of 24 birds in a single performance. It also imitated a squeaky washing machine and often answered the calls of wild birds with their own notes. It even recognized birds and called their songs when they flew by.

The domain of a mockingbird includes not only the trees and shrubs in its territory but also the turf. They keep their sharp yellow eyes trained on the ground looking for grasshoppers, crickets, beetles, caterpillars, and other delectable creatures of the grass. Like a hawk on a rabbit, they drop from their perch and grab their prey. Often the hunt involves wing flashing, a behavior that birdwatchers have never been able to explain adequately. The mockingbird lands on the ground, takes several steps, and slowly and mechanically opens and closes his wings. Some suggest the white wing patches may help scare up insects. Only the mockers know for sure, and they aren't telling. Through the year, insects average 48 percent of their diet, accounting for more in the summer. Wild berries and fruit fill out their menu and comprise 85 percent of their diet in the winter.

In the days before air conditioning required closed windows to seal out the summer heat, I can remember awakening deep in the night and hearing the echoing melodies of the mockingbird's song. Somewhere in the dark shadows cast by the pale moon, the troubadour sang his medley to anyone who would listen. Somehow, the fluid melodies in the stillness of the midnight hours stirred within me a feeling of kinship with the sleepless bird.

Mockingbirds fit in well with city life. The manicured lawns of the sprawling suburbs supply an abundance of the mockingbirds' favorite insects. Two or three yards provide ample territory for the bird to rear its family, so every block usually has several resident mockers. In the wild, these birds prefer open habitat with shrubs and trees for nesting and cover. They rarely occur in the treeless prairies of the Panhandle and the deep woodlands of East Texas. In the summer, they range into southern Canada, and live permanently from northern California, through South Dakota, to

New Jersey, and south into Mexico. In addition to Texas, the states of Arkansas, Florida, Mississippi, and Tennessee have chosen this popular singer as their state bird.

The Owl: Warrior of the Night

Great horned owl
Bubo virginianus
Eastern screech owl
Otus asio

Deep in the still of the night, the "hoohoo, hoo, hoo" of an owl echoes in our mind long after the sound disappears. The somber cry ringing through a moonless night fills us with wonder—or fear. Throughout history, owls have symbolized the evil presences that lurk in the shadows. In the minds of many, those mysterious birds represent doom and desolation, dire misfortune, death's dreadful messenger, evil, and mischief. But in the topsy-turvy world of superstitions, owls also denote wisdom, intelligence, and scholarship. Few other birds have had such an influence on the thoughts of humanity as these feathered warriors of the night.

Part of the owl's mystique is its costume. The animal's soft downy coat conceals weapons of death. Its powerful talons can dispatch a small animal in an instant. Riding on silent wings, owls deliver death without warning, snatch up their unsuspecting victims, and disappear without a trace. Only their eerie call betrays their presence. No wonder so many cultures consider these nocturnal creatures harbingers of ill fortune.

Owls represent the nighttime counterparts to the diurnal birds of prey. Different species of owls fill the same niches that hawks, falcons, and eagles do. The great horned owl is the only eagle owl in North America. Like the bald eagle, it uses the perch-and-pounce method of hunting, sitting high in a tree looking for any movement on the ground. Other owls search for prey while soaring like hawks. Screech owls represent the evening complement to small insectivorous falcons, such as the kestrel. As true masters of the night, the owls' shape, plumage, and senses show amazing adaptations for nocturnal hunting.

Catching scampering animals by starlight requires a combination of sharp vision and keen hearing. Owls have flat faces and forward-facing eyes to maximize binocular vision, necessary for capturing moving prey. The size of their eyes allows the lens to gather enough of the faintest light to trigger the cells in the retina. The size, number, and concentration of cells and the way the cells connect to the brain make an owl's eye 100 times more sensitive to light than a human's.

Nocturnal animals usually sacrifice the ability to perceive detail, or visual acuity, for the ability to see objects in low light, but not owls. With a tube-shaped eye that spreads the light over as many retinal cells as possible, owls can discern fine detail in dim light. The tube-shaped eye is highly efficient, but every design improvement has its trade-offs. Owls cannot rotate their eyes, and they have a narrower field of view than humans. To compensate for the limitations, these specialized birds can swivel their heads 270 degrees.

Owls can hunt on the darkest night. The highly developed auditory portion of their brain provides the acute hearing necessary to locate prey in low light. Some species hear well enough to catch animals they cannot see. Their flat, disk-shaped face channels the slightest sound to the large ear openings on the sides of their heads. Feathers around the ear slits scan for noise like a mammal's large ears. The right ear is higher on the head than the left, providing directional hearing, an aid in pinpointing the exact location of a noise. Owls can discern sounds reaching the ears with a 0.00003-second difference. Screech owls and other owls that prey on small critters are most sensitive to high frequencies, like leaves rustling and squeaks. The great horned owl, which hunts larger animals, is most sensitive to 1000 hertz, the same as the human ear.

Acute hearing would provide little help in detecting and tracking prey if owls were noisy fliers. The flapping of their own wings would drown out any noises made by their quarry. To baffle the noise, the owls' wing feathers have soft edges enabling the birds to fly in almost complete silence. Their large wings also minimize the amount of flapping required.

With a 4½-foot wingspread, the great horned owl is the largest owl in Texas. This eagle of the night darts adroitly through forest branches and soars over desert shrubs in pursuit of scampering prey. Not finicky eaters, the aerial hunters dine on porcupines, skunks, rabbits, squirrels, mice, birds, and reptiles. The adaptable great horned owl ranges from Alaska and the subarctic through most of the Western Hemisphere to the tip of South America. They live comfortably in any semi-open terrain, whether rugged mountains, arid desert, humid seashore, or rolling brushlands.

The fury of a great horned owl is legendary. Two of these flying tigers once attacked a naturalist inspecting their nest. One drove its claws into the man's side while the other lacerated his arm with four-inch gashes. The owl's talon penetrated a tendon and partially paralyzed the arm. In another instance, an unwary hunter went to retrieve a great horned owl he thought he had killed. The injured bird sank its talons in his wrist and punctured an artery. Sometime later, both were found still locked in a death grip.

The diminutive screech owl is the common urban owl of Texas. It ranges from Alaska and southern Canada into northeastern Mexico. Unlike their larger relative, which favors wilderness settings, screech owls often live in wooded parks and along greenbelts in our most populous cities. At night, they sally forth capturing insects in midair with a loud snap of their beaks. Besides flying and crawling insects, they eat mice, moles, birds, lizards, and almost any other small animal.

Though not as powerful as the 20-inch great horned owl, the 8-inch screech owl is just as fearless. The grip of its smaller talons can barely pierce a toughened human hand, but with claws as sharp as a cat's, a swooping screech owl can deliver a slashing wound. Screech owls do not hesitate to attack larger creatures. Late one moonlit night, I looked out my bedroom window just in time to see my howling dog reel from the blow of a screech owl. His midnight serenade interrupted, the yelping hound ran for protection underneath the house. A small owl once blinded one eye of a person trying to photograph its nest.

Though hunters by night, owls sit stoically by day, their benign appearance giving no clue to their fierce disposition. Their sedentary behavior helps conceal them from other birds, which universally hold a great enmity for the bird-eating raptors. Great horned owls often seek shelter in a densely vegetated treetop or deserted building. Screech owls commonly roost in a hollow tree. Most birds recognize the upright, rounded profile of a roosting owl and sound a loud and excited alarm. Calling every woodland bird, the smaller birds furiously harass the owl, carefully staying out of its reach. Finally the sleepy bird gives up and flies away to find a more secluded perch.

Many times I have traced a loud clamor in the treetops to a group of birds mobbing an owl. Crows have a particular antipathy for the great horned owl, while blue jays despise the smaller screech owl. Once I released a screech owl that had recovered from an injury. The owl flew into a tree, and within minutes was discovered. Blue jays, grackles, titmice, and chickadees swooped and screamed until the confused owl flew away. Birdwatchers make good use of a bird's boldness when pestering a screech owl. They either imitate the whinnylike call of the small owl or play a recording. Every bird within hearing will flock to the sound and bounce around in the bushes in clear view. At night, the call brings the resident screech owl swooping to investigate the intruder in its territory. Calling screech owls can have unexpected results. One night a friend, who does an excellent screech owl imitation, barely missed the attack of a great horned owl diving in to snare its smaller cousin for supper.

Both screech and great horned owls have feather tufts

on their heads that resemble ears. The tufts break up their outline while they perch and make them more difficult to recognize. Their mottled and barred coloration helps camouflage them while sitting in the shadows. Screech owls may be either of two color phases to help conceal them in vegetation. The gray phase occurs most commonly in deciduous and hardwood forests, and the reddish phase among conifers, which have a redder bark.

Despite their name, screech owls do not screech. Their territorial and dueting call is a long, descending whinny with tremolo, followed by an even-pitched trill. Like most Texans, Lone Star screech owls speak a dialect distinctly different from those in the eastern United States. The western screech owl, *Otus kennicottii,* which can be heard in Big Bend and westward, has a call that sounds more like rapping on wood. Screech owls begin calling in February and remain vocal through September. They often begin their courtship calls shortly after sunset, and pairs call to each other through the night as they hunt. The pairs break up in September, and the small owls live alone until January.

Great horned owls are the classic hoot owls. With a deep bass voice, they utter four to seven soft tremulous hoots that resonate over remarkably long distances. Once, while camping at Big Bend National Park, I heard the soft "hoo, hoohoo, hoo, hoo" of the large owl all through the night and at dawn when I arose. It sounded as though he were just outside my tent. I followed the hooting for about a quarter-mile before seeing the owl perched atop a yucca stalk. Like the screech owl, these owls call more in the late winter and spring.

Owls begin courting and nesting in January and February, several months before most birds get the urge. Great horned owls lay their two to five round white eggs in a bulky nest high in a tree, often using the old nest of a red-tailed hawk. The eggs hatch in 28 days, and the young can fly in 10 to 12 weeks. Screech owls nest in tree cavities, often old woodpecker holes. The male feeds the female during the 26 days she incubates the two to six eggs. Both feed the young for 5 or 6 weeks.

Nesting early helps owls find food for the young before the dense summer growth of vegetation can hide small animals. Growing owls have voracious appetites, and screech owls may make as many as 70 feeding trips per night bringing insects and small prey to the young. One naturalist counted 6 rabbits in a great horned owl nest, and another measured 18 pounds of food in a nest, including 1 rabbit, 5 birds, 2 eels, 4 catfish, 11 rats, and 1 muskrat.

Two other owls common in Texas are the barred owl, *Strix varia,* and the barn owl, *Tyto alba.* Barred owls, named after the markings on their breast, live in woodlands, river bottoms, and swamps of the eastern half of the state. Their hooting call sounds like the bird is saying "who cooks for you, who cooks for you-all." Barn owls have a distinct heart-shaped face and white underparts. They prefer prairies, marshes, and open terrain, often inhabiting old buildings around farms, as their name implies. They do not hoot, but have a wheezy cry. A total of about 11 species of owls live in Texas.

The Roadrunner:
The Paisano, Symbol
of the Southwest

Roadrunner, paisano
Geococcyx californianus

"He must surely be the most comical bird in America!"
laughed Texas author J. Frank Dobie. "He will go through
more antics and cut more didos in an hour than a parrot can
be taught in a lifetime!" Americans, particularly in the
Southwest, share Dobie's enthusiasm for this strange member of the cuckoo family, the roadrunner.

The roadrunner comes by its name and reputation hon-
estly. It would rather run than fly. This sleek, streamlined
bird darts through the low brush and cacti of the Southwest
with remarkable speed and agility. But while traveling at top
speed, it will abruptly stop, raise its colorful crest, and look
around as though pursued. Then, with a sudden burst of
speed, it resumes its race with its head low and its tail parallel to the ground. This characteristic profile of outstretched bill and extended tail has inspired painters, wood-
carvers, sculptors, potters, and souvenir-makers from Texas
to Hong Kong.

Hollywood also recognizes the entertainment value of
the bird with such strange behavior and speedy locomotion.
Every American youth laughs at the famous cartoon series
featuring the roadrunner and the coyote. The cartoon depicts the bird as a crafty jester that invariably outwits the in-
ane Wile E. Coyote. This childhood introduction to the
roadrunner justly might be considered modern American
folklore.

The roadrunner has played a prominent role in the folklore of the Southwest for centuries. Along the Mexican border, the bird is known as paisano, meaning fellow country-
man, or fellow traveler. Residents use the term to address

141

someone who has experienced many of the same pleasures and hardships in life. The vaqueros who chased longhorns through the thorny chaparral of South Texas easily identified with the dauntless bird. Like the cowboys, the paisano also raced through the almost impenetrable vegetation, but instead of chasing ornery cows, it pursued lizards, mice, snakes, and other edible delights. A bird that had to wrest its livelihood from the same rugged country was an inspiration, and certainly a paisano.

The thick, shrubby vegetation where roadrunners live influences their curious behavior more than some imagined witty nature. The best way to find a gourmet meal of insects and small animals is by cruising along at ground level. A bird soaring above the treetops would have little chance of seeing or capturing a small creature in the dense vegetation. About the only time a roadrunner uses its wings is to sail from tree limb to ground. If pursued, a brief flight takes it into the thick brush, where it takes off running.

The roadrunner depends on legwork to keep its belly full. Catching the inhabitants of the thorny brush and desert requires fast starts, fast stops, quick turns, and quick bursts of speed. Some lizards can run up to 10 mph, but the roadrunner can top 15 mph. The birds have reportedly been clocked racing along roadsides at speeds exceeding 25 mph.

Though Hollywood depicts the coyote as the archenemy of the roadrunner, folktales emphasize its notorious battles with rattlesnakes. In one often repeated story, a roadrunner comes upon a sleeping diamondback. The crafty bird carefully constructs a corral of prickly pear pads or cholla cactus stems around the unsuspecting snake. Once the roadrunner has cornered the rattler with no route of escape, it pounces on the hapless reptile for the coup de grace. Using its heavy, slightly curved bill, the bird crushes the snake's skull with staccato hammerlike blows.

Roadrunners most assuredly kill rattlesnakes, and their victims are occasionally found with a crushed head and surrounded by cacti. A snake thrashing around in a cactus patch while being pecked to death could easily clear a small area. And that area might resemble a miniature corral. Thus, a little bit of factual evidence and some creative conjecture gives birth to an enduring folktale.

A roadrunner usually kills a snake for food, not out of animosity. Sometimes the bird's eyes are bigger than its stomach, and it catches a snake longer than it can completely swallow. A roadrunner hopping around with the snake's tail dangling from its mouth only adds to its comic reputation.

The bird's unusual vocalizations also contribute to the rich folklore surrounding this feathered warrior of the chaparral. In the spring, the male sits atop a mesquite or cactus and utters a guttural "crut-crut-crut." He bows his head low as though in prayer and slowly rises skyward while calling. The bird's tracks in the sand even resemble a cross. People thought that such a religious bird must be a paisano. The male actually sings his strange song to advise other males to stay out of his territory, and to attract females.

While courting the female, the male behaves like a true gentleman. He always brings a gift to try to win the lady's attention. He struts around with a scorpion or other delicacy dangling invitingly from his beak. If he is successful in wooing the prospective mother of his children, the pair mates. As often as not, the male does not relinquish his gift, and after the encounter, he nonchalantly swallows his present.

Unlike those members of the cuckoo family who lay their eggs in other birds' nests, roadrunners are dutiful parents. Both the male and female share equally in rearing the family, and each feeds the young chicks frequently throughout the day. The adult seems to freeze for a full minute with its beak thrust deep into the baby's throat while it regurgitates the baby's meal. When the young grow larger, the parents bring lizards and other small prey to the nest. Along the Texas border, roadrunners reportedly take parenting very seriously.

143

According to legend, roadrunners, not the stork, deliver human babies to their parents.

Despite their reputation for excellent parenting, roadrunners sometimes get confused. One spring, a female kept hopping up to the window ledge outside the ranger's station at Big Bend National Park. Behind the glass barrier, rangers had made a display featuring a roadrunner's nest. Finally, in frustration with the perfect home so close yet just out of reach, the bird laid an egg on the narrow windowsill.

Even though the roadrunner is the emblem of the wide open spaces and associated with the western deserts, this adaptable bird is equally at home in the palmetto swamps of East Texas. The chaparral bird likes open areas with scrubby brush cover whether in deserts, prairies, or broken woodlands. The bird delights its human neighbors from northern California east to Kansas, southward through Arkansas and northwest Louisiana, along the Texas coast to central Mexico, and west to northern Baja California.

In the Lone Star State, roadrunners dart across highways from the Louisiana border to El Paso and from the Panhandle to Brownsville. The bird occurs most commonly in West, Central, and South Texas, where the cowboy and all those who live close to the land still consider it their close companion. As J. Frank Dobie said of the bird he loved so much, "We true paisanos of mankind include in our kinship the paisanos of birdkind."

Talking Turkey in Texas

Eastern turkey
Meleagris gallopavo silvestris
Rio Grande turkey
M. g. intermedia
Merriam's turkey
M. g. merriami

Americans may vote dogs and cats their favorite animals most of the time, but for one week the turkey gets the honors. The warty faced, fan-tailed creature is the center of attention on the fourth Thursday of each November. During the week, pictures of denuded turkeys, usually in a prone position with their feet in the air, appear in all the newspapers, and even on TV. The culmination of all this attention is the ceremonial carving and consumption of the baked and basted animal. Participants in the feast hoard scraps remaining after the feeding frenzy for future reenactments of the ritual.

The pioneer founders of this culinary festival were so eager to celebrate Thanksgiving year-round that the commonplace turkey completely disappeared from most of its original range. What few survived the overhunting had to contend with the conversion of their forest homelands into plowed fields and pastures. By 1930, only about 20,000 of these magnificent birds remained in just 21 states. States imposed hunting restrictions, outlawed hunting during breeding season when the males were the most visible, and initiated restocking programs.

Unfortunately most of the stocking efforts released crosses between domestic and wild turkeys, since the tamer birds provided easier targets. The tameness that made a hybrid variety a good game bird doomed it to certain death in the wild. Typically only about 1 percent survived the first six

145

months. In addition, they spread barnyard poultry diseases in the wild population. State biologists finally overcame the political pressure to use birds bred for easy hunting, and the restocking programs became successful. Shooting a turkey once again became a true test of a hunter's skill.

All of the three varieties of wild turkeys originally lived in the Lone Star State. Hunters gunned the Merriam's turkey out of the Guadalupe Mountains before the 1900s, and the last eastern wild turkey from the Panhandle in 1905. By 1942, less than 100 turkeys survived in the East Texas forests. The Rio Grande turkey ranges from South Texas through the Hill Country into North Texas and Oklahoma. It is the only variety that, though its numbers greatly declined, did not suffer a drastic reduction in range. Today biologists have restocked the Rio Grande turkey successfully in the Panhandle and through much of its native range. The gobble of the Merriam's turkey once again echoes through the Guadalupe Mountains, as well as the Davis Mountains. The future of the eastern turkey in East Texas remains less certain. Lumbering conglomerates own most of the pine-hardwood forests and annually convert hundreds of thousands of acres of the rich woodlands into barren pine plantations devoid of food for wildlife.

Besides their keen senses and a tendency to flee at the slightest alarm, wild turkeys survive because they eat almost anything. Their favorite foods include nuts, acorns, juniper berries, grass seeds, and insects, but they will not scorn an occasional lizard, snake, or snail. When they find a rich resource, they gorge themselves in true turkey fashion. By storing up fat, they can survive the harshest winters. They have been known to go 24 days without food and lose 40 percent of their weight, and still survive.

Turkeys form flocks of 30 to 40 in the fall after the poults, or chicks, have matured and the spring breeding aggressiveness has disappeared. The birds like to roost in large deciduous trees near water, and flocks sometimes return to the same site for 100 years. The 15-to-20-pound gobblers and 6-to-8-pound hens reach the highest limbs by short flights from branch to branch. They come to the roost as the sun sets and leave at dawn.

Turkeys have contributed to human life in North America since the Indians first domesticated them 2000 years ago. After almost disappearing from its ancestral range, the wild turkey population has increased to 2 million strong, with 500,000 in Texas.

[At this point in the chapter, I was overcome by a trance and began automatically writing under the direction of Ben Franklin. This may be the first time in recorded history that a spirit used a word processor to speak to posterity. I present the following unedited paragraphs to the reader. The facts about turkeys are accurate, but I have no way to ensure the authenticity of certain historical references—G.M.]

Even though every American history book tells how turkeys came to be the main attraction of Thanksgiving, the complete story has never been told. The choice resulted from a conspiracy, not by the bloody British but by the Puritans. After over 200 years of secrecy, I will now reveal the truth to you fortunate readers.

The colonists admired the turkey almost more than any other animal. The wild turkey reigned as the king of the game birds. With a sleek, streamlined body, powerful legs, and keen eyesight, it streaks through the woods like a racehorse, reaching speeds of 15 mph. If danger presses, it bursts into the air with a strong, swift flight, though it seldom stays airborne for over a quarter of a mile.

At a time before TVs or comic books, the colonial youth looked to male turkeys as a chief source of amusement. The gobbler's sexual behavior, a subject taboo in all forms of polite Puritan society, created the main interest, and provided ample subject matter for ribald jokes and stories.

In the spring, the male's wattle-covered face turns as red as Old Glory's stripes. He struts around with a bounding stride chasing away other toms and courting the females. Evidently the sight of the malshaped crimson face and long hairlike beard growing from his chest strikes admiration in a lady's heart. The tom advances toward a hen with a subdued gobble and his tail fanned while quivering his dropped wings. After the gobbler enjoys the company of one hen, he struts on looking for another. Since a male turkey has a large number of females in his herd, being called a turkey in colonial times was the epitome of a macho compliment.

The Puritan leaders, however, had a contrary opinion of the male turkey, an animal that seemed to live for one inexcusable purpose: sex. On top of that, the cursed animal deserts the female after getting her in the family way. The lady retreats to a secluded nesting spot and hatches between 10 and 14 eggs with the father assuming no responsibility for the children. Such behavior provided the topic for many a Sunday sermon. The Reverend Cotton Mather became famous for his Turkey Sermon.

Despite being slandered on Sundays, the wild turkey captured the imagination of the more daring colonists. Its peculiar gait inspired a dance, the turkey trot, as popular on Saturday night as a picnic on the Lord's day. Ben Franklin even led a movement to adopt the turkey as the national bird.

How could the Puritan leaders squelch the admiration for turkeys held by the country's youth and political leaders? Outright condemnation from the pulpit had failed, so they launched an indirect assault on the turkey's reputation. To save the impressionable youth from the influence of such an aberrant bird and to preserve the honor of this great nation, the T-Day conspiracy was born. The strategy was to make the turkey the center of the emerging culinary festival called Thanksgiving. Who could admire an animal eaten with relish, or even cranberry sauce, every year? The plan worked, and any reference to gobbling food or being called a turkey became an insult.

[Thanks, Ben, for the inside info.]

Vultures: Nature's Garbage Disposals

Turkey vulture
Cathartes aura
Black vulture
Coragyps atratus

"Ranger, we thought we had killed the poor bird! He flew up right in front of us and bounced onto our hood. He threw up all over the windshield before he flew away!" The ranger at Big Bend National Park tried not to laugh at the gentleman's encounter with the turkey vulture. Visitors to the park often have an unglamorous introduction to the ungainly bird. The ranger explained that vultures naturally regurgitate when threatened or frightened. They have a hard enough time getting airborne without a headwind, and the added weight of an engorged stomach doesn't help a quick take-off.

I had already discovered the vulture's disgusting habit of jettisoning its stomach contents. The Austin Nature Center had an injured turkey vulture named Groucho Marx, and my job was to make him (or her) feel at home. Groucho had a nasty habit of coating my shoes with goopy green stuff every time I entered his cage. I never knew whether he related to my shoes like a dog marking a tree, a skunk spraying a foe, or a mother vulture feeding her baby. To my relief, he finally decided to keep his supper to himself, and merely shredded my shoelaces.

One day, we tried to liberate Groucho. We took him to the nearby woods and cast him into the air, expecting him to wing his way to freedom. Instead he glided to the nearest picnic table and contentedly folded his wings. After several hours, we realized that Groucho wasn't about to trade a safe perch and a full food bowl for a hard day's work in the

149

sky. I wasn't sure how to get him back to his cage. He didn't want to leave the table, but he couldn't resist my shoes. I led him, Pied Piper style, back to his cage.

Vultures have such a hard time finding food that they only reluctantly abandon a meal, whether in a cage or on a roadside. Safe roosting sites are also at a premium. No wonder Groucho had no ambitions to abandon human charity. In Big Bend, turkey vultures find an ideal roost in the tall trees shading the campgrounds at Rio Grande Village. The large cottonwoods bordering the river provide a safe haven for a large population. At dawn, they noisily flap their three-foot wings and glide from their roosts high in the trees to the closest picnic table. After defacing the table, they hop awkwardly around on the ground until some photographer harasses them into flying. The unsightly birds remain earthbound until the sun has warmed the desert enough to create thermal updrafts.

When vultures take to the airways, they become a picture of grace soaring on the rising thermals. They ride the updrafts like a kite circling higher and higher until they become mere dots. These perfect sailplanes can glide for hours and cover miles of terrain without expending the energy of a single wing flap.

Every feather on a vulture's wing is designed for one purpose: gliding. Feathers extending beyond the wingtips act as tiny, narrow wings and prevent stalling at low speeds. They also reduce vortices along the wing edges. The broad wings give the bird a high lift factor, essential for long-term soaring without flapping. The rounded design of the wing allows the bird to maneuver in the tight circles necessary to track rising columns of air. Even the vulture's size suits its lifestyle of riding the thermal updrafts. It is large enough to provide stability in the capricious currents, but light enough to require a minimum of energy to stay airborne.

While the red-headed turkey vulture and its black-faced cousin, the black vulture, soar through the skies, their eyes remain glued on the earth below. With keen vision they scan the countryside for food. Unlike birds that kill their food and eat it fresh, vultures feast on dead animals, and the riper the better. The weak talons of these birds of prey cannot grip tightly enough to hold a live animal or to carry objects very far, and their slightly hooked bill is too weak to kill. By grouping together for a mass attack, however, vultures can kill a small animal like a skunk.

Turkey vultures have an advantage over black vultures in finding food. Both rely on their sharp vision to spot carcasses in the open, but turkey vultures have an additional sense missing in almost all other birds: they can smell. Their brain has a well-developed olfactory lobe. Smell guides them to prey hidden from sight in brush or trees until they can locate it by sight. Despite their acute sense of smell, they must see the prey to find it.

Vultures willingly serve as natural garbage disposals; they are as important as trash collectors in a city. They congregate in large numbers around the carcass of a cow or deer. A half-dozen may sit on fence posts and in nearby trees while several feast on a road-killed armadillo. In Central American countries, black vultures often eat rotten fruit and vegetables. Both species gather in large numbers in garbage dumps. These normally silent birds hiss, grunt, and growl at each other while dining. In a mixed group, the smaller but more aggressive black vulture often drives away the turkey vulture.

Despite its filthy occupation, a vulture retains a tidy appearance and, even though it sometimes wallows in its food, never lets offal besmirch its feathers. Dirty feathers mean inefficient flying, a costly mistake for a soaring bird. A vulture cleans its feathers by preening, running them through its bill, but it cannot reach its neck and head feathers, the ones most likely to get soiled. For improved sanitation, vultures are endowed with a naked head and neck.

Vultures, or buzzards as people commonly call them, prefer open country where they can see dead animals from long distances. Turkey vultures, the most abundant vulture in Texas, occur throughout the state, but are usually rare in the Panhandle and Trans-Pecos in the winter. They range from southern Canada to the Tierra del Fuego at the southern tip of Argentina. Turkey vultures reside year-round through most of their range, but must migrate from areas where winter temperatures freeze carcasses. The birds soar 3500 miles to southern climates, fasting for the two-week trip, and fly about nine hours a day, averaging 40 mph.

Black vultures range from Maryland south through the coastal states to central Argentina. In Texas, they commonly live in the eastern and southern halves of the state. Black vultures, probably the most numerous birds of prey in the Western Hemisphere, occur most abundantly in the tropics. They thrive in a hot climate because they are not as efficient at soaring as the turkey vulture, and they require stronger updrafts to stay airborne. Black vultures have shorter wings, flap frequently, and use more energy while hunting, but the tropical thermals compensate for the inefficiency. The rate at which a soaring bird descends in calm air is a measure of its gliding efficiency. Black vultures sink at a rate of 0.79 meters per second, while turkey vultures sink at 0.61 meters per second. This slight difference translates into a considerable additional energy expenditure for the black vulture over a year's period.

In the last three decades, the number of both vultures in Texas has decreased drastically. Many factors have contributed to the decline. Less carrion is available. The blowfly, which infected and killed many cattle and deer, was brought under control by 1950. Ranchers deprive vultures of food by burning carcasses to prevent the spread of disease. With less carrion available in the fields, vultures must rely on road-killed animals for sustenance, and sometimes themselves become victims of speeding vehicles. Ranchers habitually kill vultures because they believe they transmit diseases, which has never been conclusively proved. In addition, habitat destruction has eliminated nesting sites and prey availability.

The black vulture has suffered much more than its red-headed relative. In a marginal temperate climate where competition is the keenest, the turkey vulture's advantages of a sense of smell and more efficient soaring give it the edge. The turkey vulture's increased mobility enables it to search over more ground for scarce food while using less energy. As the years pass, the black vulture slowly retreats south, where optimum conditions exist for its survival.

Soaring black and turkey vultures are easy to tell apart. Look for the turkey vulture's characteristic V-shaped profile. The bird gently rocks back and forth as it glides along. The entire edge of the wings from body to tips appears grayish white. The black vulture holds its wings flat as it glides, and only the wingtips are whitish. At close range, the turkey vulture's red head is readily distinguishable, though juveniles have dark heads.

The Armadillo, *Dasypus novemcinctus*

Photo by Merlin Tuttle.

Mexican free-tailed bat, *Tadarida brasiliensis*

Plate 1

Cougar, *Felis concolor*

Coyote, *Canis latrans*

Plate 2

White-tailed deer, *Odocoileus virginianus texanus*

Bottlenose dolphin, *Tursiops truncatus*

Plate 3

Gray fox, *Urocyon cinereoargenteus*

Javelina, *Dicotyles tajacu angulatus*

Plate 4

The Longhorn

Opossum, *Didelphis virginiana*

Plate 5

Pronghorn, *Antilocapra americana*

Black-tailed jackrabbit,
Lepus californicus

Jackalope
(no designated scientific name)

Plate 6

Raccoon, *Procyon lotor*

Hog-nosed skunk, *Conepatus mesoleucus*

Plate 7

Bald eagle, *Haliaeetus leucocephalus*

Golden eagle, *Aquila chrysaëtos*

Plate 8

Cattle egret, *Bubulcus ibis*

Ruby-throated hummingbird, *Archilochus colubris*

Plate 9

Purple martin, *Progne subis*

Mockingbird, *Mimus polyglottos*

Plate 10

Great horned owl, *Bubo virginianus*

Eastern screech owl, *Otus asio*

Plate 11

Roadrunner, *Geococcyx californianus*

Eastern turkey, *Meleagris gallopavo silvestris*

Plate 12

Turkey vulture, *Cathartes aura*

Black vulture, *Coragyps atratus*

Plate 13

Golden-cheeked warbler, *Dendroica chrysoparia*

Whooping crane, *Grus americana*

Plate 14

American alligator, *Alligator mississippiensis*

Southern copperhead, *Agkistrodon contortrix contortrix*

Plate 15

Monarch butterfly, *Danaus plexippus*

Red-legged tarantula, *Dugesiella hentzi*

Plate 16

Western diamondback rattlesnake, *Crotalus atrox*

Western cottonmouth, *Agkistrodon piscivorus leucostoma*

Plate 17

Texas horned lizard, *Phrynosoma cornutum*

Baby Kemp's ridley sea turtle, *Lepidochelys kempi*

Plate 18

Three-toed box turtle, *Terrapene carolina triunguis*

Imported red fire ant, *Solenopsis invicta*

Plate 19

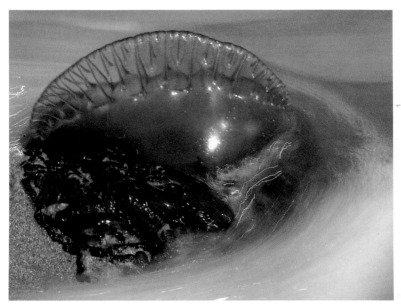

Portuguese man-of-war, *Physalia physalia*

Striped scorpion, *Centruroides vittatus*

Plate 20

The Golden-cheeked Warbler: A True Native Texan

Golden-cheeked warbler
Dendroica chrysoparia

Each spring, hordes of enthusiasts from around the nation descend on the cedar-covered hills of Central Texas searching for a treasure of gold. Instead of panning the many spring-fed streams for precious nuggets, they scan the tree-tops with high-powered binoculars. Their quest is the rare and endangered golden-cheeked warbler. After spending the winter in Guatemala, Honduras, and Nicaragua, these tiny birds migrate to the Texas Hill Country to rear their families. Every golden-cheeked in existence is a native Texan, a distinction held by no other species of bird.

What unique feature in the Hill Country attracts these colorful birds? The cedars, the same trees despised by sniffling and sneezing humans for spreading highly allergenic pollen, attract the golden-cheeks. Each winter, misery floats on every breeze as the trees shed copious amounts of the pernicious pollen. By spring the air has cleared, and the energetic golden-cheeks, like feathered butterflies, enliven the aromatic branches. The breeding range of the golden-cheeked warbler coincides with the distribution of the Ashe junipers, commonly called cedars, across the Edwards Plateau.

Excitement comes in small packages for birdwatchers. The 4¼-inch golden-cheek weighs only a third of an ounce. The birds typically arrive in the hills west of Austin around March 12. One year on that date, I met a birdwatcher from Ohio at the Travis County Audubon sanctuary. She had scheduled her birding trip to spend that one day in Austin hoping to add the rare warbler to her life list. Many birdwatchers keep a list of every species seen, and some keep it with religious zeal. The bird books gave the average arrival

155

date of the golden-cheeks, and she was ready with binoculars in hand. The birds, however, operate on their own timetables, and to the woman's consternation, the warblers were tardy that year. Without forgiving the belated birds, she rushed off to her next stop, still with an unmarked square beside the elusive golden-cheek on her checklist.

I remember the excitement the first time I saw this colorful warbler. The cedar brakes were stifling, with April temperatures already in the mid-90s. I had heard several singing males, but hadn't found them. Suddenly one popped up in the tree above me and began singing. I caught my breath when I saw him through my seven-power binoculars. No picture can capture the intensity of his jet black head, throat, and back contrasted with his blazing golden cheeks. His buzzy song seemed to burst from his throat, then the ball of energy disappeared into the brush. The females, also with golden cheeks, have a dull olive back and streaked throat. Both sexes have white bellies.

The female golden-cheek builds her nest without any help from the man of the family, who stays busy singing. She adheres to a very strict building code established by thousands of years of tradition. The ladies demand the rustic look of cedar, and always construct their homes with long strips of cedar bark. They pull loose strands from the limbs and, using spiderwebs to hold them together, weave a three-inch cuplike nest. As a finishing touch, they line the interior with soft rootlets, mammal hair, and feathers.

The males are far from idle while the females build the nest, lay, and incubate the three or four eggs. In the division of labor, each sex has an equally important role. All day—from the time he first arrives from his southern retreat—the male sings his wheezy song to proclaim his territory. Any intruding male meets a furious assault. The males battle out a division of the turf, or more properly the treetops because they never forage on the ground. Each male stakes out a three-to-six-acre domain with enough resources to rear a family successfully. Females choose aggressive mates that will protect the nest, vigorously defend their territory, and help feed the young.

Once the eggs hatch, after 12 days of incubation, the male becomes a family man. The dutiful father sings less and less as he devotes more time to feeding the hungry babies. From dawn to dusk, both parents fill the gaping mouths of the young with caterpillars, spiders, flies, moths, and any other insects they can catch. After 9 days, the young leave the nest, but remain under the protection of their parents. They learn to forage on their own in about 3 weeks. The parents appear to divide the family, each taking care of the young in its charge.

Golden-cheek nesting coincides with the peak caterpillar population in the plateau live oak, Texas oak, and other hardwood trees. The birds scour the limbs gleaning the tiny caterpillars, the major food for the voracious appetites of the young. Without the insects in the hardwoods, the young would starve. Golden-cheeks never nest in pure stands of cedar, nor in cut-over second growths. Only mature cedars, at least 50 years old, have bark that easily shreds from the trunk and limbs, so only the association of mature cedars and hardwoods provides a suitable habitat for this rare bird.

Golden-cheeks nest in 31 counties in Central Texas, but exclusively in the remaining patches of mature cedars, which are becoming as rare as the bird so dependent on them. The cedar eradication program of the Soil Conservation Service, land-clearing for pastures and agriculture, and sprawling urbanization destroy the warbler homeland at an alarming rate. A 1974 field survey estimated that in the 150-by-50-mile wedge-shaped area occupied by the birds, only 326,000 acres of suitable habitat remained, and almost half of that was considered marginal. At that time, the world's population of golden-cheeks numbered about 15,000.

Habitat destruction may eventually eradicate the golden-cheek, but the birds also have their share of day-to-day worries. The babies often suffer ill-treatment from unwelcome guests. Besides having their home burglarized by rat snakes, golden-cheeks are victimized by the brown-headed cowbird, one of nature's cleverest con artists. In some areas, these birds parasitize as many as 60 percent of the golden-cheek nests. Cowbirds prefer to let someone else shoulder parental chores, and they lay their eggs in the nests of warblers and other smaller birds. The female cowbird closely watches the other bird's nest and lays her egg just before the host begins incubating. She discards several of the rightful eggs to make room for her own. The golden-cheek often recognizes the foreign egg and abandons the nest to start over. Once a cowbird hatches, the warbler babies are doomed because the aggressive baby kills the other young. The foster parents dutifully feed the cowbird until it leaves the nest to flock with its own species.

After completing their family responsibilities, the golden-cheeked warblers pack up and head south. By August, the birds have left Texas and are winging their way through Mexico to their winter refuge. Naturalists first discovered golden-cheeks in Guatemala in 1859 and found them in Texas five years later. Texans are stewards of this precious and irreplaceable biological legacy, a golden gem hidden in the scenic Hill Country. The tiny warbler is a product and symbol of the ecological richness and diversity of the rolling hills of Central Texas. Today you can see these native Texans in about ten state parks and wildlife management areas in Central Texas, several county and municipal parks, and private sanctuaries.

What will we lose if we clear the cedar brakes and drive the golden-cheeked warbler to extinction? Like a coal miner's canary testing for poisoned air, the status of the pretty warbler alerts us to a far greater danger: a destructive attitude toward the world, the source of our existence. In the complex web of life, the disappearance of one species indicates that many links in the ecological chain have been broken. If we drive the golden-cheek to extinction, we will have extinguished not just a single bird but also a vast segment of the environment. If, like children playing irresponsibly with the family heirlooms, we discard the biological treasures around us, we only demonstrate our avarice and immaturity. Like the cowbird, we will be parasites exploiting the riches of the planet, proving that we have the capability of driving nature itself into bankruptcy. Such an attitude not only destroys the quality of human life in the short run, but, if continued indefinitely, will lead to the extinction of the human species.

The Whooping Crane: Texas' Most Celebrated Visitor

Whooping crane
Grus americana

One hundred and fifty pairs of eyes strained for a better view of the 4 stately subjects in the distance. Those with binoculars and cameras leaned perilously over the rail to get a few inches closer. Suddenly all were quiet, then a simultaneous gasp. The whooping cranes had burst into the air and, with their long necks fully extended, flew directly in front of the tour boat. Their wings, stretching seven feet from black tip to black tip, beat gracefully, almost in slow motion. Clicking cameras sounded like the rumble of a distant cattle stampede. The flying foursome brought to 28 the number of whoopers we had seen on the four-hour excursion into the heart of the rare bird's feeding grounds. The captain had beached the boat twice so we could get better than a passing view. After that climactic scene, the skipper turned around and brought the satisfied tourists back through Aransas Bay to the marina.

Thousands of people visit the Texas coast each autumn to see one of the state's most celebrated attractions, the only wild flock of breeding whooping cranes in the world. In mid-October, the birds begin arriving from their summer home 2600 miles away in Wood Buffalo National Park in northern Canada. They roam the rich coastal marshes until early April, then return to their Canadian breeding grounds. In 1987, a record 134 birds, including 24 chicks, made the arduous flight to Texas.

Whoopers were never very numerous. The National Audubon Society estimates that their population probably never exceeded 1300 or 1400. The birds once wintered all along the Gulf Coast and into central Mexico. For thousands of years, they bred from Texas and Louisiana north through the central states into upper Canada. The early pioneers who encountered the five-foot white cranes named them for their trumpetlike call, which resembled the war whoop of attacking Indians. By 1870, ranchers and farmers had settled most of their range and converted prime whooping crane habitat into prime beef, corn, and wheat habitat. Whoopers last bred in Texas in 1878 near Eagle Lake, and in the United States in 1889. In 1894, a pair nested in Iowa, but no eggs hatched. By 1918, the wintering grounds of these magnificent birds had been reduced to three isolated localities. Twenty-five birds wintered in the coastal marshes in Aransas County, 16 on the King Ranch in Kleberg and Kenedy counties, and 6 in Louisiana. The White Lake marshes of Louisiana harbored an additional 12 resident birds. The last whooper left the King Ranch in 1937, and only 15 stalked the marshes around Aransas Bay by 1941. The sole bird remaining in Louisiana left the state via helicopter in 1950 to join the Aransas flock.

In 1937, Congress established the 54,829-acre Aransas National Wildlife Refuge to protect the last of this disappearing species. The marshes and shallow ponds bordering Aransas Bay and Matagorda and San Jose islands provide ideal habitat for the whooping cranes. Each family unit, usually a pair with their young, requires between 300 and 600 acres to provide enough food to satisfy their voracious appetites. Like ballet dancers in slow motion, they wade through the shallows spearing blue crabs, clams, crayfish, and other aquatic organisms. The family members feed together harmoniously, but chase intruding whoopers from their territory.

Texans get to view the whoopers from October through April, but unfortunately, they rarely see their spectacular mating dance. In the early spring just before migrating north, whoopers begin courting. They may dance occasionally during migration, but do not perform in earnest until they arrive at the 11-million-acre preserve in Canada. These graceful birds exchange bows as though they were attending a formal reception, then leap high into the air like an excited child. Wild wing-flapping, gyrations, and acrobatics accompany the stiff-legged prancing and leaping. The clarion call of the cavorting birds echoes across the marsh like a bugler sounding a charge. The dance strengthens the bond between the couples, who mate for life, and forms new pairs among maturing young.

Between May and early June, the female lays two eggs on a mound constructed of vegetation in the middle of a shallow pond. Most species of birds begin incubation after laying their full clutch of eggs so the young will all hatch the same day, but not whoopers. The female begins incubating the first egg, which hatches several days before the second. The older chick usually pecks the smaller chick to death or outcompetes it for food. Only rarely do both survive. The chicks, feasting on minnows and other aquatic and plant life, grow rapidly. By migration time in September and October, they have almost reached adult size, but they still wear their rusty juvenile plumage. The youngsters accompany their parents to the Aransas refuge and, begging for food, wade beside them through the marshes.

From 1981 to 1984, wildlife biologists followed and observed the birds along the entire 2600-mile migration route using solar-powered tracking transmitters placed on the juveniles' legs. The whoopers typically leave their nesting grounds in the southern Northwest Territories in mid-September, but may delay in Saskatchewan for several weeks to feed in wheat and barley fields. By mid-October, the family begins its flight south in earnest and may cover 450 miles a day if winds and weather cooperate. Inclement weather may cause them to lay over for a week or more. During the 30-plus days of the birds' trip, they cross the corner of Montana, the Dakotas, Nebraska, Kansas, and Oklahoma and enter North Texas. They may spend only 15 to 20 days in the air, with an average flight speed of 30 mph. While en route, the cranes feed in ponds, marshes, and grain fields, most of which are privately owned. Grains provide an important food source during migration. In pastures they turn over dried cow patties looking for insects.

The long trip between Texas and Canada poses a grave threat to a whooper's life. Hunters sometimes mistake them for snow geese, which also have white wings with black tips. The state has set a $4000 to $10,000 fine for killing a whooping crane. Power lines frequently take their toll. In 1981, one juvenile carrying a transmitter had a fatal encounter in Saskatchewan, and a yearling died near Waco, Texas, the following year. In 1983, a juvenile died in Aransas from disease, and in 1984 another crane died from a head wound, probably from a great horned owl. In 1984, a whooper at the Bosque del Apache Refuge died of lead poisoning. Since 1951, 10 cranes have died and 15 disappeared at the Aransas Refuge. At the Canada breeding grounds, the chicks must survive cold, drought, starvation, disease, and predators. Since 1977, at least 142 chicks have hatched, but only 75 lived long enough to arrive at Aransas. Oil spills, polluted water, and dredging present continual and serious threats at the Aransas refuge.

The total number of captive and wild whooping cranes reached a low of 23 in 1941. The Aransas flock of 15 contained only 2 to 3 breeding pairs. The population slowly increased at a rate of 3.6 percent per year during the next four decades. In 1972, one-fourth of the flock mysteriously died. By fall 1985, the Aransas whoopers numbered 97, and about 40 lived in captivity, most in the Patuxent Wildlife Research Center in Laurel, Maryland. In 1986, 28 whoopers nested successfully in Canada, fledging 20 chicks.

Texas can boast the only breeding flock of whooping cranes, but hopefully not for long. With only marginal success at captive breeding at the Patuxent center, biologists decided to establish a second wild flock using sandhill cranes as foster parents. Since only one of the two eggs a whooper lays usually survives, one can be removed without adversely affecting the breeding flock. The smaller sandhill cranes will incubate the whooper egg and dutifully care for the adopted young. After six years of study, biologists chose the sandhills in Gray's Lake National Wildlife Refuge, Idaho, as the foster parents. The Idaho sandhills seemed well suited for the task since they had a relatively short migration route to Bosque del Apache National Wildlife Refuge in New Mexico, and most of their stopovers occurred on protected refuges. Biologists began transferring whooper eggs to the sandhills in 1975.

By 1986, the experimental flock had grown to 37. Biologists transferred 15 more eggs from Canada that year. Unfortunately no female whoopers have survived long enough to reach sexual maturity. Some males have begun establishing territories at Gray's Lake, but the younger females have shown no interest. Instead of spending the summer together where pairs could form, the flock has scattered over parts of Idaho, Montana, and Wyoming. In 1986, biologists captured three females in Wyoming and transferred them to Gray's Lake. It is hoped that they will form pairs with the males there. Banded birds in the Aransas flock began breeding after four or five years. With the Gray's Lake population steadily growing, biologists believe that it is only a matter of time before the flock will have enough mature individuals of both sexes to begin breeding and rearing young.

The success of the programs to save the whoopers results from the collective efforts and cooperation of many agencies within the U.S. and Canadian governments and the private sector. The plight of these noble birds captures the imagination of the public. In our urbanized society, the whooping crane has become the symbol of the wildness of nature that is so rapidly disappearing and, as Aldo Leopold stated, "the symbol of our untameable past."

Reptiles

The old western movie *The Good, the Bad, and the Ugly* could as easily have been made about reptiles as about outlaws. In which category you place these scaly creatures depends primarily on your culture and your time in history. With representatives of the nearly 6000 species of reptiles occurring on every continent except the frozen Antarctic, people have lived close to reptiles since the beginning of human history. Reptiles, particularly snakes, have played a dominant role throughout the ages in mythology, folklore, and superstitions. Various snake deities reportedly guarded the treasures of the Egyptians and the secrets of the Phoenicians, and taught astronomy to the Indians. The Bible and most of its adherents curse the snake as the tempter in the Garden of Eden and consider it the symbol of evil and suffering in the world. Conversely, the American Indians, from the pre-Columbian Toltecs, Aztecs, and Mayas with their feathered bird-serpent Quetzalcoatl, to the modern Hopis with their snake dance ceremonies, have viewed snakes as symbols of the deity. The Romans associated the snake with the god of healing, and even today the snake-coiled staff remains the internationally accepted symbol of the medical profession.

Six major groups of reptiles exist in the world today: lizards, snakes, crocodilians, turtles, the tuatara, and the amphisbaenians (not to be confused with the amphibians, a separate class of vertebrates). Reptiles thrive in every inhabitable environment on the earth. These adaptable animals live from just north of the Arctic Circle to within five degrees of the Antarctic Circle. The marine iguana in the Galapagos

Islands dines on seaweed beneath the ocean surface, while a lizard in Nepal scampers across rocks on 18,000-foot mountaintops. Reptiles thrive in inhospitable deserts, humid swamps and marshes, boreal, temperate, and tropical forests, scrublands, and prairies. They burrow through the soil, crawl legless across the ground, climb trees, cling to vertical surfaces, plod slowly along, race swiftly away, and swim in both salt and fresh waters.

Unlike birds with feathers and mammals with fur, reptiles have no single distinguishing characteristic. Scales, which provide a tough, waterproof shield, cover their bodies, but fish, birds, and some mammals also have scales. All reptiles are ectothermal, or cold-blooded, a misnomer since their blood is not cold. They cannot maintain a constant internal temperature like birds and mammals, but must depend on the environment to warm their bodies sufficiently for the chemistry of muscle action and digestion to function. Reptiles must seek shade to prevent overheating, and most prefer an 80-to-100-degree F range.

With approximately 3000 species, the lizards make up slightly more than half of the living species of reptiles. Though they typically have well-developed legs, a long tail, sharp teeth, ears, and keen eyes with eyelids, many species depart radically from this generic description. The bodily features of each species enable it to survive in a particular environment. The size and shape of its body, legs, and toes, the acuity of its sight, hearing, and other senses, and its diet, reproductive strategy, and behavioral habits match it to a specific niche and habitat. The toes of a gecko have pads with as many as one million microscopic bristles with suction cups. The specialized toes enable the gecko to climb vertical surfaces and even hang upside down to catch the insects it eats. Many lizards living in sand dunes have long, fringed toes to help them scurry across the loose sand. A lizard's long legs give it speed and also allow it to elevate its body off the hot desert sand and rocks. A following section describes the extreme modifications of the Texas horned lizard that uniquely adapt it to feed on its primary food, ants.

Every child, or adult, who has tried to catch a lizard has learned that most have tails that pop off if grabbed. The broken appendage wiggles violently, startling or confusing the attacker while the lizard scampers to safety. A special set of vertebrae, with a muscle to clamp off the blood flow, allows a lizard to sacrifice its tail without harm. Amazingly, the tail regenerates, though the new growth has no vertebrae and is never as long. Some lizards have other defenses equally as bizarre as a detachable tail. The horned lizard, besides having a spine-covered body, squirts blood from its eyes, a chuckwalla jams itself in a crevice by swelling up, and a chameleon changes colors. Most lizards depend on camouflage and speed for their defenses.

Perhaps no group of animals has aroused the imagination and ire of humans more than the serpents. Only in Ireland, New Zealand, and Greenland do people live free from the fear of snakebite. Unfortunately for the rest of the clan, numbering about 2700 species, the poisonous snakes have created such a bad public image that most people indiscriminately fear and kill all snakes, at least in the Western world. Many Asian cultures consider them a gourmet food item and an important pharmaceutical ingredient for medicines.

Snakes have adapted to a greater variety of environments than any other cold-blooded animal. Besides the terrestrial habitat, some live in the oceans and fresh waters, in trees, or underground. Beyond the remarkable adaptations in body shape and scale structure that enable some snakes to swim and others to climb or burrow, a snake's body represents an extreme example of specialization. When survival pressures began molding the lizard predecessors of snakes into slender, tube-shaped creatures that could hide in cracks and tunnel underground, a number of internal and external modifications were required. During 60 million years of underground existence, snakes lost their legs, a hindrance to burrowing creatures, as well as their ears and keen vision, unnecessary senses in a subterranean world. Developing a long, flexible body required extensive modifications of the spine, ribs, and skull. Some snakes have as many as 400 vertebrae with movable ribs. The tubular body also required a rearrangement of internal organs. One lung disappeared and the other elongated. The respiratory system, including a modified trachea, occupies three-quarters of the snake's length. Today only boa constrictors and sunbeam snakes have a functional left lung. Snakes have an elongated stomach and no bladder, with the other organs staggered through the body. These slender creatures store the food reserves necessary for reproduction and hibernation in special fat bodies in their tails.

Snakes have developed various methods to catch and subdue live prey, the diet of all serpents. A constrictor wraps itself around its victim and prevents it from breathing. These snakes suffocate, not crush, their prey. Venomous snakes have a special poison-delivery system to inject fast-acting toxins into animals. The poisons combine a complex mixture of modified digestive enzymes specialized to attack the blood, internal organs, and nervous system. Other snakes simply chase down and overpower their prey.

No reptile can chew its food into small pieces. For a snake to swallow a creature that may be two or three times its diameter requires extreme anatomical modifications. A highly specialized skull allows a snake to flex and rotate the two halves of its lower jawbone independently and pull its food inward with its backward-facing teeth. The lower jaw completely unhinges from the upper, and the neck and body skin stretches to allow a snake to swallow food. A reinforced windpipe prevents the snake from suffocating while engulfing large prey: a 25-foot captive python once swallowed a 74-pound goat in two hours. The astounding adaptations of snakes make them among the most biologically interesting creatures alive.

The third largest group of reptiles, the turtles, swim the open seas, rivers, and lakes, and trudge through the deserts, plains, and forests of the world. Turtles, with their unique body covering, have a radically different appearance from all other reptiles. Their shells provide protection, and in some species are hinged to close tightly. Contrary to folktales, a turtle cannot crawl out of its shell, which is fused to its backbone. The 250 species living today vary from fist-size box turtles to the giant land tortoises of the Galapagos Islands and eight-foot leatherback sea turtles. Scientists consider the land tortoises the most intelligent reptiles. Turtles live longer than any other vertebrate, with an American box turtle holding the record of 123 years.

The crocodilians, including alligators, crocodiles, caymans, and gavials, comprise another order of reptiles. These semi-aquatic creatures, with 29 species worldwide, thrive in the tropics and subtropics. The American alligator, described in a following section, has only one other member in its family, the Chinese alligator, while the gavial of India is in a family of its own. The other species belong to the crocodile family.

Crocodilians of all sizes, from the 4-foot dwarf species to the giants, come well equipped for both killing live food and defense. With sharp teeth and powerful jaws, designed for crushing and ripping bite-size chunks from dead prey, even small specimens can easily inflict serious injury. In general, crocodiles have a temperament that makes the American alligator gentle in comparison. The Nile crocodile of Africa and the saltwater crocodile of Asia reach 20 to 25 feet in length, weigh 2000 pounds, and have a disposition intolerant of people. These monsters habitually prey on humans and are greatly feared by people living in areas where they are abundant.

Two other groups of reptiles have few members and are rarely encountered. The amphisbaenians are snakelike creatures with no external ear openings; only a few members have visible limbs. The worm lizard, the only member in North America, lives in central Florida. This unusual subterranean animal has no eyes or legs and closely resembles an earthworm, one of its primary food items. Tiny scales cover its 12-inch body, and it has a lizardlike head. The last group of reptiles has one surviving member, the tuatara of New Zealand. This 2-foot lizardlike relic of antiquity has a bony cranial structure dating back to the beak-head reptiles of 150 million years ago. The tuatara, as well as some lizards, including the fence lizard of Texas, has a vestigial third eye on the forehead, complete with lens, cornea, retina, and nerve connections to the brain. The organ probably is sensitive to day length, which influences reproductive functions, and helps the animals regulate their exposure to the sun.

Reptiles were the first terrestrial vertebrates to develop after some ancient species of fishes left their watery home and evolved into amphibians. The key to the success of reptiles, the factor that propelled them beyond the dependence on water of their amphibian predecessors, was the development of an egg covered with a leathery, but porous, shell. No longer did reptiles have to return to the water to lay their eggs—they could bury them in the soil and let the earth and sun incubate them. Also, the embryo could develop fully in the protected egg and skip the larval, or tadpole, stage. Today some lizards and snakes keep the eggs inside their bodies until they hatch, giving birth to live offspring.

Fishes first adapted to life on dry land during the Devonian Period. Fossil remains of 400-million-year-old fish show unmistakable signs of lungs and thick, fleshy fins that would have allowed them to crawl from one pond to another. Today's walking catfish and lungfish use the same methods to survive droughts. Scientists consider the fossilized fishlike creatures to be links between fish and the first amphibians. The amphibians adapted to life on dry land, and some eventually evolved into reptilelike animals. By Permian time, 250 million years ago, fossils record a great abundance and variety of reptile forms. Reptiles dominated the landscape for the next 190 million years, to the close of the Cretaceous period: dinosaurs, varying from the size of cats to 90 feet in length, roamed the earth; pterodactyls, some with 40-foot wingspans, soared through the sky; while 50-

foot aquatic reptiles swam the depths of the oceans. Fossils record a line of reptiles that exhibit many mammalian characteristics and are considered predecessors to all living mammals. Another series of fossils reveals reptilelike creatures with feathers, representing the ancestors of today's birds, which still retain many reptilian features, including scales on their legs.

Paleontologists trace today's reptiles back through the fossil records to their ancestors in the past. Turtles are the old-timers of all reptiles. They saw the dinosaurs come and go, and today remain basically the same as they were 275 million years ago. The oldest lizard fossils date back to the Triassic period 190 million years ago. Snakes first appear in the fossil record about 135 million years ago.

Predation pressures from small, agile dinosaurs probably forced many lizards to live in rock cracks and crevices and to burrow underground, habitats that favored slender, flexible bodies. In a subterranean habitat, legs, eyelids, and ears were not as important as a tube-shaped body with the necessary internal organ modifications. The extreme restructuring of the lizard's body into the form of a snake indicates intense pressure either to change radically or to perish. Snakes adopted a completely subterranean lifestyle until about 65 million years ago, when a great extinction eradicated all large terrestrial, marine, and flying reptiles. The extinction theory currently supported with the most evidence proposes that a large meteor struck the earth and that the massive amount of particulate matter displaced into the atmosphere obscured the sun for a number of years. Without sunlight, plants and the animals that depended on them died. With the major predators gone, the snakes emerged and proliferated. At least one group of modern snakes retains evidence of their ancestral form. Boas and pythons have clawlike vestigial hind limbs on either side of their vent.

Texas, with its great environmental diversity, is well populated with reptiles. The state hosts about 110 species and subspecies of snakes (far more than any other state), sixty-one species and subspecies of lizards, and thirty-five species of turtles, as well as a healthy population of alligators. Unfortunately the taming of Texas, and the rest of the world, is having a tragic effect on reptiles. Habitat lost to farms, ranches, and cities and the use of insecticides and other poisons have placed 40 species of reptiles in the threatened and endangered classification. The official list of threatened and endangered wildlife, compiled by the Texas Parks and Wildlife Department, includes about 36 percent of the snake species, 11 percent of the lizards, and 28 percent of the turtles.

In the next seven sections, you will discover more about the poisonous snakes in the Lone Star State, where they live, and the latest medically approved methods for treating snakebite. You will learn the amazing adaptations of the strangest lizard in Texas, read about a 25-year effort to save a rare turtle, and find the success story of one reptile that was saved from the brink of extinction.

The Alligator:
Gator-Aid in Texas

American alligator
Alligator mississippiensis

Children pressed their noses against the restaurant windows and adults left their lunches to watch the spectacle. I felt like a Roman gladiator facing a hungry lion while the masses cheered, favoring the lion more than me. Right on cue, Charlie the alligator swam to the pond's edge, and waited with his head raised halfway out of the water and his mouth gaping menacingly. I unwrapped the chicken. The kids screamed "Jaws!" and the adults gasped when I tossed it a foot to the right of the gator's mouth. With a reflex born from millions of years of instinct, the ten-foot gator struck the food with lightning speed. With two crunches, Charlie's powerful jaws positioned the meal. Then he swallowed it whole and settled back into the water. The show wasn't long, but it satisfied the customers and sold hamburgers.

Alligators trace their ancestry back to the distant age of reptiles when flesh-eating creatures roared and roamed through the swamps. They have remained unchanged for 35 million years, sufficient time to tune their survival instincts to machinelike precision. A Port Arthur hunter who almost lost his retriever to an alligator called them "the meanest killing machines that crawl the face of the earth." To most people, they seem as threatening as the movie monsters that terrorize cities.

In times past, alligators reached 19 feet in length and slid into southern swamps by the millions. In the nineteenth century, hunters killed 25 million in Florida alone. Many considered these giant reptiles big game animals and searched the marshes for the largest trophies. Midway into the twentieth century, alligators had disappeared from most

175

of their range and, like the passenger pigeon, seemed doomed to extinction. Only about half a million had survived the 150 years of slaughter and habitat destruction. Today the American alligator ranges throughout swamps and marshes from the mouth of the Rio Grande to North Carolina. In Texas, most live in the coastal marshes, but a few survive along the river courses into Central Texas. About 15 find refuge in the Highland Lakes from Town Lake in Austin to Lake Buchanan.

These vanishing relics from prehistory received federal protection in 1967 under the Endangered Species Act. By 1980, the Texas population had grown to 68,000, numbering about 140,000 by 1985. Protected from their primary predator, humans, alligators increased rapidly until Texas, like Florida and Louisiana, classified them as threatened and allowed controlled harvesting. In 1985, Texas hunters killed 747 in a closely supervised hunt.

The rapid increase from near extinction to abundance shows us how well alligators are adapted for survival. These silent hunters patrol the waterways consuming fish, mammals, birds, and carrion; they catch floating animals by swimming underneath them, surfacing, and lashing sideways with jaws open. The mighty jaws, studded with teeth, can crunch a turtle like a boiled egg, snap bones like match sticks, and tear an animal into shreds. When the food is too large to swallow whole (alligators can't chew) they rip off a large chunk by biting down and violently jerking their head back and forth, like a shark.

Although alligators eat smaller creatures, many of these same animals depend on the large predator for their own survival. Marshes periodically dry up, and the many fish, amphibians, turtles, birds, and mammals dependent on water would perish if numerous small ponds did not exist. The lifesaving ponds are not just natural depressions, but "gator holes." Alligators use their mighty tails like bulldozers and thrash out a wildlife oasis 10 feet deep and 40 feet in diameter. Each gator has its private pool and a den that may reach

10 to 15 feet into a mud bank. Despite their reputation, alligators play an imperative role in the ecology of the marshes, and all wildlife suffers when they disappear.

Alligators survive by eating anything they can catch and, when food is scarce, by going long periods without food. Like all reptiles, an alligator's internal temperature depends on the surroundings. These ectothermic, or cold-blooded, animals require a water temperature of about 80 degrees F to warm them up enough for their digestive system to function. For years, the ten-foot gator at the hamburger restaurant ate 1, sometimes 2, chickens a week from late June through September, and nothing during the rest of the year. His yearly diet consisted of approximately 15 fryers, an amount of food easily obtained in his natural marshy habitat. In the winter, alligators retreat to their dens and hibernate. I could drag Charlie out of the frigid water by his tail to wash his pool, a feat that would have been suicide in the summer. Since the water in his pool never froze, Charlie easily survived the Austin winters, even when the air temperature dropped well below freezing.

After reaching several feet in length, alligators have little to fear from other animals. The reptile's large size, sharp teeth, and powerful jaws persuade neighbors to avoid any confrontation. With no enemies and an easily satisfied diet, alligators have thrived in the southern United States for countless millennia. Another adaptation for survival, the ability to produce many offspring, has enabled their population to rebound after reaching the dangerously low numbers of recent times. In the spring, the throaty bellow of the male echoes through the marshes like a car with a rusty muffler. A bull alligator fiercely repels intruding males from the female, and violent battles may churn a tranquil bayou into a bloody froth.

The female constructs a nest mound of mud, sticks, and vegetation three feet high and ten feet wide. She lays from 30 to 60 hen-size eggs and covers them with more vegetation, which keeps the eggs warm as it decomposes. Unlike most reptiles that abandon their eggs, the mother alligator dutifully guards the nest during the nine or so weeks of incubation. When the eggs begin hatching in late August and early September, the babies make noises that tell the mother to dig them up. Sometimes the mother even takes the babies to water in her mouth. She protects her young for several months, but most fall prey to raccoons, herons, gar, and other alligators, which find the eight-inch babies tasty morsels.

Young alligators eat tadpoles, minnows, crayfish, insects, and other small animals. I once had an 18-inch gator that I hand-fed minnows, which it grabbed with the typical sideways lashing attack with its head. After a few nasty encounters with its sharp teeth, I decided it could catch its own fish in the small pool that was its temporary home. Alligators grow about a foot a year for their first six to ten years, then about an inch a year. Most gators in the wild today measure between 6 and 10 feet and weigh 100 to 200 pounds. A 12-foot gator could weigh as much as 450 pounds. Even with today's limited hunting, an alligator will probably never reach the 20-foot size of the creatures that glided through the swamps of the past.

People boating or swimming generally react with fear at the sight of a nearby alligator in the water. Though retiring by nature, any alligator represents a potential threat, whether on the land, in shallows, or in deep water. An alligator attacks by thrashing sideways, and any person or animal within striking range, about half the length of its body, cannot move fast enough to escape the jaws or tail. The powerful animal uses its tail like a bludgeon, and it can whip it sideways with enough speed and force to break a leg. Alligators appear docile and sluggish, but if the occasion arises, they can run as fast as a human for short distances. Wild alligators, however, seldom will attack a human, unless cornered. Their reptilian brain may lack intelligence, but they are smart enough to recognize a threat. Gators usually avoid any animal as large as a human. I have seen fishermen standing in shallow lakes in Florida with alligators only a few yards away, each ignoring the other. Injuries sometimes do occur when people feed alligators regularly, and the animals lose their fear of humans. An alligator accustomed to eating food thrown from the water's edge is expecting a meal when a person or pet jumps into the water.

In 1979, a University of Texas student illegally collected alligator eggs from an area on the Texas coast destined for development, hatched them in his apartment, and released 316 in the lakes around Austin. Despite the media hysteria (with headlines such as "Guess Who's Coming to Dinner—You!") alligators did not eventually infest the lakes. Raccoons, birds, and gar probably ate most, if not all, of the hatchlings. An 18-inch gator did appear on an Austin newspaper columnist's desk, which caused quite a commotion in the newsroom, but it was too large to have come from the clandestine eggs. A few adult alligators do live in the Highland Lakes, but they rarely are seen.

Alligators and their ancestors have a 200-million year legacy in Texas. In the distant past, when West Texas was a swampy marsh, giant alligators basked in the sun and slithered into the tepid waters. Archaeologists in Big Bend National Park unearthed the 6-foot fossil skull of a gator that would dwarf today's critters: the prehistoric creature measured at least 45 feet long. Alligators have survived massive loss of habitat by planetwide climatic changes, advancing and receding oceans, and ice ages. Though human hunters and developers nearly drove these adaptable reptiles to extinction, the future of the alligator now seems secure, thanks to the efforts of conservation groups and the protection of state and federal agencies.

The Copperhead:
The Reclusive Viper

Southern copperhead
*Agkistrodon contortrix
contortrix*
Broad-banded copperhead
A. C. laticinctus
Trans-Pecos copperhead
A. C. pictigaster

If snakes could talk, I know one copperhead that would
have yelled, "Hey, watch your step, lady!" Our group had
hiked deep into the Big Thicket for several hours when one
lady stepped right on the middle of the perfectly camouflaged snake. She screamed and jumped straight into the
air, and the snake slowly squirmed away, unharmed. When
we all gathered around for the most exciting sight of the
day, the aroused serpent coiled in its defensive position and
vibrated its tail. In the loose leaves, the buzz sounded an
unmistakable warning, like that of a rattler. A few feet away
by a rotting log lay another copperhead, silently observing
the predicament of its companion. Thanks to the unaggressive temperament of these retiring serpents, no one was bitten that day.

A high school buddy of mine was less fortunate. While
in the woods, he saw a colorful piece of rope on the ground
and reached down to pick it up. Suddenly the rope came
alive and bit him on the thumb. The mottled white and
brown pattern of a copperhead conceals it so well that it becomes almost invisible on the leaf-littered forest floor. The
bite my friend received was frightening and painful, though
not serious, but he almost lost his hand from the tourniquet
his terrified friends wrapped around his wrist.

Despite their venomous threat, copperheads are one of
the most beautiful snakes in North America. Bands of rich

golden tan, the color of fallen oak leaves or pine needles, alternate with beige to off-white bands. The combination of rich earth colors and lighter markings camouflages the snake perfectly in the dappled shadows of its woodland environment. Its variegated pattern and the habit of lying motionless instead of slithering away when threatened are a copperhead's best defense, and offense. The cryptic coloration enables the snake to remain undetected when danger approaches, or while waiting for prey to come within striking range.

In East Texas, where they are the most common venomous snakes, copperheads inflict the majority of poisonous bites, yet fatalities seldom occur regardless of treatment. A copperhead's venom has only 66 percent of the lethal potency of a western diamondback rattlesnake's, and 33 percent of the blood-destroying capacity. With fangs less than $5/16$ inch long, copperheads usually inject their poison into the skin layer, not the deeper tissues and muscles. A bite from a large copperhead can deliver only about 10 to 15 percent of the poison necessary to kill an adult human; however, the snake sometimes strikes repeatedly. A bitten hand or arm may swell to twice its size, and severe poisonings may cause loss of digits or limb. Most permanent injuries from copperhead bites result from ill-advised tourniquets and the cut-and-suck treatment instead of from the effects of the venom.

The three subspecies of copperheads in Texas favor riparian woodlands with a dense leaf litter. The southern copperhead of the eastern third of Texas and the southern states lives primarily in pine and deciduous forests. It is especially abundant in wet, low-lying areas, and may reach densities of six to seven per acre in rich environments. The broad-banded population extends approximately from Dallas south to Victoria and west to Del Rio and Abilene, and northward to Kansas. This snake favors post oak woodlands with a sandy soil covered with leaves, and the oak and juniper savannahs and rocky ledges of the Edwards Plateau.

The Trans-Pecos copperhead, the rarest of the three, lives near permanent water in the desert, usually in association with cottonwood or tamarisk trees, though it has been seen in the shrub desert miles away from water.

The optimum body temperature for a copperhead is between 70 and 80 degrees F, which it regulates by basking in the sun when the air temperature is cool, and avoiding the heat of the day in the summer. A copperhead caught out during a torrid West Texas day could easily exceed the fatal body temperature of 104 degrees. In the spring and fall, they hunt at dawn and dusk, emerging later in the evening as the summer temperature increases.

With excellent night vision for a snake, heat-sensing facial pits, and a sophisticated venom, copperheads are superbly adapted for hunting small animals in the dark. These opportunistic feeders mainly catch white-footed, harvest, and deer mice, but in the late summer they often gorge on cicada nymphs. Insects comprise about 20 percent of their annual diet. Lizards, small snakes, frogs, toads, and skinks also find their way onto the copperhead's varied menu.

Unlike snakes that stalk or chase their prey, copperheads ambush their victims. These sluggish 20-to-30-inch snakes expect curb service and lie in wait on an animal trail until their food comes to them. Their expenditure of energy for an evening's meal might be as little as a 5-inch strike. With their acute smell, they sometimes find the nests of mice and ground nesting birds.

The juveniles use another technique to find food. Copperheads naturally lie perfectly still so their camouflaged coloration hides them. The young hold the bright yellow tip of their tail straight up and slowly wave it back and forth. Frogs and other small critters mistake the tail for a meal, and become the meal themselves. Whether the snake intentionally waves its tail as a lure or it is a nervous response to waiting for the strike is undetermined, but the ploy works. Young water moccasins use their tail as a lure in the same manner.

With stout bodies adapted to a sedentary life, copperheads seldom wander far. In a rich environment, females may spend their entire life within 1 or 2 acres, while males range through 8 to 25 acres. A group of marked young in a North Texas study plot strayed less than 100 yards during the first year. Occasionally these terrestrial snakes crawl into grapevine-covered trees to avoid high water and to search for food. During the spring and fall mating seasons, the males often abandon their nocturnal habits and search for females during the day.

Most females reproduce every other year because of the time required to store the necessary fat reserves. From 5 to 14 young are born alive from late July to September and early October. The seven-to-ten-inch babies begin life with a full load of venom and aggressively strike at any disturbance, which undoubtedly saves many from hungry predators. Moles reportedly burrow underneath the young and snatch them from below, while skunks, opossums, and larger snakes search through the leaf litter for the morsel-size tidbits. Adult copperheads have fewer foes, though hogs, with a thick skin and layer of fat, devour them with impunity. Birds of prey probably seldom pounce on the well-hidden snakes, yet a great horned owl did attack one in a herpetologist's outdoor pen. In an unusual outcome, the snake killed the owl.

Copperheads often live in wooded suburban areas, especially in East Texas. They survive in overgrown vacant lots, in brush piles, and along creeks until they are discovered and killed, or their habitat is cleared. Southern copperheads were the most common land snake I saw while growing up in a wooded area north of Beaumont, and I can recall many encounters with the colorfully banded snakes. A particularly favorable microhabitat, such as a good winter den, a well-suited basking area, or a location with abundant food, may attract a number of snakes, including copperheads. Two stacks of corrugated iron siding at an abandoned farm in North Texas sheltered a dozen broad-banded copperheads.

Most snakebites occur not in the wilds of nature but in backyards of homes in the most populous cities in the state. Children and teenagers, the largest group of victims, receive 46 percent of the bites. You can go a long way toward preventing snakes from living in your yard by removing piles of lumber, brush, rocks, and rubbish that might harbor both the serpents and the rodents they eat. Clearing dense vegetation eliminates cover and hiding places for snakes. These precautionary steps provide much better protection than the chemical snake repellents on the market. Most are either completely ineffective or too toxic to be used around children and pets, or where runoff would pollute streams and lakes.

The Coral Snake: "Red Touch Yellow, Kill a Fellow"

Coral snake
Micrurus fulvius tenere

Most of the phone questions I received during my tenure with the Austin Nature Center concerned snakes, and "What kind of snake is this?" was the most common. One person wanted to know how to identify a coral snake. I quoted the rhyme learned in my childhood, "Red touch yellow, kill a fellow," referring to the arrangement of the snake's stripes. Before I could finish with "Red touch black, venom lack," the caller sympathetically replied, "Oh, I'm so sorry the fellow died!"

I remember the first coral snake I saw, in the woods along Armand's Bayou near Houston. Fascinated, I followed the snake crawling nonchalantly through the thick leaf litter, and repeated "Red touch yellow, kill a fellow" like a child trying to memorize a lesson. Finally, just as the beautiful but deadly creature disappeared under a rotten log, I was convinced my eyes weren't deceiving me.

Though common throughout the eastern two-thirds of the state, from Dallas to Brownsville and west to the Pecos River, coral snakes seldom come to our attention. These gaily patterned serpents prefer to hide their vibrant colors in woodlands with thick leaf litter and in areas with abundant outcroppings of rocks. They live in the rocky streambeds of Central Texas, chaparral thickets of South Texas, the Cross Timbers woodlands, and East Texas Piney Woods. Thick terrestrial cover provides both a hiding place for the snake and the habitat for their reptilian prey.

Given the proper cover, coral snakes coexist contentedly in suburban settings, particularly in parks and wooded areas. They venture forth in the morning and evening searching for their favorite food: other snakes. Once, on the

187

sidewalk of an Austin park, I found one that had swallowed all but the last four inches of a rat snake. Other reptiles in their diet include rough green, earth, and flat head snakes, as well as other corals and an occasional skink.

A coral snake kills its prey with the most potent venom of any North American serpent. It is about eight times more toxic than western diamondback rattlesnake venom, and it equals that of most cobras. Between 5 and 10 milligrams will kill an adult. The snake's poison attacks the central nervous system, unlike pit viper venom, which is composed primarily of digestive enzymes that destroy tissue. The prey of a coral snake dies from respiratory and cardiac failure. With small creatures, death is rapid so the snake can consume its victim, but with humans fatal symptoms may take hours to develop. One teenager appeared unaffected by a bite, but died six hours later.

A San Antonio zookeeper bitten just momentarily on the back of his hand experienced immediate intense pain, which lasted for 24 hours. He was treated with antivenin and remained in intensive care for three days but recovered fully. He suffered none of the muscle damage and extended period of weakness usually associated with pit viper bites. Because of the sudden and sometimes delayed failure of the central nervous system, doctors recommend administering the venom antidote immediately, whether or not symptoms occur. If bitten, wrap an elastic band between the bite and heart, splint the limb, and seek immediate medical attention. Fortunately less than 40 percent of coral snake bites result in serious poisoning, partly because of the snake's tiny fangs.

A coral snake seldom strikes unless provoked, and practically all bites occur to people handling a snake. Though some corals allow repeated handling without biting, most will strike immediately if treated roughly. These serpents do not have the long, hollow hypodermic fangs of rattlesnakes and other pit vipers: the poison flows down narrow grooves on the front surface of their $1/8$-inch fangs. A membrane covers the peglike fang providing a closed passageway for the flow of venom.

The choice of prey, behavior of the snake, and potency of its venom are all interrelated. A coral snake's lethal venom enables it to dine on snakes that it otherwise could not subdue and kill. Since snakes cannot chew, they must attack prey small enough to swallow whole; and since they eat freshly killed animals, they must rapidly dispatch their victims. Unlike a rattler, which strikes, injects its venom, and withdraws instantly, coral snakes usually bite and hold their prey tenaciously—thus, the scientific name *tenere*. The biting grip enables as much poison as possible to trickle into the victim. A test bite on the finger of a welding glove showed numerous scratches from the twisting, biting action of the snake.

Scientists have long speculated about the advantages of a coral snake's brilliant colors. One popular theory proposes that the bright colors and distinctive bands warn other animals of the snake's venomous defense. Similar warning coloration has been demonstrated in other animals, such as wasps. To learn to recognize the colors as a warning requires a predator to attack the snake, get bitten, and survive the ill results. A predator can learn to avoid animals having mild venom, but not those whose bite kills outright. If the attackers never survive, no learning takes place and the bright colors cannot serve as a warning.

Another theory suggests that the bright colors actually camouflage the snake. In moonlight red appears gray, and the bands look like mottled shadows. Coral snakes, nonetheless, forage primarily during the day, not night, so they would be glaringly apparent to animals that could discern colors. However, most of the mammals that kill and eat snakes—armadillos, opossums, moles, and raccoons are color blind, so the colorful pattern may in fact help them blend in with their environment.

The harmless milk and scarlet snakes, which also have a combination of red, yellow, or black bands, traditionally have been considered to mimic the deadly coral snake. Supposedly animals would mistake them for the coral snake and leave them alone. But tests show that snake-eating animals rarely have any inhibitions about attacking corals, supporting the idea that the colors do not act as warning beacons. More likely, these species independently developed the patterns and colors because they helped camouflage them from color-blind predators.

An alternate theory speculates that coral snakes themselves mimic less toxic snakes, ones predators could learn to avoid without being killed. Most of the more than 30 species of coral snakes occur in the tropics, and some are less virulent than our species. In the distant past, ancestors of the North American species might have lived farther south, where they could mimic less poisonous relatives, and then gradually expanded their range to the present distribution.

Regardless of the evolutionary reason, coral snakes are one of the most colorful and easily recognized snakes in Texas. Narrow canary yellow bands separate the broad jet black and red bands that encircle their bodies. The red bands usually have mottled black spots giving a dusty appearance. The similarly colored milk snake has red, yellow, and black bands, but only the coral snake has yellow touching the red—hence the often repeated rhyme. Additionally, only the coral snake has bands that completely encircle its body.

A coral snake's head and tail are colored identically. Both have a black tip followed by a series of yellow and black bands. When in danger, the coral snake frequently uses its tail as a threat to frighten predators. It covers its head with its foreparts, sticks up its tail in a menacing fashion, and snaps it forward simulating a strike. This posturing both protects the snake's head from attack and apparently deters the aggressor. Tests show that many animals retreat when they see the tail waving.

While most people think of coral snakes as small serpents, the adult females average about 26 inches and the males 24 inches. The record, ¼ inch shy of 4 feet, was captured in Brazoria County in 1958. Most of the large corals are females. They lay between three and five leathery white eggs from May through July. The 6-to-7-inch, pale-colored babies hatch about the size of earthworms. Within one week, the young shed and sport the brilliant colors they will wear for the rest of their lives.

The Cottonmouth: Beware the Gaper

Western cottonmouth, water moccasin
Agkistrodon piscivorus leucostoma

Just as West Texas has its legends of giant rattlesnakes, East Texas abounds with stories about the cottonmouth, or water moccasin. The sight of this serpent strikes fear in the hearts of outdoor adventurers throughout the eastern half of the state. Most hunters in the Piney Woods and coastal marshes and recreationists on the region's many lakes have personal tales of their experiences with this fearsome reptile.

The large-bodied, dark-colored water moccasin only partially deserves its reputation as a belligerent snake. Most would rather avoid people than fight, but like any cornered animal, it will defend itself to the death. A cottonmouth threatens by holding back its head and opening its mouth wide with fangs erect. The gaping posture and the white interior of its mouth give it the common names "cottonmouth" and "gaper" and the scientific name meaning "forward-fanged, fish-eating, white-mouthed serpent."

Water moccasins usually hunt at night and eat frogs, minnows, tadpoles, and other aquatic creatures, as well as a variety of terrestrial animals. They kill small mammals with their venom and often have to track down and find the dying animal. The aquatic habitat and hunting behavior of the water moccasin have engendered a number of popular folktales. Since moccasins are accustomed to feeding on freshly killed animals, a stringer of fish looks like an easy dinner. Night fishermen always advise, "Never shine your light on a water moccasin or it will crawl right into your boat!" So what do you do if you see one? Do you turn off your light and wonder where the poisonous creature is? I never met a fisherman content with letting a moccasin swim around his boat in the dark.

Every boater in the state has heard the folktale about the

agonizing death of the water skier who fell into a nest of water moccasins. The snakes attacked him with a fury, and with more bites than could be counted, he died before reaching the hospital. The story changes little through the decades, yet such an incident has never been documented by newspapers or medical records. According to another common myth, water skiers are perfectly safe because the snake cannot open its mouth underwater to bite or it will drown. Tell that to the fish that water moccasins voraciously consume.

The story of the attacked water skier may have been born when someone saw several snakes along a lakeshore. Locations with abundant food, such as shallows where small fish cannot escape, attract water snakes, and all of the 12 species of nonpoisonous aquatic snakes in Texas are considered cottonmouths by most people. Water-filled depressions in a creek bed or rocky lakeshore provide a natural refuge for aquatic critters, including snakes. I once saw five snakes, none poisonous, in a three-foot pothole when the Pedernales River was running low. Snakes may congregate at a favorable spot, but they do not "nest" in mass like some birds and herding animals.

Despite their name, water moccasins are only semi-aquatic, and may forage a half-mile from water, hunting in fields and woodlands for rabbits and rodents. Like other pit vipers, they have heat-sensing organs located in a tiny pit on either side of their nose to help them accurately strike warm-blooded prey. A high-speed film of a moccasin striking a mouse revealed that the fangs were in the animal's body only $\frac{1}{50}$ second, and the snake could adjust the angle of each fang independently while striking. When hunting cold-blooded fish and amphibians in murky water, cottonmouths strike blindly at any ripple or movement. Research showed that fish and amphibians comprise one-third to one-half of the snake's diet, with reptiles making up nearly one-third and birds and mammals one-third. Cottonmouths readily devour other snakes, even poisonous ones. This preference may explain why other water snakes are rare in areas with an abundant population of moccasins.

Most moccasins display little fear of humans, but although they gape and display fearlessly, few people are bitten. Less than 7 percent of the hospitalizations from snakebite in Texas result from the water moccasin. I can attest to their reluctance to bite. As a junior high student, I stepped on one in the schoolyard without the snake striking. I once sat within a foot of one, water skied over one, and, following eight other hikers along a trail, stepped over one coiled among tree roots. Cottonmouths not only show less of a propensity to strike than rattlesnakes, but their venom is about 30 percent less toxic than the western diamondback's. Though they can inflict debilitating and permanent muscle damage, less than one person a year in the United States dies from being bitten.

An adult cottonmouth has a grayish black back with often indistinct crossbands, which makes them difficult to distinguish from the nonpoisonous blotched, yellowbelly, and diamondback water snakes. The large, triangular, flat-crowned head with vertical cat-eyed pupils provides the best field mark for the cottonmouth; however, you may prefer leaving a close inspection of a live snake's eyes to a snake charmer. No other aquatic snake vibrates its tail and gapes motionlessly when threatened on land. In the water, a cottonmouth swims with its body on the surface, while other water snakes generally swim with only their heads above water. Juvenile water moccasins have a distinct pattern of crossbands and a yellow-tipped tail. Their tail acts as a lure to trick minnows and frogs. A minnow sees the flicking tail and, thinking it is a juicy worm, rushes not to its dinner but the snake's.

Between August and October, the female cottonmouth gives birth to 3 to 12 live babies. The 7-to-11-inch young must fend for themselves immediately, and avoid being eaten by other snakes, birds, and largemouth bass. By November, the moccasins begin denning up for the winter, choosing rocky slopes in the western part of their range and crayfish and rodent holes along the coast. They hibernate until March or April, although they often emerge on warm days. Cottonmouths and their close relatives, the copperheads, are some of the first snakes to become active in the spring.

In Texas, the western cottonmouth ranges west to San Angelo, south to Corpus Christi, and north to Wichita Falls. It has a patchy distribution on the western edge of its range, being rare on the Highland Lakes of the Colorado River, and absent along the Brazos River around Waco. On the Edwards Plateau and in North Texas, they live in woodlands along river bottoms and lakes. Water moccasins do not occur in South Texas, the Panhandle, and the Trans-Pecos. Their range extends east along the Gulf Coast to Alabama and north to southern Missouri.

When food is abundant, cottonmouths thrive in large numbers, especially along sloughs, bayous, and irrigation canals in the Coastal Plains. One observer near Corpus Christi recorded 30 moccasins in 250 yards. As a boy growing up in Beaumont, I considered hunting moccasins along rice canals a great sport. The thick-bodied snakes would stretch out on willow limbs a few feet above the water. The challenge was to sneak up close enough for a shot before the snake dropped into the water. Sometimes the snakes basked in the sun on the levee and dashed for the water straight toward me, which only added to the excitement.

I now find pleasure in admiring the creatures I once shot, both for their important ecological role and for their value as fellow inhabitants of this planet who have a right to live their own lives. Many people disagree and place a value on animals, and all of nature, relative only to their needs and likes. Whether this self-centered view of life is an artifact of our consumer-oriented society or a survival instinct is irrelevant. Though in certain situations hunting benefits an animal population or is necessary for human safety, the same viewpoint that justifies the needless killing of animals for personal pleasure also pollutes the air, poisons the rivers, and decimates the forests for personal profit. At some point humans must learn to act responsibly toward the rest of creation. Otherwise, we will exhaust our resources and eventually suffer the same fate as the thousands of species we will drive to extinction by the year 2000.

The Horned Lizard: The Strangest Lizard in Texas

Texas horned lizard
Phrynosoma cornutum
Mountain short-horned lizard
Phrynosoma douglassi hernandesi
Bleached horned lizard
Phrynosoma modesrum

In 1897, workers constructing a new courthouse in Eastland County carefully sealed Old Rip in the cornerstone. The courthouse and its unwilling tenant remained in place for 31 years before a demolition crew began tearing down the old building. A curious crowd gathered as the workers reached the cornerstone. What had happened to Old Rip during the intervening years? Nobody took bets that he would be alive. Yet when workers removed the final stone, Old Rip looked up and blinked at the first sunlight he had seen in more than three decades. To the astonishment of the unbelieving audience, the bizarre lizard scampered away! Presumably it had hibernated all those years within the cool confines of its rocky enclosure.

Old Rip became the first horned lizard in the world to become nationally famous. Of course, many doubters considered the lizard a hoax, but witnesses testified to the authenticity of the event. Unfortunately Old Rip's fame and publicity were short lived. The illustrious lizard died within a year of being liberated from his stone prison. The remains of this celebrated reptile lie in state in a glass-fronted coffin in the Eastland County courthouse. Public viewing is welcomed.

Without a doubt, horned lizards are one of the most unusual animals to scamper beneath our feet. Their heads sport a crown of horns, and rows of prickly spines line their sides. The thorny growth covers the entire upper surface of their prehistoric-looking bodies. Instead of being long and slender like most lizards, they have squat, saucer-shaped bodies. Confused by their flat body, many people call these strange-looking creatures horny toads. The confusion is particularly acute in Fort Worth, where students of Texas Christian University adopted the animal as their mascot but insist on calling it a horned frog.

Horned lizards live in a world far removed from the aquatic habitat of frogs and toads. They like hot and dry places, which makes most of Texas ideal. Three species live in the state, mostly west of Houston and Dallas. At one time these novelties were common, but today they have disappeared from much of their range. I've talked to old-timers who said they once could buy them for a nickel apiece and use them for fish bait, although I can't imagine a fish striking such a ball of thorns. Some suffered from the curiosity of inquisitive children who captured them and kept them in a box. Usually the lizards outlived the interest of their young captors, who eventually returned them to the wild.

Before laws afforded them protection in 1967, pet dealers and pesticides posed the greatest threat to these slow-moving miniature dinosaurs. The widespread use of poisons killed their primary food source, ants, and animal merchants scooped them up by the bushel to ship all over the country. The transported lizards suffered the same fate as Old Rip once he was placed on display. Horned lizards cannot live very long in the temperatures we humans consider comfortable. If you kept your house above 90 degrees F, horned lizards would feel right at home.

Horned lizards, like all reptiles, depend on the sun to warm them sufficiently so their metabolic processes will work. Until they soak up enough heat, these sluggish creatures cannot convert food to energy for muscular action. Even if they are force fed, the chemistry of their digestive system does not function. At room temperature, horned lizards languish away, too warm to hibernate and too cold to eat.

Each species of animal, or plant for that matter, has an optimum set of environmental conditions under which it survives the best. The creature's behavior, color, size, and diet influence its ability to survive in its particular habitat. The optimum conditions for an animal are like trumps to a bridge player; more trumps in a hand, or habitat, mean a better chance to win, or survive and produce the next generation.

Ants are the ace of environmental trumps for horned lizards. Few other animals dine on ants, probably because they have so little nutritional content. So horned lizards have practically no competition for food, which is like having the only key to the supermarket. Specializing in ants has influenced every aspect of the horned lizard's life. It must eat vast quantities of the little morsels to get enough calories and protein to survive. To hold a sufficient meal requires a large stomach, so large that its body must be round instead of tube shaped. Horned lizards have the largest stomach of any lizard living in a similar environment.

Catching ants does not require rapid movements, a fortunate coincidence since the lizard's tanklike body design could never win a race. But sacrificing speed means sacrificing one of the best defenses most lizards have for escaping enemies. These cumbersome lizards had to develop an alternate defense. Stickers provide ample protection for cacti, so why not lizards too? Their thorn-covered bodies protect the lizards from most snakes, birds, and other predators.

When threatened, these little pincushions exhibit a temperament befitting their ferocious appearance. They arch their back, jump forward, and hiss. If the bluff fails, and the predator grabs the little animal, it discovers that horned lizards know how to use their barbed headgear. The lizard twists and jerks its head around to impale its horns in the foe and, when it can, bites and holds tightly.

Besides a studded coat of armor, horned lizards use the most successful defense in the animal world: camouflage. They can lighten and darken their colors and dappled pattern to match the soil and rocks of their environment. Cryptic coloration hides an animal only if the creature remains still, because predators easily detect movement. Horned lizards lie so flat that they cast no shadow and seem to disappear in the sand. They refuse to move until almost stepped on, then they scamper off to hide again.

If camouflage is unsuccessful and sharp horns fail to discourage aggressors, horned lizards have an unconventional weapon in reserve. When the lizards become alarmed, the blood pressure rises in their heads. Sometimes the pressure builds up enough to rupture the capillaries in the corners of the animals' eyes, and a fine stream of blood squirts out for several feet. The lizards suffer no ill effects from the episode, and the spray often deters the predators.

Lying in the sun all day eating ants or hiding in the sand would spell doom for most lizards, but the remarkable horned lizards can withstand internal temperatures that would fry most reptiles. They have the widest tolerance for high body temperatures of any lizards living in a similar environment. The ability to remain active over a broad range of temperatures gives them time to find ant beds, which may be widely scattered throughout the area.

The horned lizard's specialized diet affects its body size, defensive strategy, and even its reproduction. While most lizards lay only a few eggs, the broad body of a horned lizard enables it to carry from 25 to 35 eggs. Such a mass would slow down fleet-footed lizards, making them vulnerable to predators; however, the added weight presents no problems to slow-moving horned lizards.

The forces of natural selection have dealt the horned lizard a hand that is hard to beat. Its unique set of adaptations enables it to survive in specialized habitats in torrid desert basins and on 9000-foot mountain slopes. The 27 species in the genus live from Guatemala to Canada, from California to Texas. Whenever you see a horned lizard, remember that these little reptiles represent the versatile and creative power in nature.

The Rattlesnake:
The Rattle of Danger

Western diamondback
Crotalus atrox
Prairie rattlesnake
C. viridis viridis
Timber rattlesnake
C. horridus
Northern black-tailed rattlesnake
C. molossus molossus
Mojave rattlesnake
C. scutulatus scutulatus
Mottled rock rattlesnake
C. lepidus lepidus
Banded rock rattlesnake
C. lepidus klauberi
Western massasauga
S. catenatus tergeminus
Desert massasauga
S. catenatus edwardsii
Western pigmy rattlesnake
S. miliarius streckeri

Once, as a child traveling through West Texas, I was capti-
vated by a stuffed rattlesnake at a roadside service station.
Coiled and ready to strike, the snake looked just like the
pictures I had seen of the deadly serpents. I inched closer to
investigate until my nose was within a foot of the angry-
looking critter. Suddenly, the snake came to life with the
loudest rattling I had ever heard. I fell backward in surprise
and terror, amid peals of laughter. To the delight of the lo-
cals who frequented the store, the owner had pushed a button activating a raucous buzzer under the snake. The trick,

probably repeated several times daily, was undoubtedly the most exciting thing happening in the entire county.

No other animal in Texas inspires as much fear, hate, and tall tales as the rattlesnake. The dread of snakebite is as much a part of growing up as sandstorms in West Texas, mesquite thorns in South Texas, and mosquitoes in East Texas. Texans have ten species of rattlesnakes to avoid, from the ill-tempered western diamondback to the diminutive pigmy rattler. The diamondback claims the western two-thirds of the state as its own, sharing portions with the Mojave, black-tailed, mottled, and banded rock rattlers, and the western and desert massasaugas. Timber and pigmy rattlers inhabit East Texas and prairie rattlers the Panhandle. Only a few counties in extreme East Texas and the Panhandle and some heavily farmed counties have no rattlesnakes.

The size of the western diamondback and the amount of venom it can deliver make it one of the most dangerous snakes in the world. Fortunately for humans, a majority of rattlers would rather flee than fight, attacking only when escape seems impossible. They depend on retreat and concealment by camouflage as their best defenses. If discovered, their rattle warns the unwary to move away. This strategy worked well with bison and other large herbivores, but in modern times it has put the snake at a disadvantage. The taming of the West brought with it the universally accepted law of killing all rattlers, a general rule usually interpreted to include all snakes. Rattlesnakes less inclined to rattle seem to be more adapted for surviving in today's world.

Rattlesnakes belong to the pit viper family, a group of snakes including copperheads and water moccasins that have a unique set of sense organs. These snakes have pits on either side of their nostrils containing a high concentration of extremely sensitive heat receptors. The ability to "see" the body heat of warm-blooded creatures enables pit vipers to hunt effectively at night. Like a heat-sensing missile, they seek out their prey and strike with deadly accuracy.

A snake has no ears or ear openings, a benefit to an animal that crawls and burrows in the ground. Although deaf, these creatures can sense the ground vibrations of approaching large animals, such as humans. Keen vision is another sense sacrificed by a snake's ancestral burrowing lifestyle. With hearing and sight of little value to a snake, smell has become its most vital sense. Scent is so important that snakes, and some lizards, have a pair of extremely sensitive sensory organs in the roofs of their mouths to help them find the live food that they eat. A snake flicks out its forked tongue to pick up airborne chemical molecules and transfer them to the receptors, called Jacobson's organs. Since their other senses are so limited, snakes use these organs as their primary contact with the world, as evidenced by their constant tongue flicking. A male snake also uses its nose to follow the pheromone, or scent, trail of a female ready to mate, and a poisonous snake uses smell to track prey that scamper a few yards away before dying.

Unlike nonpoisonous snakes that depend on speed to catch their prey, the heavier-bodied rattlers lie in wait and use venom to kill the rodents and other small mammals they eat. After killing the animal, the primary function of the venom is to begin the digestive process from the inside out. Most of the toxic components contribute to breaking down tissue and muscle, allowing the snake to assimilate the food rapidly. In human poisoning, the digestive toxins may cause serious internal hemorrhaging and swelling. With deep fang penetration, extensive muscle damage can result in impairment or loss of limb.

Snake venom is a complex fluid containing 12 to 30 peptides and enzymes. Some destroy blood, others begin digesting tissue, and others attack the nervous system. Some components attack particular organs, and others break down tissue to increase the effectiveness of other components. The Mojave rattler, with more neurotoxin in its venom than the diamondback, has the most deadly venom of any rattler in the state. Venom immediately combines metabolically with the surrounding tissue, making removal by suction impossible. Tourniquets, which have caused more injury and loss of limbs than snakebites, prevent the spread of toxins, but without life-giving blood, the cells in a limb will die in 30 to 40 minutes. Once a limb dies, it must be amputated.

Rattlesnakes play an important, though often over-looked, role in controlling rodents and rabbits on the range. As the rodent population increases, the numbers of snakes and other rodent-eating predators increase proportionally. Without the predators to keep the rodents in check, rats, mice, and rabbits would soon overrun the range. The government spends millions of dollars annually in Texas fighting rodents, which inflict heavy economic losses on ranchers and farmers, yet nature provides the best and least expensive form of vermin control.

As night falls and the summer heat abates, rattlesnakes emerge from hiding and begin their search for food. When hunting, rattlesnakes do not forage randomly throughout their range. An Oklahoma study that outfitted 83 rattlers with radio trackers discovered they prefer selected routes that provide protective cover. In the hottest part of the summer, they may forage for only a few hours around midnight and then retreat to a protected den for the day. They sometimes hunt during daylight in the spring or after a cooling summer rainstorm, but usually remain nocturnal. In the winter, Texas rattlers do not truly hibernate and may emerge from their dens on sunny days to bask. In South Texas, they remain active during most of the year.

South Texas diamondback rattlers feed well into the winter months, enabling the females to reproduce every year. Northern rattlesnake species require a year of storing fat in order to produce a litter. They do not have enough time between parturition and hibernation to accumulate enough reserves to reproduce the next year. The 9 to 16 young, born alive usually during September, average 9 to 13 inches in length depending on the species. The babies emerge with a button and a lethal load of venom. They shed and get another rattle in about one week. A snake adds a rattle each time it sheds, about every six to eight weeks when food is plentiful. During an eight-month feeding season, a rattler can add four to five rattles, but long strings are unusual because the rattles break off easily in the brush and rocks.

The western diamondback holds the record for size, both in length and in the fictitious tales it has inspired. Texas author and historian J. Frank Dobie compiled an entire book of rattlesnake folklore. He described a specimen said to be about 15 feet long that once decorated a rail car running between Brownsville and St. Louis. Since a skin will stretch as much as 33 percent, the snake must have been about 12 feet long, if really a rattler. Stuffed pythons have been painted convincingly and, with rattles attached, passed off as giants. W. S. "Snake" King of Brownsville, well known for both his king size snakes and stories, claims to have captured a 9-foot, 6½-inch diamondback. Seven-foot individuals are well documented, which is probably as large as diamondbacks grow. The majority of adults grow to 3 or 4 feet, regardless of age, yet populations of snakes, like the human population, include a few genetic giants. King's offer of $100 per inch for any western diamondback over 6 feet went unclaimed for years.

Most stories about rattlesnakes involve giant size, snakebite, or folk remedies. According to legend, a rattlesnake bite is so poisonous that it will kill a tree if the snake accidentally misses its victim and strikes the plant. To prove its point, the story relates the time a rattler bit a wagon tongue. The tongue began swelling, and the driver had to cut it off to save the wagon. A mythological snake once bit a tire, and the high-pressure air rushed through its hollow fangs, filling the unfortunate creature like a balloon until it exploded.

One of the most persistent fables, dutifully passed on to me in my youth, concerns a beautiful woman and her fiancé. On their wedding day, he bought new boots and on the way to the church received a fatal bite on the foot. After the funeral, his best friend began courting the bride-to-be, and they eventually announced their plans for marriage. Since his late friend's boots fit him, he decided to wear them. During the ceremony, he suddenly dropped dead. A third friend consoled the grief-stricken woman, and as time passed, they too fell in love. On the day of the wedding, he decided to wear the ill-fated boots. While putting them on, he noticed a broken snake fang waiting to inject its lethal venom into the unlucky person who inserted his foot.

Every snakebite story can be matched by the tale of a sure-cure remedy. Many involve an elusive herb called rattlesnake weed. None of the stories ever really identify this mysterious plant that when chewed, applied as a poultice, or made into a tea cures snakebites, but numerous plants bear the common name. Other alleged cures, besides the traditional bottle of whiskey, include jabbing the wound with yucca or agave spines and using fresh liver or meat to draw out the poison.

The apparent success of the folk remedies depended on how much venom, if any at all, the snake actually injected into the victim. One-fifth of the time rattlesnakes deliver no poison, and about 70 percent of the bites inject venom only superficially. Doctors today advise that the standard cut-and-suck treatment taught to every Boy Scout should be discarded with the whiskey and rattlesnake weed remedies. No treatment at all is better than cutting, tourniquets, or packing with ice for long periods. The recommended first aid is to wrap an elastic bandage around the limb between the bite and the heart. Secure the bandage snugly enough to compress the lymph system but not restrict the flow of blood. Immobilize the affected limb in a splint, remove shoes or rings in case of swelling, and rush to a hospital.

Today rattlesnakes continue to be as much a part of modern Texas culture as in times past. Each spring Sweetwater, Freer, Taylor, and other towns sponsor carnival-like rattlesnake roundups. To the cheers of excited masses, contestants see who can bag the most snakes without getting bitten, stay the longest in a sleeping bag filled with rattlers, and take part in other events exhibiting equally absurd bravado. Visitors can dine on rattlesnake burgers and buy snakeskin hat bands and belts, rattler key chains, and other oddities. Many animal lovers protest the debauchery and inhumane treatment of the reptiles, but rattlesnakes find few advocates in the ranks of Texas lawmakers. Perhaps someday we humans will learn to value all life, and not treat other creatures as objects for our entertainment.

Turtles:
The Animals with
a Mobile Home

Modern vacationers who set out in their recreational vehicles each summer have adopted a lifestyle turtles perfected 200 million years ago. Like the turtle, today's travelers live in safety and comfort by taking their homes with them. Through the eons, this strategy has proved successful for the turtle. Dinosaurs, the largest and fiercest reptiles, vanished from the changing world, yet the unaggressive turtle lives on. This small reptile, with its home on its back, crawled out of the golden age of dinosaurs, across the drifting continents, and into the present age of mammals.

While many people have a hysterical fear of snakes and find lizards repulsive, turtles capture the imagination of us all. From children to adults, people all over the world like them. Pottery, paintings, and myths show that even ancient cultures favored turtles. Today art, children's stories, and sage expressions glorify and anthropomorphize this creature's characteristics. "Observe the turtle," the saying advises, "it doesn't get anywhere unless it sticks out its neck." Remember the tortoise and the hare? We may laugh at the turtle's slowness, but we admire its persistence.

Baby turtles often become children's first pets, their introduction to the world of nature. A quarter-size red-eared slider, *Trachemys scripta elegans,* paddled around in my first aquarium. Later I found an ornate box turtle, *Terrapene ornata ornata,* and fed it moths attracted to our front porch light. After discovering how hard these toothless critters could bite, I released it, but not before painting my phone number, LO-2975, on its back. The next day, a friendly neighbor three blocks away called for me to retrieve the wandering turtle. The distance that poky little creature traveled left a lasting impression on its young captor. I learned later that painting a turtle is like painting your skin, an unhealthy thing to do, and that most pet turtles die from the inadequate diet of commercial turtle food.

The ancestors of modern turtles saw the ice ages come and go, mountain ranges build and wear away, continents collide and reform, catastrophic meteor showers, and massive plant and animal extinctions. To survive these extremes, turtles had to be exceedingly resilient to environmental changes. These well-adapted creatures even can withstand radiation levels that would kill most animals. Perhaps turtles, along with cockroaches, will eventually inherit the earth.

In surviving the millennia, turtles have solved three of an animal's biggest problems: food, protection, and shelter. Some animals specialize in a particular type of food, but most turtles eat anything, plant or animal, that they can grasp in their horny jaws. Their varied diet kept them well fed while the plant and animal community around them continuously changed through the ages.

Many animals spend most of their waking hours trying to avoid becoming another animal's meal, but turtles carry their protection on their backs. Their bony armor both protects them from hungry predators and provides an instant home. The turtle's shell is its most remarkable adaptation for survival, and separates these animals from all other creatures. A turtle's ribs and vertebrae are fused into its upper shell, or carapace, placing its hip bone inside the rib cage, a unique arrangement among vertebrates. A bony bridge on each side connects the carapace to the bottom shell, the plastron. Living encased in a horny bunker offers protection, but makes locomotion cumbersome. Many, but by no means all, turtles circumvent this problem by taking to the water, a much more buoyant medium than air. But even water turtles return to land to bury their leathery eggs. The female digs a shallow hole and lets the soil, heated by the sun, incubate the eggs.

To illustrate their incredible ability to adapt to extreme environments, some turtles, instead of swimming through lakes and rivers, trudge across the sand in the hottest, driest deserts in the world. The desert tortoise of the Mojave Desert and the Texas tortoise, *Gopherus berlandieri,* both relatives of the giant tortoises of the Galapagos Islands, lumber through cactus-covered landscapes eating grass, stems, leaves, and prickly pear pads and fruit.

Turtles and other reptiles have another basic survival strategy that many animals find limiting: their body temperature rises and falls with the external temperature. Mammals and birds expend vast amounts of food energy maintaining a constant temperature, while reptiles merely climb on a rock or limb and let the sun do the work. Once their body reaches a temperature warm enough for the chemistry of muscle action and digestion to function, reptiles become as agile and fleet as mammals. These creatures can survive on a tenth of the food energy required by a mammal, a reasonable trade-off for the ability to function at low temperatures.

Turtles are particularly abundant in North America. Of the approximately 200 species in the world, about 86 live in the United States, with some 35 calling Texas home. In contrast, 6 species live in Europe, 19 in Australia, and 35 each in Africa and South America. Most turtles live in fresh water, and many of the larger river basins in the nation have their own unique species and subspecies.

The alligator snapping turtle, *Macroclemys temminckii,* occurring from East Texas to West Florida and along the Mississippi River, holds the size record for a freshwater turtle. These mammoths of the lakes and rivers sometimes weigh more than 200 pounds. They have powerful jaws to crush their prey and have been known to break the fingers of unwary humans. To trick fish to venture within striking range, alligator snappers have a wormlike lure on the inside of their mouth.

Perhaps the strangest turtles of all ride the ocean

waves. The seven species of sea turtles in the world have adapted well to their watery existence. Their front feet are elongated flippers that propel them along as fast as 20 mph. The leatherback turtle, *Dermochelys coriacea,* grows to be the largest living reptile. In 1923, fishermen captured an 8½-foot, 1286-pound leatherback in Monterey Bay, California. Unlike other turtles, the leatherback, as its name implies, has no horny carapace but many small bones embedded in a thick, leathery skin.

Except for brief trips to selected beaches by the females to lay eggs, sea turtles spend their lives swimming the tropical and subtropical seas. These creatures have mystified sailors and scientists for centuries. Marine biologists have watched the females laboriously digging their nest chambers on isolated beaches and laying 100 to 150 eggs each, seen the hatchlings scampering toward the surf, and occasionally captured an adult swimming at sea. But where the juveniles spend their lives remains for the most part a mystery. Despite years of research, biologists know little about what happens between hatching and maturity.

The Kemp's ridley sea turtle, *Lepidochelys kempi,* a denizen of the Gulf of Mexico and Atlantic seaboard, puzzled scientists the longest. For 18 years, marine biologists searched in vain for the breeding sites of this mysterious beast. Some people considered it a hybrid between the loggerhead and green sea turtles, since a female with eggs had never been found. Finally in 1961, a film made in the 1940s stunned the audience at an American Society of Ichthyologists and Herpetologists meeting in Austin. A Mexican had filmed approximately 40,000 ridleys nesting in one day on a 15-mile stretch of beach near Tampico.

Villagers long had known what had eluded the biologists, and when the turtles massed offshore they waited with bags, boxes, and trucks to gather the eggs. The eggs, considered an aphrodisiac, brought handsome prices as far away as Mexico City. By the time the scientific community discovered the nesting beach, less than a thousand turtles remained and the species was on the brink of extinction. In 1966, the Mexican government finally legislated protection and sent soldiers to patrol the tiny stretch of beach that is the birthplace of every Kemp's ridley sea turtle.

Outdoorsman Dearl Adams and his wife, Ethel, of Brownsville realized that the ridley needed more than conservation to save it from extinction. A second nesting colony would double the magnificent turtle's chance of survival. Between 1963 and 1967, they transferred 5000 eggs from Mexico to South Padre Island, which closely resembles the turtles' native beach. Assisted by Ila Loetscher, who became nationally known as the Turtle Lady of Padre Island, they lived on the beach each year to protect the eggs and hatchlings until the tiny turtles swam away in the rolling surf. Finally, in 1976, their dedication was rewarded. A 100-pound ridley swam ashore and laid 97 eggs.

The U.S. government realized the value of the project, and in 1978 began a large-scale operation to transfer eggs to Padre Island National Seashore. Each year, scientists bag 2000 eggs, pack them in Padre Island sand, and take them to the seashore to hatch. The hatchlings are given a brief taste of freedom in the sea, and then netted and taken to facilities in Galveston for a year. The scientists hope that the exposure to the sand and sea of Padre Island will imprint the new location in the babies, and they will return there as adults to nest.

In the wild, only about 1 percent of the baby sea turtles reach maturity. The rest become meals for everything from crabs and gulls to fish and sharks. By rearing the young in a protected environment for the first year, about 30 percent are expected to reach breeding age. Workers tag and release the eight-inch yearlings about 15 miles at sea.

The life history of the ridley still remains a mystery. Except for a few washed across the Atlantic by strong currents, adults occur only in the Gulf of Mexico. Juveniles

215

have never been recovered in the Gulf, only in bays on the Atlantic coast. Perhaps the young leave the Gulf for a period and return as adults.

The future of the Kemp's ridley sea turtle remains uncertain. The Padre Island transplants may take 10 to 15 years to mature sexually. In 1986, 8 years after the start of the program, rangers began patrolling the beach regularly looking for nests, but only rare, sporadic nesting has occurred on the island. In the meantime, fewer females nest in Mexico each year. The number of eggs decreased from about 100,000 in 1978 to 45,000 in 1986. To compound the problem, shrimpers' nets increasingly threaten the few turtles that escape predators and reach maturity. The industry has fought the use of turtle-excluding devices that would keep the air-breathing animals from drowning in the nets. Apparently, only legislation will force shrimpers to use the lifesaving device.

After millions of years of swimming freely in the open sea, the ridley sea turtle now depends for survival not on its natural adaptations but on the cooperation of the Mexican, United States, and Texas governments, conservation groups, and the fishing industry. Time will tell if this mysterious creature of the deep will survive the pressures of the twentieth century.

Invertebrates

If an extraterrestrial were cataloguing life on this planet, invertebrates would lead the list in numbers. The invertebrates include all animals without backbones, from sponges to the ubiquitous insects, from tiny soil nematodes to the giant octopus. Only a few classes of animals with a centralized brain and a complex neural system have backbones, and these are far outnumbered by the invertebrates.

The land, sea, and soil teem with invertebrates. The minuscule zooplankton of the sea are the foundation of the food pyramid that supports all ocean life. Larger invertebrates, like shrimp and clams, and many fish, filter the tiny organisms from the water, and in turn become food for larger fish. Without the abundant invertebrates, life in the sea would collapse. Insects play a pivotal role in the terrestrial ecosystem. Without insect pollinators, many plants, and all the animals that depended on them, would disappear. Without the soil organisms decomposing the dead animals and plants, the nutrient balance would be disrupted. Without the insects and other invertebrates providing the basic fodder for the land animals, the food chain would shatter.

In comparison with the invertebrates, the more highly developed forms of life play an almost insignificant role in the biosphere. If the mammals, birds, and reptiles suddenly disappeared, life on the planet would proceed with little change, but removing the invertebrates would totally disrupt the fabric of life on the earth. Vertebrates may be the star performers in the pageant of life, but the play would fold overnight without the supporting role of the invertebrates.

Scientists have divided all life into five distinct king

doms. The Monera kingdom contains bacteria, and probably will be divided into two separate kingdoms. The cells of these organisms have no nucleus and, in terms of evolutionary development, represent the simplest forms of life. The Protista kingdom consists of predominantly single-celled organisms like the amoeba and algae. Scientists undoubtedly will divide this kingdom when the origins of its diverse members are better understood. Molds, mildews, mushrooms, and yeasts belong to the fungi kingdom. No one knows where to place the viruses, but they probably will have a separate kingdom of their own. The rest of life fits into the two more familiar, but vastly complex, plant and animal kingdoms.

Biologists have subdivided the animal kingdom into nine major categories according to the complexity of cellular, tissue, organ, and body development. All are invertebrates except for the few classes of animals with backbones. Sponges have a body composed of a few specialized cells largely independent of each other. Corals and jellyfish, including the Portuguese man-of-war described in a following section, have cells organized into tissues with only a few rudimentary organs, such as tentacles. Animals with major organs are divided into those with no body cavity, the flatworms, and those with a fluid-filled body cavity. Major divisions within the latter group include the earthworms, nematodes, mollusks, arthropods, sea urchins, and chordates. The joint-leg arthropods, the most diverse group of living animals, include crabs, shrimp, spiders, mites, and insects. The chordates include the vertebrates, composed of the fishes, amphibians, reptiles, birds, and mammals, as well as some invertebrates.

If our extraterrestrial explorer were choosing the most successful land animals to use to colonize a distant planet, the choice undoubtedly would be the insects. Terrestrial life is largely a celebration of this incredibly diverse class of invertebrates. Insects outnumber all other plants and animals in both species and individuals. The six-legged critters comprise about 80 percent of the animals on the earth. Scientists have described nearly one million species, and as many as one million more may wait their turn to be discovered.

Insects became the most numerous, widespread, and diverse forms of life because of their ability to adopt extremely specialized lifestyles. By dividing the food resources into narrow niches, numerous species can exist side by side without competing with each other. An insect's mouth, with either chewing or sucking parts, and its digestive system adapt it to a particular food source, often only one narrow group or species of plants or animals. Mosquitoes have mouths designed for sucking blood, most butterfly caterpillars feed on a single type of plant, and scarab beetles specialize in eating manure. A leaf miner burrows through the inside of a leaf, a gall wasp lays its eggs in the leaf, twig, or branch of a single plant species, and the tarantula wasp attacks only spiders. Insects and plants have evolved a complex dependence on each other: showy, fragrant blooms attract insects, which pollinate the flower and receive a nutritious reward for their efforts. In contrast, a plant that depends on the wind to spread its pollen has tiny, nondescript flowers.

Having a narrow food preference enables insects to diversify, and their robust ability to survive adverse conditions allows them to exploit every imaginable habitat. They live in glacial snowfields, arid deserts, deep lakes, and on stalactites in caves. In California, a fly larva lives in pools of crude oil in petroleum fields, and another eats mold in vats of corrosive formaldehyde. Insects even live in such extraordinary microhabitats as the nostrils of reindeer and the water in hollow leaves.

After 300 million years of adapting, insects have the odds of survival in their favor. Most insects cover their bets with a simple strategy of copious reproduction. If each female produces thousands of offspring, some invariably will be able to survive almost any adverse condition. We spray them with poisons, but succeed only in eliminating the susceptible ones. Each generation will have genetically resistant individuals that live to produce more poison-tolerant young. Many of today's insects can walk through DDT with impunity. One species of grasshopper even concentrated a particular insecticide in its body. If the poison deters other animals from eating the grasshopper, we have increased its ability to survive instead of killing it. Insects could have written the book on natural selection and survival of the fittest.

Except for the few creatures that have an impact on our daily lives, most invertebrates live in a complex world that we normally overlook. Ants and termites have an intricate social system that governs colonies as populous as our large cities. Bees communicate the location of nectar-rich flowers by an elaborate dance. Insects can see spectra of light beyond the sensitivity of the human eye and hear frequencies beyond the audio range of our ear. A Saturniid moth has such a keen sense of smell that the male can detect a female as far as five miles away. Insects developed flight 100 million years before birds soared through the sky, which helped them spread around the globe and diversify into the millions of living species. Insects vary in size from the $1/100$-inch hairy winged beetle to several moths with a 12-inch wingspan.

Invertebrates greatly influence our daily life, both positively and negatively. We may curse the discomfort caused by blood-sucking mosquitoes, pesky flies, and stinging ants, wasps, and scorpions, but we thrill at a dancing butterfly, savor lobster, shrimp, and oysters as culinary delicacies, enjoy our silk clothes, and consider honey a staple food. Insects pollinate the vast majority of the plants, provide a source of food, either directly or indirectly, for most of the other animals, and complete the food cycle by decomposing dead plants and animals into nutrients that plants can assimilate. Just one acre of forest soil contains about 65 million soil insects. Insects and insect products, such as beeswax, provide medicines, dyes, shellac, lubricants, salves, ointments, wax, polish, and varnishes. Although whole industries have developed to help control insect damage to agriculture, most species benefit the farmer and rancher by controlling weeds and other plant pests and aerating and fertilizing the soil. Even though insects spread disease and destroy food, timber, and other necessities worth $3.5 billion annually in the United States, these animals directly benefit the economy by $4.5 billion, a net gain of $1 billion.

The next six sections describe some of the hidden mysteries of the invertebrate creatures that we commonly encounter in our backyards, at the beach, and in the woods. Read about a colony of organisms that float on the ocean waves, a fragile butterfly that migrates thousands of miles, and critters that sting, itch, and suck our blood.

Chiggers and Ticks: Pint-size Pests

Chigger
Trombicula alfreddugesi
American dog tick
Dermacentor variabilis
Lone Star tick
Amblyomma americanum

The humans, oblivious of the blood-hungry predators, marched merrily through the dense vegetation. Hidden in the foliage, the carnivorous beasties waited with claws outstretched, ready to snare their victims, tear into their bodies, and gorge themselves on the juicy flesh and blood. This may sound like the opening scene of a horror movie, but it is only a typical spring picnic. While we play and cavort in the park, chiggers and ticks hang on the tips of grass and leaves with outstretched legs waving in the air, waiting to grasp any animal that passes by. Once they have hitched a ride, they search for a tender patch of skin for their own picnic. For humans, these parasites cause irritation, infection, and, at worst, disease.

Chiggers and ticks both belong to the class Arachnida, which also includes scorpions and spiders. Each develops in a completely different way, and each poses different problems for humans. While chiggers mainly cause physical discomfort, ticks can carry the potentially deadly Rocky Mountain spotted fever (RMSF).

Texans are lucky. Of the more than 2000 species of chiggers in the world, only 2 bother people in our state. Some chiggers in other parts of the world specialize in a particular animal, but ours dine on a large number of hosts. Besides human flesh, they feast on mammals, birds, reptiles, and even amphibians.

Chiggers pass through four life stages: egg, larva,

223

nymph, and adult. The nymphs and adults, only $\frac{1}{20}$ of an inch long, perform a service to humans by eating insect eggs, small insects, and other tiny organisms. The pin-size larvae, $\frac{1}{150}$ -inch, are the tiny culprits that inflict king-size misery in humans. These minuscule pests invariably homestead on the tenderest parts of our bodies, especially waists, armpits, groins, and behind the knees.

The larva works its way into a skin pore or hair follicle and attaches with two pairs of barbed mouth appendages. Then begins a scene that surpasses any monster movie ever produced by Hollywood or Japan. The chigger slowly begins to dissolve away the body of its victim. Fortunately a microscopic parasite can only liquefy microscopic amounts of flesh. The digestive enzymes the chigger pumps in form a hollow strawlike tube that the critter uses to lap up the dissolved skin cells. The larva gluttonizes for three or four days and, when engorged, drops off to develop into the nymph stage.

Chigger bites itch so intensely because humans are not the perfect hosts. Our body recognizes the pest as an intruder and reacts strongly. A puffed-up red bump forms around the parasite and usually persists for several days after the villainous arachnid departs. Once you become a chigger landlord, you will probably have to live with the unwelcome tenants until they leave voluntarily. Tape may pull them off, and medicines may kill them, but the itch remains. I know from experience that the itching from several hundred bites will almost drive you insane. The three or four days of constant misery seem like an eternity. Some chiggers in Asia and Australia are adapted to humans and cause no itching, but they spread deadly diseases.

The best way to survive chigger season, spring through late summer, is to avoid the pests as much as possible. Spray insect repellent on your ankles and pants legs, and scrub with soapy water after being outdoors. Chiggers hate sulfur, and dusting your ankles with an old sock filled with the yellow powder works as well as expensive sprays. Some people even dust their yards, which may deter the pests until the next rain. Most drugstores sell powdered sulfur.

Ticks are another pint-size parasite eager to exploit the protein available in the human body. Using specialized mouth parts, a tick buries its head in the victim's skin and, like a tiny vampire, begins sucking blood. Ticks feed on the blood of animals during every stage of their life except as eggs. A female tick lays 3000 to 6000 eggs in the spring, which hatch into tiny "seed" ticks. The larval seed ticks begin the lifelong process of grasping for any animal that passes by. They engorge, molt, and grow into nymphs, then finally into reproducing adults. At any state of development they can transmit diseases to humans.

Ticks carry Rocky Mountain spotted fever and, as vectors of the disease, pass it to other animals. The malady, also called tick-borne typhus fever, occurs throughout the United States and south to Brazil. Ticks become infected by feeding on diseased animals and carry the pathogen for life, about 18 months. Females transmit the fever to their many offspring. Prime tick season in Texas and the rest of the United States occurs from April through October. During this season, anyone who spends time in wooded, bushy areas should inspect for ticks daily.

The incidence of the fever increased from 433 cases nationwide in 1969 to 1165 in 1981, but the number of cases fluctuates with peak and low years. Texas recorded 108 cases in 1983, yet only 33 in 1985. The fatality rate averages about 5 percent. Hunters and campers contract the disease much less than those who live in tick-infested areas. Most cases occur in wooded East Texas among rural inhabitants. Children under 15, especially between 5 and 9, contract RMSF more than any other age group, probably because of continuous exposure to the outdoors and from ticks on pet dogs.

Only about 1 percent of the ticks carry the RMSF microorganisms. Symptoms of the disease develop within three to ten days, beginning with a measleslike rash on the hands and feet that spreads over the entire body. Severe muscle aches and headaches, chills, and fever accompany the rash. The general nature of the symptoms and the fact that most doctors have no experience diagnosing the disease can have serious consequences. Without treatment, the symptoms last for two to three weeks with a death rate of about 20 percent. When treated by the first or second day of the rash, the fever usually falls within 48 hours. With the cure the victim receives a bonus: lifelong immunity.

Of the many species of ticks, only two carry the disease in Texas, the American dog tick (*Dermacentor variabilis*) and the Lone Star tick (*Amblyomma americanum*), named for the white spot on its back. In the West, the Rocky Mountain wood tick (*Dermacentor andersoni*) also transmits the disease. To spread Rocky Mountain spotted fever, a tick must be attached for two to six hours. The Federal Centers for Disease Control advise against using a hot match, petroleum jelly, or any other method that kills the tick while it is embedded. Injuring the tick could cause it to discharge its fluids, including the disease organisms, directly into your body. The crushed tissue or body fluids can also transmit the fever. For this reason, never mash a tick between your fingers. You can safely remove a tick with tweezers or tissue-covered fingers. Grasp the tick by the head as close to the skin as possible and roll the body upward without jerking or twisting. Ideally the tick comes out alive with a bit of skin still in its mouth. Thoroughly wash and disinfect the bite and fingers.

You can greatly decrease the chance of a tick bite by tucking in shirttails and pants legs. Spray with a commercial insect repellent before heading into the woods or backcountry. Closely check clothing for loose ticks. The critters may crawl around for several hours before attaching. Also, brush long hair and check your scalp. If you develop a rash or fever within ten days of exposure to tick country (only 80 percent of fever victims recall an actual bite), consult your physician immediately.

The Fire Ant:
Wildfire with Six Legs

Imported red fire ant
Solenopsis invicta

They swarm, they sting, they attack with a fury. Just as locusts smote the Pharaohs of Egypt and plague-ridden fleas decimated Europe, the imported red fire ant has assaulted the United States. Undetected, the $1/8$- to $1/4$-inch ants hitched a ride on a Brazilian cargo ship sometime in the 1940s and jumped ship in Mobile, Alabama. By 1953, they had pillaged their way through the South like General Sherman and reached the Texas border. Texans may have wrested their vast state away from the Indians and Mexicans, but they could not stop the relentless advance of the fire ants. Nearly a quarter of the entire state has fallen to the invaders. Like flags of conquest, the conical mounds of these indomitable insects now decorate 113 of the state's 254 counties. Fire ants outnumber Texans ten million to one!

Fire ants are more than a pest—they represent a serious menace to ranchers, farmers, and urban dwellers. The one-to-two-foot-high mounds of a mature colony may contain 250,000 ants, which swarm out ready to attack on the slightest provocation. Even a gentle puff of air on the mound will incite the belligerent critters. Infested areas have as many as 50 mounds per acre.

The crusty mounds can render a pasture or field virtually unusable for ranchers and farmers. Cattle wisely avoid pastures infested with the aggressive ants, and farmers find the sun-hardened mounds worse than speed bumps on a freeway. The mounds damage equipment, jam combines, and dull blades. Farmers sometime leave their crops in an overrun field if harvesting would seriously damage their equipment. The ants often ruin hay by homesteading in the bales. Each year Texans spend about $1.5 million, and Americans spend $6 million, trying to control fire ants. Soil, plants, sod, hay, and logs are a few of the quarantined items that cannot be transported from infested counties into uninfested areas without stringent control measures.

Of the 10,000 species of ants worldwide, the imported fire ant poses the most serious threat in North America, especially in residential areas. They find manicured lawns, parks, school grounds, and roadsides perfect homesites. A well-watered sunny expanse of turf and the absence of other ants present the perfect invitation to these adventurous insects. Most people in the eastern half of the state have had close encounters of the stinging kind with fire ants, and many in their own yards.

Fire ants derive their name from the intense pain caused by their sting. A burning sensation begins as soon as the ant injects its venom; the skin turns red and a pustule forms. The pus irritates the surrounding tissue, causing itching. Bacteria may enter and cause secondary infections if the pimplelike sores are broken by scratching. The sores usually heal in about a week.

Angry fire ants sting until killed, and their swarming attacks occasionally hospitalize their unfortunate victims, particularly small children. A surprised highway patrolman in East Texas abruptly forgot the speedster he was ticketing when he discovered he was standing in a fire ant bed. Doctors in one county in Georgia treated almost 30,000 fire ant sting cases in one year. Once I asked my wife and two children to pose for a picture on a stump. As I took the picture, my daughter said, "Daddy, there're ants in the log!" The apprehensive expressions in the snapshot foretold the dancing and screaming that immediately followed.

When a person develops an extreme allergy to fire ant venom, a single bite can prove fatal. In 1985, two people died in Texas. One, a truck driver, laid his head in an ant bed while changing a tire. He recovered from the painful experience, but suffered a fatal heart attack several months later when three ants bit him on the toe. If the symptoms of anaphylactic shock develop—dizziness, sweating, swelling of the throat—seek immediate medical attention. A half-and-half solution of water and chlorine bleach or a paste of meat tenderizer provides some relief from the stinging, itching, and pustule formation if used immediately. A doctor at Texas A&M University found that injections of puréed fire ants help desensitize people to the venom.

Unwelcome, but unhesitating, fire ants move into any neighborhood and may even try to share your house. A New York couple that moved to Austin found them in their washing machine and the walls of their laundry room. By taking advantage of the warmth of our houses and the dampness of our irrigated lawns and crops, these tropical ants can spread beyond the natural barriers of cold and dryness. Although the dry West Texas summers and a winter monthly average low of 10 degrees should have halted their expansion into North Texas, these pests have survived some of the harshest winters in history in Lubbock, and they may eventually become scattered throughout the Panhandle.

Despite the combined efforts of federal and state agricultural departments, the invaders have not been stopped, or even slowed. Since their introduction into the United States, they have advanced steadily at a rate of 5 to 12 miles per year. From a modest beginning of perhaps only one queen, fire ants have infested 11 states, an area of more than 230 million acres, with 50 million acres in Texas. If they inadvertently are transported to the West Coast, they will spread from Arizona to Washington.

Texas has three species of native fire ants that cause few problems compared with the imported species. They are less aggressive and have smaller colonies, and natural factors control their spread. The native fire ants require three to five years to produce queens, while the imported red fire ant takes only seven months. A single colony of imported ants may produce 4500 queens per year, but fortunately for the world, 90 to 99 percent never survive to establish colonies.

Imported fire ants are prime examples of animals adapted to pioneering into new territory. Colonies of ants form when new queens mature and leave the nest. On sunny, windless days in the spring and summer, the virgin queens and drones mass at the mound surface and fly skyward to mate. After the nuptial flight, the fertilized queen lands ¼ mile to 1 mile away and loses her wings. Now earthbound, she lays 10 to 15 eggs that hatch as tiny workers in about 28 days. Gradually the number of foragers, nurses, and other caste members increases until new queens can be produced.

When foraging for food, imported red fire ants outcompete the native species. Besides being more aggressive, they win by numbers alone. A native fire ant colony contains anywhere from 100 to 5000 individuals, but there are 250,000 per colony of the imported species. Red fire ants build subways about ½ inch underground to reach their foraging sites safely. The tunnels radiate as far as 75 feet in all directions from the mound. Workers exit through openings along the way and forage at random until they find a food source. Then they return to the mound, leaving a pheromone, or scent, trail for other workers to follow.

A foraging imported red fire ant stalking through the weeds is a vicious predator armed with a potent weapon. It uses its venom to kill spiders, ticks, insects, earthworms, and other small invertebrates. It may even attack ground-nesting birds. As predators, fire ants sometimes aid farmers by controlling crop-damaging insects, such as boll weevils and corn earworms. However, the native ants they displace may perform this service as well or better. Although hunters, these omnivorous ants eat almost everything in their path. They eat plant sap, germinating seeds, and buds, and tend aphids for the honeylike secretions the aphids produce.

Until banned by the U.S. Environmental Protection Agency in 1978, Mirex, a fat-soluble compound more persistent than DDT, was the pesticide most used to control fire ants. In some areas 44 percent of the people had accumulated residues of this chlorinated hydrocarbon in their bodies. After 16 years of widespread use, Mirex proved to be carcinogenic, caused birth defects, and killed a large number of nontargeted animals.

Amdro, the pesticide now approved for broadcast application for nonagricultural land, does not accumulate in the environment and dissipates within 24 hours. It will kill 85 to 90 percent of the ants of all species when spread on rangeland, pastures, and lawns, but in 6 to 9 months fire ants will reinvade. Since the chemical degrades so fast, it must be used in the cool of the morning or evening, when the foraging workers will carry the poison back to the mound to feed the queen.

After years of research, a juvenile hormone pesticide, Logic, has been approved for areawide broadcast. Worker ants carry the pesticide into the mound and feed it to the larvae. The hormone disrupts the larvae's metamorphosis into adults, and the colony dies from lack of workers. Although formulated to kill ants, Amdro and Logic also kill aquatic organisms and should not be used around water. Research continues on other ways to control the imported fire ant biologically. In Brazil, researchers have discovered about ten different pathogens and parasites that naturally limit the fire ant population.

Areawide application of pesticides is not always the best way to control fire ants because the native ants in an area help keep the imported species in check. When all species of ants have been killed by pesticides, imported fire ants repopulate more efficiently than the native species. Within a year after broadcasting pesticides over an area, the fire ant population may have increased 3000-fold. For this reason, only individual mound treatment is recommended for low-density infestation, less than 15 mounds per acre.

A number of pesticides are approved for individual mound treatment. You can spread baits for the workers to carry back to the colony, or soak the mounds with drenches. The baits should be spread uniformly for three feet around the mound, or use at least three gallons of liquid to soak the mound. For homeowners, boiling water, which kills 60 percent of the mounds, may be the easiest and safest approach. Do not disturb the ants when treating a mound. Excited ants immediately carry the queen deep inside the mound, which may extend three feet below the surface, and a colony will survive until its queen is killed. Never use gasoline or other petroleum products because of their flammability and damage to the environment.

Each year, specialists from around the nation gather for a symposium to report the latest biological research and developments for controlling the imported fire ant. Control, not elimination, is the goal. Reagan Brown, the former Texas commissioner of agriculture, expressed the feelings of both the researchers and everyone who has stumbled into a swarming mound of fire ants when he said, "This is not an infestation, it's an invasion!"

The Monarch Butterfly: Jeweled Wings and Dancing Colors

Monarch butterfly
Danaus plexippus

In the wondrous world of nature, one of the most intriguing groups of animals has the flight agility of birds and the gorgeous colors of a field of wildflowers. These delicate creatures are painted with intricate patterns in a rainbow of hues. Who can doubt the creative force within the world of nature when a butterfly goes fluttering by?

The monarch reigns as the most popular and most recognized butterfly in North America. The life of this fragile animal proves that the natural world is full of hidden mystery and majesty. The first surprise is that monarchs migrate thousands of miles between their wintering grounds in the mountains of Mexico and their breeding grounds in the prairie states extending from North Texas to southern Canada. Each spring and fall, hundreds of millions of monarchs come flitting through Texas. The monarchs reach Texas by mid-March and Canada by June. They are the only butterfly with a true back and forth migration between wintering and breeding grounds. Many species disperse as their populations increase and follow the seasonal flower blooms. About 175 species migrate into Central Texas from September to November to feed on the fall wildflowers.

From late September to early November, hordes of monarchs sweep into Texas heading south for the winter. A 20-mile-wide front of the butterflies, resembling a multicolored flying carpet, flew over Dallas one day late in October. As evening fell, they flocked into trees and covered the barren limbs like leaves fluttering in a gentle breeze. As soon as the air warmed the next day, they began leaving and had departed by noon. Within 24 hours, an estimated 1,055,000 had passed over Big D. Monarchs can fly 30 mph, but between breaks for sipping nectar they typically cover only about 40 miles per day.

Whether these delicate creatures so easily swept away by wayward breezes migrated kept the scientific community puzzled for decades. Since insects can overwinter as eggs, larvae, pupae, and adults, no one was sure if the monarchs actually left or overwintered in one form or other. Studies eventually documented that they did leave their northern breeding grounds in the fall and return in the spring, but where they wintered remained a mystery. In 1952, Dr. Fred A. Urquhart of the Toronto Museum in Canada began a massive banding program. Each year, people from across the continent glued tiny stickers with the museum's address and a code number on the wings of tens of thousands of butterflies. Eagle Pass, where monarchs from across the central states funneled through Texas on their way to Mexico, proved to be a prime location for banding during the study. In good years, monarchs covered the trees like colorful leaves. In October 1957, volunteers banded almost 10,000 monarchs en route to Mexico.

As the data accumulated, the migration mystery began to become clearer. Monarchs from northern Wyoming, Montana, and Alberta—the Northern Great Basin—migrate to the Pacific Coast of California. In northern California, with cold temperatures, the butterflies congregate on tree limbs in massive numbers and hibernate. Butterflies cannot fly if the temperature drops below 55 degrees F, and they do not feed until the temperature exceeds 60 degrees. They can withstand mild frosts. Millions cover the trees in the city of Pacific Grove on the Monterey Peninsula. In warmer southern California, they do not need to hibernate and remain active all winter.

Monarchs from the eastern part of their breeding range migrate through Texas and to the Gulf Coast, where many remain active all winter. Only at Lighthouse Point, Florida, do they gather in "butterfly trees." Despite the multitudes of banded butterflies, no one knew the exact destination of the millions that flew through Texas. Finally, in 1975, the mystery of the century was solved—after 40 years of research, Urquhart discovered the winter destination in a high mountain valley in the state of Michoacán, Mexico, west of Mexico City. Hundreds of millions of monarchs, some from 2000 miles away in Canada, cover the trees. The density of the hibernating butterflies reaches four million per acre. If the winter bivouac had not been discovered, it and the monarchs that live there might have disappeared forever. The local populace depends on logging for its livelihood, and would have timbered the winter roosts if the government had not declared a logging ban. Now armed guards protect the butterfly colonies from curiosity seekers and the wrath of unemployed workers and landowners.

The beginning point and destination of the migrating monarchs tell only a fraction of the complex life cycle of these gems of nature. From late winter to early spring, monarchs begin the return trip to their summer homes. They pass through Texas from mid-March to early July. Monarchs mate soon after beginning the long trip north, and they start laying en route as soon as the eggs develop. The eggs hatch and mature, and the offspring follow their parents. Most of the monarchs that arrive in the northern breeding grounds in June and July are the generations that hatched along the migration route. They have never seen their summer destination or their Mexican wintering grounds, but they have the road map indelibly imprinted in their chromosomes.

Millions of monarchs die during the spring and fall migrations, and millions more die while hibernating. With such a high mortality, each female monarch must reproduce prodigiously if the species is to survive. Each female lays about 400 eggs, and the young mature and begin laying in about 30 days. Monarchs in the southern portion of their breeding range produce three or four generations, while northern populations produce one or two. If only half the eggs from a single female survived with half being males, the progeny of each migrating female would number two million within three generations, or about three months. Evidently the survival rate is much less than half or the world would be overrun with butterflies.

A female monarch, like most butterflies, is very particular about where she lays her eggs. Certain milkweed plants provide the perfect day care center for a baby monarch. The monarch's breeding range coincides with the North American distribution of the *Asclepias* genus of milkweed, especially *Asclepias syriaca*, and extends primarily between the latitudes 32 degrees N and 48 degrees N. Monarchs find a majority of the milkweed species in the state unsuitable for their progeny, and most pass through South and Central Texas without laying. Some do remain in the Davis Mountains, South Texas, and North Texas and spend their summer flitting from flower to flower and searching for the plants they require to lay their eggs.

The female selects a young milkweed with new leaves so the caterpillars will have tender vegetation to eat. The taste sensors on her legs tell her she has selected the right plant. She lays each egg, about the size of a pinhead, on the bottom side of a leaf. Shaped like exquisite gemstones, the eggs have about 36 facets and 22 vertical ridges. At 70 degrees F, the eggs hatch in three to four days.

The monarch passes through four distinctively different life stages: egg, caterpillar or larva, pupa, and adult. A caterpillar is designed for one purpose—eating. At hatching, the 2-mm monarch larva begins munching milkweed leaves and doesn't stop until it is about to pop, literally. The caterpillar outgrows and sheds its skin four times during its first two weeks. Then its eating machine turns off, and it takes its last bite. The caterpillar spins a tiny silk pad attached to a protected leaf or twig. As the pupa begins to form within its skin, it secures its rear feet in the pad and sheds for the last time. The new skin hardens into a protective cover called a chrysalis. Inside the chrysalis, the magical metamorphosis takes place. In about 12 days, the chrysalis bursts open and a creature as different from a caterpillar as a worm is from a bird crawls out. But the butterfly's maiden flight must wait until it pumps up its wings and the delicate membranes dry. After a life of crawling, the butterfly is earthbound no more.

A monarch's flight may seem weak and haphazard, but in reality the butterfly is a strong, purposeful flier. While searching for nectar-rich flowers, it saves energy by gliding on the fickle air currents. It cruises with a wingbeat covering 30 degrees, while its 30 mph power flight, used to escape danger and during migration, sweeps through 120 degrees. While courting, the male chases the female in an upward spiral. If the lady is unreceptive, she flees with a rapid zigzag flight. The male tries to appear appealing by wearing a sweet-smelling perfume. It even has a special pocket in its hind wings to store the scent, which is produced by glands on the tip of its abdomen.

A butterfly may seem like a tasty morsel to a hungry bird, but the monarch has a secret weapon. The caterpillar concentrates toxins in its system from the milkweed leaves it so voraciously consumes. The compounds, cardiac glycosides, are powerful heart drugs for vertebrates, and cause vomiting as well. Each monarch has three to nine times the dose of cardiac glycosides prescribed for a human with congestive heart failure. The poison is concentrated in the monarch's wings, the most likely part to be attacked. Tests with blue jays showed that a naive bird that had never seen a monarch readily attacked, but became ill after one bite. One nibble gave the bird a retching experience it never forgot. With the bird overcome with nausea, the monarch flies away only slightly scarred from the escapade. Many monarchs in the wild have nibble marks on their wings, showing they have survived a close encounter.

The viceroy butterfly, *Limenitis archippus,* which has a similar outline and the same basic coloration, benefits from the monarch's bad reputation. A bird that has tasted a monarch will avoid any butterfly that resembles the distasteful species. The ruse fools birds so well that they avoid the unprotected look-alike. Viceroys are masters of deception and use a different disguise through each of their four life stages. Their eggs resemble leaf galls, the caterpillars have fierce-looking horns, and the chrysalis looks like a bird dropping. Many species of butterflies mimic butterflies and other objects, especially in the tropics.

Monarchs are a marvel of nature. Though so lightweight and easily swept by the wind, they migrate thousands of miles. They appear defenseless, yet possess a powerful deterrent to predators. They reproduce by the millions, and when hibernating cover trees like colorful ribbons. Monarchs play an important role as pollinators as they sip the sweet nectar provided by flowers. Besides their ecological importance, butterflies have an aesthetic importance for humans. Whether we are young or old, butterflies delight our senses. Children thrill when one lands on their shoulder, and adults, with expensive cameras in hand, chase the elusive insects through fields and meadows. I'll never forget my daughter's excitement when she saw a butterfly flitting from flower to flower: "Look, there goes a flutterby!"

The Portuguese Man-of-War: Danger Rides the Surf

Portuguese man-of-war
Physalia physalis

Long before the Portuguese, or any other human, hoisted a sail, the Portuguese man-of-war ran freely before the ocean winds. Driven by breezes, currents, and tides, armadas of these boneless sea creatures landed on the sandy shores of the New World. Men-of-war sail the seas in the true sense of the word. They have a gas-filled float that serves both as a boat to keep the animals from sinking and as a miniature sail. The float, resembling a small balloon, catches the wind in a flattened scalloped ridge along the top.

Today, as in times past, Portuguese men-of-war, or blue jellyfish as they are sometimes called, ride the rolling surf, which eventually casts them up to die on dry land. Sometimes the receding tide leaves behind thousands of the unusual sea animals littering the beach. At times men-of-war seem to invade the beach, their blue-tinted floats bobbing up and down in the waves. Swimmers learn that, like a disguised pirate vessel, these innocent-looking mariners are more than meets the eye. Below the 4-to-12-inch balloonlike float dangle tentacles that present a serious threat to humans.

Portuguese men-of-war belong to a group of aquatic invertebrates called Cnidaria, which includes jellyfish, sea wasps, and other floating creatures. They have no skeleton, organs, blood, or central nervous system. One distinguishing feature makes this group important to humans: they have tentacles covered with stinging cells to kill the fish they eat. The tentacles trail through the water and automatically discharge their poison into any creature they encounter, whether fish or human. Each stinging cell, or nematocyst, less than 50 microns (0.002 inch) in size, contains a coiled, hollow thread in a tiny capsule. When mechanically disturbed, the barbed thread shoots into the victim, releasing its poison. The venom has a paralyzing effect on the motor nerve endings, which stuns or kills small fish. The tentacles contract to bring the fish up to the mouth and digestive cavity of the animal. A man-of-war's numerous tentacles contain about 900 nematocysts per inch.

Humans encountering the tentacles experience immediate and excruciating pain. Minor cases may involve intense burning, stinging, and formation of red welts. Extensive contact can result in throbbing or shooting pains, muscular cramps, nausea, vomiting, abdominal rigidity, severe backache, inability to speak, frothing at the mouth, constriction of the throat, respiratory difficulties, paralysis, delirium, convulsions, and unconsciousness. Swimmers are the most frequent victims. The stinging cells on the tentacles of men-of-war washed ashore may remain potent for several days. At least one human death, a child in Florida, has been attributed to the Portuguese man-of-war. Other fatalities have been reported, but such cases are difficult to document.

First aid for a sting from a man-of-war, jellyfish, or sea wasp can help relieve pain and partially alleviate the effects of the toxin. Splash generous amounts of rubbing alcohol on the affected area to deactivate any stinging cells that have not discharged their poison. Sprinkle the sting area with liberal amounts of unseasoned Adolph's Meat Tenderizer (or any brand containing papain) to help neutralize the toxin. The victim may require antihistamines to lessen allergic responses, and in severe cases should seek immediate medical attention. Intravenous injections and other support measures may be required to combat pain, muscle cramps, and respiratory and cardiac problems.

The tentacles of a large man-of-war may trail 100 feet beneath the animal as it drifts aimlessly across the sea, though most that wash up on the beaches have tentacles 5 to 10 feet long. The gas-filled float of this unusual dweller of the deep is a remarkable adaptation enabling a sea animal unable to swim to navigate the waters and search for food. A gas-producing gland fills the float with just the proper amount of gas to keep the man-of-war buoyant. A valve on the top regulates the pressure inside the bladder, and if it becomes deflated, the gas glands can fill the float within 30 minutes.

The Portuguese man-of-war has a complex life history, and the animal we see floating in the surf represents only half the story. Aristotle was unsure about these strange creatures and considered them an intermediate life form between plants and animals. Actually the man-of-war passes through two radically different stages of life, known to scientists as alteration of generations. The floating organism with dangling tentacles is called a medusa, after the Greek mythological woman with snakes for hair. The medusa itself is a colony composed of four distinct types of individuals, each specialized for different functions. The float keeps the colony buoyant; the feeding tentacles bring the food to the digestive chamber on the bottom side of the float; the stinging cells reside in the feeding tentacles; and the reproductive members produce the eggs and sperm.

The medusa generation reproduces sexually, but the offspring bear little resemblance to the parents. The free-swimming larvae of the second generation attach permanently to an underwater surface and grow into a polyp, a tubelike creature resembling a plant. The polyp branches and forms many slender stems. Some stems have tentacles to capture food, and others bud and break off to become the free-swimming medusae.

In the unpredictable world of the deep, some creatures have learned to use to their advantage the most effective poisons of other animals. Even the deadly tentacles of the man-of-war become a haven of safety for the small harvester, or man-of-war fish, the *Peprilus*. This fish may not be immune to the poison, but it somehow has conditioned the floating creatures not to sting it. This type of association between two widely different creatures in which one or both benefit from the characteristics of the other is widespread in the ocean. Another fish has learned to take advantage of the potent stinging cells, but at the expense of the man-of-war. It eats the tentacles without discharging the nematocysts, and somehow manages to store the armed cells in its body to use for its own defense.

Some of the most unusual inhabitants of the earth live in the sea, and many can be found along the crescent-shaped coast of Texas. At low tide, look on the exposed rocks of jetties for anemones with their waving tentacles. In addition to sand dollars and shells with intricate patterns, beach-combers find colorful jellylike creatures, sea cucumbers, and other bizarre animals that hint of a complex life structure just beyond the surf. Scientists exploring the deepest ocean trenches find animals far stranger than the most imaginative fiction. Portuguese men-of-war live in a mysterious world where nature's creative force holds unbounded surprises. No wonder Aristotle could not decide whether many of these complicated creatures belonged to the animal or plant kingdom.

The Scorpion: Miniature Monster

Striped scorpion
Centruroides vittatus

How would you like to live in a world teeming with giant flesh-eating, blood-sucking monsters? Humans are lucky. By some quirk of fate, all the monsters are too small to present much of a threat. But try looking at life from an insect's viewpoint. Miniature monsters more awesome than any found in science fiction stories populate the world around us. Behind every twig and under every rock, some vicious beast lies in ambush with claws, teeth, or stinger ready to pounce. Yet one of these minuscule monsters, despite its two-to-three-inch size, strikes fear in the heart of every human. The scorpion, with tail poised ready to strike, gets as much respect as a deadly rattlesnake.

Scorpions come well equipped to survive in the world of the small. Since their ancestors adapted to life out of the sea, about 400 million years ago according to fossils, these critters have faced few foes their own size. With powerful lobsterlike pincers and a venom that instantly kills their prey, scorpions stalk through leaves, rocks, and vegetation. When the sun sets, scorpions emerge to hunt spiders, centipedes, crickets, and other small insects. By day, the reclusive animals repose under rocks, fallen logs, and other objects. Despite their effective armament, scorpions have learned to stay hidden in a world populated with creatures that can crush them with a single step, or devour them with a snap of their jaws. Armadillos, skunks, opossums, and pallid bats consider scorpions, poison stingers and all, tasty tidbits.

While stalking prey through the darkness of night, scorpions depend not on sight but on the senses of touch and

243

smell to find their victims. Some species also have well-developed hearing. Comblike chemical receptor organs on their undersides contact the ground as they crawl and help them track prey. Scorpions have long hairs, or setae, on their eight legs and pincers that are super-sensitive to touch. These hunters walk with claws outstretched feeling for small animals. The hairs on the legs of the sand scorpion in the Mojave Desert detect movement and direct the animal toward its meal. Sand scorpions use a complex sensing system to measure the time difference between compression waves caused by insects walking across the sand dunes. These perceptive creatures can detect movement 18 inches away, and can judge perfectly the distance and direction of prey, whether crawling or burrowing, within a 4-inch range.

A scorpion catches food by grabbing and crushing its prey with its powerful pincers. With lightning action, the tiny predator swings its tail over its body and stings the victim. The creature jerks convulsively and, paralyzed by the venom, dies in the scorpion's rigid grasp. The scorpion then chews the body into a semi-liquid state that it can suck up with its tiny mouth.

The poison glands in the swollen tip of the scorpion's tail secrete a venom that is deadly to insects and causes extreme discomfort in humans. Yet, except for a few species, none of which occur in Texas, scorpions present no serious threat to humans. Arizona harbors two species with a potent neurotoxin that can kill humans, particularly children. About two dozen deaths have been recorded. A more deadly scorpion, which reportedly can kill an adult in one hour, lives in the state of Durango in central Mexico. In a 35-year period, 1600 people died from the Durango scorpion. The government placed a bounty on the scorpions and collected 100,000 annually, but the effort did little to reduce the scorpion population. Fortunately, an antivenin that now saves many lives has been developed for the Durango and Arizona scorpions.

The sting from a nonlethal scorpion burns like fire and

244

leaves a welt, but like a wasp sting, the pain eventually subsides. Cooling the area with ice and taking antihistamines if an allergic reaction develops are the only recommended medical treatments. In hypersensitive individuals, however, the sting from a nonlethal scorpion like the species in Texas can cause severe complications and even death. If swelling or pain persists or breathing difficulty occurs, contact a physician immediately. A Johnson City man, stung on the finger while carrying firewood, died before he reached the hospital.

Scorpions, along with spiders and ticks, are members of the Arachnid family. Some tropical species grow to 7 inches in length, but in Texas, the common striped scorpion, *Centruroides vittatus,* only reaches 2½ inches. The 20 to 30 species in the United States live as far north as Canada, but favor the Gulf Coast and the hot, arid Southwest. Scorpions tolerate a limited range of temperatures and humidity, even in the desert. These creatures are perfect examples of animals that find a micro-habitat exactly suited to them. Like humans inside an air-conditioned building, scorpions avoid the daytime heat by staying protected under a rock or other object. The sand scorpion burrows 4 inches into the sand, where the temperature is about 60 degrees F lower than the surface and the humidity approaches 90 percent. Only in the cool of night do scorpions venture forth.

Scorpions do not socialize. Besides accidental encounters that usually result in cannibalism, only the sexual urge brings two scorpions together. They have an elaborate courtship that may last for hours: the two grasp each other's pincers and jaws and dance back and forth. Finally the male deposits a sac of sperm on the ground and pulls the female over it. She picks up the capsule with a special organ on her abdomen. After birth, the young crowd onto the mother's back and remain there until they shed their first skin. The sight of the babies covering the female's back inspired the folktale that the young eat the parent.

Several close relatives of scorpions resemble them but

do not sting. The whip scorpion has the same body shape without pincers and a long whiplike tail with no stinger. The vinegarroon also has a whiplike tail with no stinger, but has heavy pincers. The pseudoscorpion has pincers but no tail at all.

I spent one enjoyable summer swimming in Lake Travis and turning over rocks collecting scorpions for a study of their behavior. I used a black light to find the prowling predators at night. Their bodies fluoresce beautifully in the darkness, but a hand-held black light must be within several feet before the Texas species begin to glow. Scorpions are not desirable pets, since they can squeeze through the slightest crack. My entire collection disappeared from the aquarium and, fortunately, never appeared again.

To avoid scorpions around your home, move stacks of logs, rocks, and trash away from buildings and play areas. They seem particularly attracted to rocks and masonry. Carefully examine rocks and firewood before picking them up. Since scorpions take refuge under bark, delay bringing firewood into the house until you are ready to burn it.

The Tarantula:
The Mild-mannered Mygalomorph

Red-legged tarantula
Dugesiella hentzi

Suddenly a shriek of alarm rang through the woods, and I immediately thought "RATTLESNAKE." The group on my nature hike had parted like the Red Sea, as one of the most feared critters on earth crawled across the path. Someone yelled, "Get a stick, kill it!" I decided to take a chance and reached down and scooped up the fearful-looking creature. I heard gasps of disbelief as the animal slowly crawled across my palm and over my wrist.

"Does anyone want to hold a tarantula?" I asked casually. Finally, one brave lady held out her hand and let the hairy spider tiptoe across her arm. The demonstration helped dispel another common misconception about the animal. Despite their reputation, tarantulas are not deadly, although their large fangs can deliver a painful bite. Even though poisonous to insects, the venom of these giant spiders of the suborder Mygalomorphae presents no more of a threat to humans than a mosquito bite, or a bee sting at worst.

Ironically the tarantula's true nature bears little resemblance to its reputation. These secretive, ground-dwelling spiders spend most of their life hidden in their burrows. Unlike some spiders, tarantulas have poor vision and, even with eight eyes, cannot see farther than a few inches. They cannot run fast or jump more than the length of their body. Tarantulas, aided by a thick covering of sensitive hairs, communicate with the world mainly through the sense of touch.

The pet industry long ago discovered the gentle nature of tarantulas, and pet stores often sell them as novelties. They don't bark, have smelly litter boxes, or require property deposits. But they may cause heart attacks and strain friendships. My tarantula, Legs, had been missing for three days when a friend came to visit. She left in a huff when, like little

247

Miss Muffet, she found Legs sitting beside her.

When alarmed, tarantulas can appear as threatening as their evil reputation suggests. They rear back, wave their long, hairy legs, and expose the formidable fangs on their underside. These frightful-looking creatures have a secret weapon to complement their fearsome posturing and powerful fangs: a distinctive patch of poisonous hairs on their abdomen. If attacked, they rapidly scrape off a cloud of the tiny hairs that irritate the eyes and nose of their antagonist. The hairs penetrate the mucous membranes of mammals, and can cause a rash, or even partial blindness. Before the attacker recovers, the spider dashes to the safety of its burrow. Some Mexican species can cause swelling and stinging in humans.

Besides being the largest spiders, tarantulas live longer than any other terrestrial invertebrates. They take 8 to 10 years to mature sexually. The females may live for 30 years, but the males, who do not molt after becoming an adult, die within a year after they mature. Southwestern tarantulas spend most of their long lives in or within a few meters of their burrows, which they may call home for several decades. At the slightest sign of danger, they hide in their hole and cover the entrance with a silken tapestry. The mature males gad about during the mating season. Virtually all the tarantulas seen crossing roads between June and December are males searching for females.

Skunks and armadillos, unaffected by the fear complex so prevalent in humans, view tarantulas as culinary delicacies. They root them out of the ground, along with scorpions and other equally tasty critters. Birds also dine on the spiders, especially the smaller juveniles. In addition to hungry mammals and birds, tarantulas have some unconventional enemies that do not fight by the rules of the Geneva Convention. Two of the tarantula's most insidious enemies want the large spider alive, not dead. To them, the eight-legged creature represents a living food larder, a supermarket for their offspring. The tarantula's large size and powerful fangs do not always ensure victory against smaller foes. Tarantulas must contend with adversaries that use time bombs and a poison that places them in suspended animation. Small-headed flies of the family Acroceridae lay their eggs on the bodies of tarantulas. Like tiny time bombs, the eggs eventually hatch and the maggots voraciously devour the hapless spider.

The tarantula hawk, a wasp in the genus *Pepsis,* hunts the large spiders like a cat after a mouse. When the wasp encounters a tarantula, the two spar like a pair of gladiators. The wasp circles and darts in trying to avoid the deadly fangs of her larger opponent. In this fight to the death, the tarantula has no retreat. The wasp will pursue the spider right into its burrow. Eventually the wasp either ends up in the grips of her intended victim or delivers a paralyzing sting to the spider. Once stung, the tarantula does not die, but may live for several months unable to move. The victor drags the bulky tarantula to a burrow she has excavated and deposits it with her eggs. When the eggs hatch, they have a ready supply of fresh food.

Usually the tarantula plays the role of the terrorist. In the summer, the hungry predator ventures out every night in search of food. Beetles, grasshoppers, sow bugs, millipedes, and other spiders and insects that wander into the giant's neighborhood seldom survive. The tarantula, like all spiders, predigests its victim by flooding the dead creature with enzymes. The spider then sucks up the softened tissue. South American species, larger than our tarantulas, devour frogs, toads, lizards, and even mice. A captive South American speciman fed for 24 hours on a mouse, leaving only a shapeless, empty skin.

The largest tarantulas live in the tropics. South Americans call them bird spiders because the giant creatures sometimes catch birds. One even killed a small rattlesnake by pouncing on its head. A Brazilian species has a $3^1/_2$-inch body, a $9^1/_2$-inch leg span, and weighs 3 ounces. Another species in Guiana has a 10-inch leg span. About 30 species of tarantulas live in the United States, mostly in the arid Southwest. The largest has a 2-inch body, 6-to-7-inch leg span, and weighs half an ounce.

No description of this hairy, long-legged spider that looks like some creature from a horror movie would be complete without mentioning its bizarre sex life. Spiders in general have strange sexual practices, especially the species with females that may eat the smaller males during the act of mating. Both sexes of the tarantulas are about the same size, but the males still must be cautious of the ladies' temperament and appetite. Females often kill males during courtship and mating.

The transfer of sperm from the male to the female requires specialized equipment for both sexes. The male has two specialized claws shaped like syringes on the ends of its two pedipalps, appendages on its head. He weaves a little silken purse to hold a globule of sperm, and places a package in each syringe on his pedipalps. The female has two pouches on her abdomen designed to receive the sperm packages. She can store the sperm for weeks or even months. As she lays her eggs, she bathes each one in a fluid containing the sperm.

North American tarantulas lay about 600 to 1000 eggs at a time on a silken sheet that the female weaves. The spider covers the eggs with another sheet and seals the edges. The large, flabby bags are about three inches in diameter. The female takes the bag to the surface of the burrow to warm in the sun, and carefully guards her treasure for about seven weeks until hatching. The babies scatter to dig their own burrows and battle the odds of survival. The vulnerable young suffer greatly from predation, and few reach sexual maturity. When they finally mature, the males have longer legs than the females, are darker, and have reddish hair on their abdomens. Some of the South American giant species mature in three to four years.

The mygalomorph spiders received their common name from a large wolf spider named after the town of Taranto in southern Italy. European explorers thought the giant spiders of the New World resembled the tarantulas in Italy, and gave them the same name. During the Middle Ages, epidemics of tarantism, or spider bites, swept through southern Europe. Music provided the only antidote. The victims gathered in an elaborately decorated hall to perform the tarantula dance, the tarantella, to the cheers and encouragement of a sympathetic audience. For an effective cure, the participants had to leap, jerk, and dance incessantly until perspiration drove out the poison. The cure was complete when the dancer dropped from exhaustion. For a fee, villagers often allowed spiders to bite them, so tourists could witness the amazing cure. The event had striking similarities to pagan exhibitions prohibited by the Catholic Church.

People almost universally detest spiders, and particularly tarantulas. Poems and nursery rhymes terrify children. Hollywood even showed macho super spy James Bond paralyzed with horror when a hairy tarantula crawled across his chest. Except for the black widow and brown recluse, which have particularly toxic venom, spiders rarely intrude into human life beyond cobwebs in the attic. But even though the tarantula has a gentle disposition, you had better avoid this giant spider. According to Zuni legend, the tarantula is an expert trickster and will trick you out of your clothes if you are not careful.

Texas' Vanishing Wildlife: Endangered and Threatened Animals

MAMMALS

Extinct Species

Black-footed ferret, *Mustela nigripes:* poisoning of prairie dogs, its main prey; presumed extinct until 1981, when several were discovered in Wyoming; only 25 remaining in captivity.

Gray wolf, *Canis lupus:* habitat destruction, eradication of bison, predator control.

Texas grizzly bear, *Ursus texensis:* eradicated in 1890.

Merriam elk, *Cervus elaphus merriami:* extinct subspecies.

Texas mountain sheep, *Ovis canadensis texiana:* extinct since the 1950s; different subspecies now introduced in Trans-Pecos.

Endangered Species

Jaguar, *Felis onca:* habitat destruction, hunting, predator control.

Jaguarundi, *Felis yagouaroundi:* habitat destruction; not sighted in Texas in ten years.

Manatee, *Trichechus manatus:* occurs in Florida and Caribbean, historically has ventured as far west as Texas.

Ocelot, *Felis pardalis:* habitat destruction, hunting, road kills.

Red wolf, *Canis rufus:* habitat destruction, predator control, hybridization with dogs; very few left in the wild.

Black bear, *Ursus americanus:* incompatible with humans; few or none remaining in mountains of Trans-Pecos.

Coati, *Nasua nausa:* very few occur in Texas since the southern portion of the state is the northern limit of its range.

Threatened Species

Rafinesque's big-eared bat, *Plecotus rafinesquii:* habitat loss, pesticide use.

Spotted bat, *Euderma maculatum:* habitat destruction.

Southern yellow bat, *Lasiurus ega:* habitat destruction.

Atlantic spotted dolphin, *Stenella plagiodon:* commercial fishing.

Palo Duro mouse, *Peromyscus comanche:* habitat loss to wildfire and impounded lakes.

Texas kangaroo rat, *Dipodomys elator:* habitat loss to agriculture and urbanization.

Coues' rice rat, *Oryzomys couesi:* habitat loss to agriculture.

BIRDS

Endangered Species

Whooping crane, *Grus americana:* habitat loss.

Eskimo curlew, *Numenius borealis:* migrates through Texas.

Bald eagle, *Haliaeetus leucocephalus:* pesticide use, hunting; about 20 breeding pairs occur in Texas.

American peregrine falcon, *Falco peregrinis anatum:* pesticide use.

Brown pelican, *Pelecanus occidentalis:* pesticide use.

Greater Attwater's prairie chicken, *Tympanuchus cupido attwateri:* habitat loss.

Interior least tern, *Sterna antillarum athalassos:* nesting disturbance by human recreation, water control projects.

Ivory-billed woodpecker, *Campephilus principalis:* habitat loss, probably extinct.

Red-cockaded woodpecker, *Picoides borealis:* habitat loss from lumbering.

Aplomado falcon, *Falco femoralis:* no recent breeding in Texas.

Black-capped vireo, *Vireo atricapillus:* habitat loss to urban development, nest parasitism by brown-headed cowbirds.

Threatened Species

Arctic peregrine falcon, *Falco peregrinus tundrius:* breeds in Canada but winters in Texas.

Reddish egret, *Egretta rufescens:* human disturbance of nesting sites.

Common black hawk, *Buteogallus anthracinus:* habitat loss.

Gray hawk, *Buteo nitidus:* habitat loss to agriculture.

White-tailed hawk, *Buteo albicaudatus:* loss of nesting habitat.

Zone-tailed hawk, *Buteo albonotatus:* habitat loss.

White-faced ibis, *Plegadis chihi:* pesticide use

Swallow-tailed kite, *Elanoides forficatus:* a Texas migrant.

Ferruginous pygmy owl, *Glaucidium brasilianum:* breeding habitat loss to agriculture.

Wood stork, *Mycteria americana:* no longer breeding in Texas.

Golden-cheeked warbler, *Dendroica chrysoparia:* habitat loss, nest parasitism to brown-headed cowbirds.

Rose-throated becard, *Pachyramphus aglaiae:* habitat loss to agriculture.

Tropical parula, *Parula pitiayumi:* habitat loss to agriculture.

Bachman's sparrow, *Aimophila aestivalis:* habitat loss to lumbering.

Botteri's sparrow, *Aimophila botterii:* habitat loss.

Sooty tern, *Sterna fuscata:* nest disturbance by human recreation.

Northern beardless tyrannulet, *Camptostoma imberbe:* habitat loss.

REPTILES

Endangered Species

Atlantic hawksbill turtle, *Eretmochelys imbricata imbricata:* hunted for shell, drowns in fishnets.

Leatherback turtle, *Dermochelys coriacea:* occurs infrequently in Texas waters, drowns in fishnets.

Speckled racer, *Drymobius margaritiferus margaritiferus* (snake): common in the tropics but barely persisting in South Texas because of habitat loss.

Kemp's ridley turtle, *Lepidochelys kempi:* egg vandals at the Mexican nesting site, drowns in fishnets; attempts to establish a nesting colony on Padre Island National Seashore still inconclusive.

Concho water snake, *Nerodia harteri paucimaculata:* habitat loss to impounded lakes.

Loggerhead turtle, *Caretta caretta:* once abundant, now seen infrequently; drowns in fishnets.

Northern cat-eyed snake, *Leptodeira septentrionalis septentrionalis:* habitat loss, pesticide use.

Louisiana pine snake, *Pituophis melanoleucus ruthveni:* habitat destruction by lumbering.

Big Bend mud turtle, *Kinosternon hirtipes murrayi:* water depletion, habitat loss.

Western smooth green snake, *Opheodrys vernalis blanchardi:* habitat loss, pesticide use.

Threatened Species

Brazos water snake, *Nerodia harteri harteri:* dam construction.

Reticulated gecko, *Coleonyx reticulatus (lizard):* pesticide use, habitat loss.

Reticulate collared lizard, *Crotaphytus reticulatus:* habitat loss, pesticide use.

Texas horned lizard, *Phrynosoma cornutum:* overcollecting, pesticide use.

Mountain short-horned lizard, *Phrynosoma douglassii hernandesi:* habitat loss, pesticide use.

Black-striped snake, *Coniophanes imperialis imperialis:* habitat loss to agriculture.

Texas indigo snake, *Drymarchon corais erebennus:* habitat loss to agriculture, overcollecting.

Texas lyre snake, *Trimorphodon biscutatus vilkinsonii:* overcollecting, habitat loss.

Baird's rat snake, *Elaphe bairdi:* over collecting.

Texas Tortoise, *Gopherus berlandieri:* overcollecting, habitat loss.

Atlantic green turtle, *Chelonia mydas mydas:* over collecting, drowns in fishnets.

Big Bend blackhead snake, *Tantilla rubra:* habitat loss, pesticide use.

Texas scarlet snake, *Cemophora coccinea lineri:* overcollecting, habitat loss.

Northern scarlet snake, *Cemophora coccinea copei:* habitat loss, overcollecting.

Alligator snapping turtle, *Macroclemys temminckii:* habitat loss, commercial exploitations, pesticide use.

Books for Further Reading

Bedichek, Roy. *Adventures with a Texas Naturalist*. Austin: University of Texas Press, 1967.

Bent, A. C. *Life Histories of North American Birds of Prey*. New York: Dover Publications, 1961.

———. *Life Histories of North American Flycatchers, Larks, Swallows, and Their Allies*. New York: Dover Publications, 1961.

———. *Life Histories of North American Marsh Birds*. New York: Dover Publications, 1961.

———. *Life Histories of North American Nuthatches, Wrens, Thrashers, and Their Allies*. New York: Dover Publications, 1961.

Breland, Osmond P. *Animal Life and Lore*. New York: Harper and Row Publishers, 1972.

Brown, Leslie. *Eagles*. New York: Arco Publishing Co., 1970.

Burt, William H. *A Field Guide to the Mammals*. New York: Houghton Mifflin Co., 1964.

Burton, John A. *Owls of the World*. New York: A & W Visual Library, 1973.

Carrington, Richard. *The Mammals*. New York: Time-Life Books, 1963.

Chapman, Joseph A., and George A. Feldhammer. *Wild Mammals of North America*. Baltimore: Johns Hopkins University Press, 1982.

Cruickshank, Allan, and Helen Cruickshank. *1001 Questions Answered About Birds*. New York: Dover Publications, 1958.

Dalrymple, Byron W. *North American Game Animals*. New York: Outdoor Life, 1978.

Davis, William B. *The Mammals of Texas*. Austin: Texas Parks and Wildlife Department, Bulletin 41, 1974.

Dobie, J. Frank. *The Longhorns*. Austin: University of Texas Press, 1980.

———. *Wild and Wily Range Animals*. Flagstaff: Northland Press, 1980.

———. *A Vaquero of the Brush Country*. Austin: University of Texas Press, 1981.

———. *Rattlesnakes*. Austin: University of Texas Press, 1982.

Duplaix, Nicole, and Noel Simon. *World of Mammals*. New York: Crown Publishers, 1976.

Engelmann, Wolf-Eberhard, and Fritz J. Obst. *Snakes, Biology, Behavior, and Relation to Man*. Los Angeles: Exter Books, 1981.

Garrett, Judith M., and David G. Barker. *A Field Guide to Reptiles and Amphibians of Texas*. Austin: Texas Monthly Press, 1987.

Gertsch, Willis J. *American Spiders*. New York: Van Nostrand Reinhold Co., 1979.

Gibbons, Whit. *Their Blood Runs Cold*. University: University of Alabama Press, 1983.

Lane, Gary. *Life of the Past*. Columbus: Charles E. Merrill Publishing Co., 1978.

Layton, R. B. *The Purple Martin*. Jackson, Miss.: Nature Book Publishers, 1969.

Madison, Virginia. *The Big Bend Country of Texas*. Stonington, Conn.: October House, 1968.

Oberholser, Harry C. *The Bird Life of Texas*. Austin: University of Texas Press, 1974.

Pearson, Erwin W., and Milton Caroline. Predator Control in Relation to Livestock in Central Texas. *Journal of Range Management* 34 (November 1981): pp 435–41.

Perrins, Christopher, and C. J. O. Harrison. *Birds, Their Life, Their Ways, Their World*. New York: Reader's Digest Association, 1979.

Pulich, Warren M. *The Golden-Cheeked Warbler*. Austin: Texas Parks and Wildlife Department, 1976.

Robbins, Chandler S., Bertel Bruun, and Herbert S. Zim. *A Field Guide to the Birds of North America*, New York: Golden Press, 1983.

Rood, Ronald. *Animals Nobody Loves*. New York: Stephen Greene Press, 1971.

Schmidly, David J. *The Mammals of Trans-Pecos Texas*. College Station: Texas A&M Press, 1977.

Skutch, Alexander F. *The Life of the Hummingbird*. New York: Crown Publishers, 1973.

————. *Parent Birds and Their Young*. Austin: University of Texas Press, 1976.

Tennant, Alan. *The Snakes of Texas*. Austin: Texas Monthly Press, 1984.

————. *A Field Guide to the Snakes of Texas*. Austin: Texas Monthly Press, 1985.

Texas Animal Damage Control. U.S. Fish and Wildlife Service, Annual Report FY 1983.

Wauer, Roland H. *Naturalist's Big Bend*. Santa Fe: Peregrine Productions, 1973.

Wetmore, Alexander. *Water, Prey, and Game Birds of North America*. Washington, D.C.: National Geographic Society, 1965.

Whitfield, Philip. *The Hunters*. New York: Simon and Schuster, 1978.